PHYSICAL GEOLOGY
Principles and Perspectives

SECOND EDITION

PHYSICAL

GEOLOGY
Principles
and
Perspectives

Edward A. Hay / A. Lee McAlester

De Anza College
Cupertino, California

Southern Methodist University
Dallas, Texas

Prentice-Hall, Inc., Englewood Cliffs, New Jersey 07632

Library of Congress Cataloging in Publication Data

HAY, EDWARD A.
    Physical geology, principles and perspectives.

    Rev. ed. of: Physical geology, principles and
perspectives / A. Lee McAlester, Edward A. Hay. 1975.
    Includes bibliographies and index.
    1. Physical geology.   I. McAlester, A. Lee (Arcie
Lee), date   . II. McAlester, A. Lee (Arcie Lee),
date   . Physical geology, principles and perspectives.   III. Title.
QE28.2.H38 1984   551   83-24447
ISBN 0-13-669549-3

PHYSICAL GEOLOGY: Principles and Perspectives, 2nd ed.
by Edward A. Hay and A. Lee McAlester

Editorial/production supervision: Virginia Huebner
Interior and Cover design: Suzanne Behnke
Manufacturing buyer: John Hall
Page Layout: Meg Van Arsdale
Title Page photo: Geological Survey of Great Britain (Crown Copyright Reserved)
Cover photo: Colin Molyneux, The Image Bank

Printed in the United States of America
10 9 8 7 6 5 4 3 2 1

ISBN   0-13-669549-3

Prentice-Hall International, Inc., *London*
Prentice-Hall of Australia Pty. Limited, *Sydney*
Editora Prentice-Hall do Brasil, Ltda., *Rio de Janeiro*
Prentice-Hall Canada Inc., *Toronto*
Prentice-Hall of India Private Limited, *New Delhi*
Prentice-Hall of Japan, Inc., *Tokyo*
Prentice-Hall of Southeast Asia Pte. Ltd., *Singapore*
Whitehall Books Limited, *Wellington, New Zealand*

For Martha
and her Grandchildren
Ali, Chris, and Stu

To Virginia

Contents

3

IGNEOUS AND METAMORPHIC PROCESSES 66

4

SEDIMENTARY PROCESSES 106

5

THE GEOLOGICAL TIME SCALE 150

6

CRUSTAL ROCK DEFORMATIONS 187

7

SEISMOLOGY AND OTHER GEOPHYSICS 217

12

GEOLOGY AND HUMAN CONCERNS   380

13

EXTRATERRESTRIAL ROCKS   408

GLOSSARY   438

INDEX   451

Preface

The Second Edition of this book attempts to provide an introduction to physical geology that is brief and accessible, yet scientifically uncompromising. Every effort has been made to place the essential principles of the subject—minerals, rocks, geologic time, earth structure, plate tectonics, and land sculpture—in a rigorously up-to-date context. The book is written for an introductory physical geology course in which the principal instruction results from lecturing and laboratory or other problem solving activities that are directed by the professor in charge. In order to produce a relatively brief book, many topics are treated in a succinct, non-compendious fashion, thus requiring experiences in lecture, and or laboratory, to develop certain subjects more fully. Neither this book, nor any book, we suspect, should be used as the principal vehicle by which a college student learns. We have tried to deal with concepts and attitudes that are fundamental to the geological sciences, and in so doing we have omitted some of the specific information that any given professor might want to include in his course. This does not pose a problem, it seems to us, because it is only common and natural that good teaching involves augmentation of materials and elaboration of ideas. In the Introduction we have also tried to set the geologic stage by stressing the evolutionary nature of scientific conclusions and the philosophical foundations upon which rests our modern understanding of the earth sciences.

Two colleagues, in particular, were helpful during the early stages of preparing the Second Edition of this book, thus we wish to thank Willim R. Cotton and N. Timothy Hall. Reviews of preliminary material provided important insights for improving our final product. Accordingly, we are indebted to Prof. William M. Jordan, Millersville State College, Prof. Gary C. Allen, The University of New Orleans, Prof. Robert B. Furlong, Wayne State University, Prof. Robert E. Lemmon, The University of North Carolina at Charlotte, Prof. Stuart J. Inglis, Chabot College—Valley Campus, Prof. Clayton H. Johnson, The University of Missouri—Columbia, Prof. Wallace D. Kleck, Orange Coast College, Prof. Henry E. Kane, Ball State University, and Prof. Don Ringe, Central Washington University.

Finally we recognize the valuable roles played by Doug Humphrey, Virginia Huebner, and Suzanne Behnke at Prentice-Hall in producing this book; we extend our thanks to them.

EDWARD A. HAY
A. LEE MCALESTER

PHYSICAL GEOLOGY
Principles and Perspectives

Introduction: Geology in Perspective

GEOLOGY IS ONE OF THE many fields of science, and science itself is but one of many broad areas of study. As an introduction to the main business of this book, we shall illustrate the manner in which sciences in general may be compared to other fields, and further, how geology contains elements that are unique with respect to other sciences such as chemistry and physics.

I.1
WHERE SCIENCE FITS IN

The difference between the sciences and other disciplines is not so much in their goals as in their *processes of inquiry*. Some discussions of this topic even suggest that a rather special procedure exists called "the scientific method." Such a term is often misleading in its implication that a formula for the achievement of "truth" exists in the form of this "method." The observation Nobel Prize winner Percy W. Bridgeman made in 1945—that the method of science is "doing one's damnedest with one's mind, no holds barred"—is an excellent statement of how scientists work. But the fact still remains that the scientist does proceed with his investigations often by using approaches that are different from those employed by other scholars. Why is this so? By virtue of the scientist's concern with questions about the workings of the universe, he finds himself in the enviable position of being able to observe, measure, and experiment with objects of interest. He may engage in the exciting activity of prediction, and whether or not his predictions prove correct, the results of his experiments provide him with valuable input into the redesign of further experiments. Almost certainly, such chains of experimentation will lead to his more nearly complete understanding.

Why is it, then, that scholars in other fields do not as successfully employ these same tools? We must remember that the tools useful to a given craftsman depend on the task to be performed. Algebra and microscopes are as inappropriate to the historian in his search for understanding the causes of the Civil War as sledge hammers and jigsaws are to the watch repairman. The scientist is thus seen to employ the tools best suited for finding out how the universe works. He attempts to discover relationships of the sort we think of as subject to so-called natural laws—gravity, relativity, and the like.

Because the interactions of matter and energy studied by the scientist are concerned with very *fundamental* properties, they lend themselves to controlled laboratory experiments and mathematical descriptions. Consider, for example, the differences in complexity between considerations of how an object goes faster after falling longer as compared with trying to understand Hitler's rise to power in Germany after World War I. The physicist has only two variables to consider—time and velocity—whereas the historian must try to weigh and evaluate literally hundreds of events, social forces, and human interactions that took place over an extended period of time in many far-flung places. Clearly, the physicist will be able to experiment and numerically describe his investigations with dramatically greater success than the historian. It is thus little wonder that scientists have achieved more impressive results than historians in their search for understanding: The problems they have chosen to attack are less complex and therefore easier to solve. Although most people not familiar with mathematics may find it paradoxical, the simple truth is that the sciences are able successfully to employ sophisticated mathematical methods by virtue of the *relative simplicity* of what is being investigated! (Figure I.1).

FIGURE I.1 Spectrum of complexity. As the phenomena being studied become more complex, there is greater difficulty in formulating "laws."

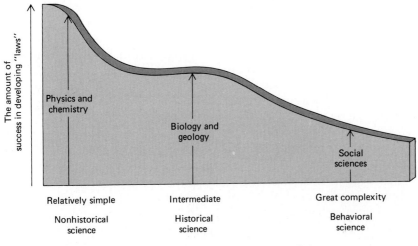

GEOLOGY'S SCIENTIFIC UNIQUENESS

Our example of how the historian and the physicist necessarily use different tools in their investigations describes what may be considered opposite ends of an academic spectrum. It now seems appropriate to ask where geology fits into these considerations. Is geology simply the discipline that applies chemistry and physics to problems concerning our planet? Or is there something about geology that makes it in some respects unique? Geologists have argued both points of view without reaching complete agreement about how much importance should be attached to the factors that make geology different, and we shall not enter into that debate here. We should, however, ask, "What is this difference and how has it come about?"

Geological sciences are concerned with the earth and how it has changed through time. Thus by their very nature they are historically oriented and therefore confronted with certain kinds of problems not encountered in nonhistorical sciences. We should not be surprised to find that geology occupies a sort of middle ground between chemistry or physics on the one hand, and history or sociology on the other. When the changing conditions over long periods of time become an important factor, problems become significantly more difficult. The geologist can conduct experiments to learn about the *mechanisms* of erosion, for example, but he is faced with a completely different kind of problem in trying to understand the origin of Yosemite Valley or of the Grand Canyon, for these represent "one of a kind" sequences of erosional events occurring over millions of years, and these precise events are nonrepeatable. In discussing this matter, George Gaylord Simpson (1963), a well-known American paleontologist, has suggested that many of the concerns of the geologist involve "postdiction" rather than prediction. In other words, because the earth has had such a long and complex history, understanding it requires methods of study beyond the approach employed so successfully in physics and chemistry, where controlled laboratory experiments are conducted to obtain *predictive* results.

Because of the complexity of the earth's history and the great difficulty in understanding it, the history of geologic thought has seen a wide range of speculations important to the progress of geology. As Thomas S. Kuhn (1962) has observed, the range of scientific speculations acceptable at any given time within a particular field of science (such as geology) will depend on the assumptions currently held by members of that scientific group.* In reference to this, the

* See reference by Kuhn in reading list at end of chapter.

term **paradigm*** has recently begun to receive wide use. What are paradigms? Simply stated, they are models or generally agreed-upon "ground rules" that limit a given investigation. Whether they realize it or not, people are constantly excluding many possible explanations because they are not consistent with a currently accepted paradigm or assumption. During the time of Jesus, for example, who would have seriously proposed sailing westward from Rome in order to get to China? Such a suggestion would have been rejected during that era, even though today we know it to be reasonable and correct, because the earth was then widely believed to be flat. This speculation would have been "premature" because no appropriate paradigm existed then to legitimize it: Going westward to reach a land to the east could not have been related to the accepted knowledge of the day. The implications of such a proposal, had it been made then, would therefore be unexplored and unappreciated until people adopted—or facts forced them to adopt—a paradigm consistent with it. Perhaps even today we fail to seize upon important ideas because they are not easily connected to currently held views.

Figure I.2 and the following discussion will be used to depict two of many major paradigm changes (scientific revolutions) that took place in the early days of the geological sciences. Three different explanations of the sketch will be presented, each derived from a once-acceptable and widely held view, although the specific quotations are hypothetical.

FIGURE I.2   Different rocks exposed in a cliff. See text for discussion.

Rock Y

Rock X

Sea shells

Cliff exposure

Fragment of rock X

Rock Z

* Terms appearing in bold type are defined in the glossary.

Statement 1 Greek poet, 600 B.C.
This remarkable cliff enables us to see the manner in which the earth was formed by the Gods out of chaos. It has remained essentially unchanged since its origin, with the exception that Poseidon [god of the sea] has flooded the surface with sea water so as to allow the sea shells to reside near the hill top.

This poet is clearly reflecting a popular attitude, or paradigm, of his day. The ancient Greeks explained all natural phenomena as functions of the whims and dictates of gods. Given such a philosophy of life, it would be totally unlikely—indeed unacceptable—to seek impersonal cause-and-effect relationships in natural processes as a means of discovering interactions between matter and energy. The whole notion of scientific laws is dependent on very different attitudes from those expressed in Statement 1. If gods supply "purpose" to earth processes, then man cannot hope to discover reproducible relationships. Thus, ideas of invariable, impersonal cause-and-effect associations are essential to the emergence of modern science. It is apparent, therefore, that science could not have flourished under the paradigm of divine control.

Statement 2 A student of A. G. Werner (Werner was an influential professor at the Mining Academy of Freiberg), A.D. 1795
This exposure allows us to document the order of deposition of rock types that have settled-out from a world-encompassing ocean to form the crust of the earth. Rock X is the *oldest because it is granite*, and granite is always the oldest rock in any region where it is found. It is a primitive chemical precipitate from the primordial ocean, as is the basalt of Rock Z. The sandstone of Rock Y is a mechanical sediment deposited after an appreciable lowering of the ocean. It is obvious that the fossils [shells] were dissolved in the universal water and have been precipitated from it. This landscape has not changed significantly since the ocean receded to its present level.

Professor Werner was the major proponent of the widely held eighteenth-century view called **Neptunism**, namely, that all rocks have precipitated from a world-encompassing ocean. The statement by Werner's student shows how once an investigator accepts a particular model, he automatically and subconsciously puts on "blinders" to a host of speculations that might otherwise have been considered. The view that order existed in the universe had been accepted by this time, but many investigators were too inclined to *pronounce* how things should be rather than carefully attempt to *discover* how they are. Werner was such a man. The model of Neptunism held sway for many years but was eventually overthrown by a way of looking at the earth called **uniformitarianism** during the early decades of the nineteenth century.

Statement 3 A follower of Charles Lyell (Lyell—British geologist, 1797–1875—is viewed by many as one of the founders of modern geology), A.D. 1835

By carefully observing the three exposed rock types and the nature of the contacts between them, we can determine the origin of each and the historical events leading to their association with each other. The granite of Rock X is much older [by millions of years] than the others, and was formed by the slow crystallization of molten rock material at great depth beneath what was then the surface of the earth. In contrast to the large crystals formed by slow cooling in Rock X, Rock Z has small crystals and, therefore, must have cooled quickly, perhaps as a lava flow on the earth's surface. Fragments of Rock X that have been incorporated within Rock Z provide clear *evidence* that Z is younger than X. A great period of erosion would necessarily have been required to cause Rock X, formed at great depth, to be exposed at the surface of the earth prior to the eruption of volcanic material of Rock Z. Rock Y, a sandstone, has resulted from the compacting and cementing of many worn grains of sand, following transportation by streams into the sea. There they accumulated with shells of once living organisms, eventually to be formed into rock. This region has an involved and dynamic history. By using present geologic processes such as erosion, deposition, and volcanism as keys to our understanding of how the earth can change, given sufficient time, it is possible to reconstruct uplifting, prolonged erosion, subsidence, and many other subtleties of earth history from a cliff exposure such as the one seen here. We need not invoke any supernatural or exceptional explanations to reconstruct the history of the earth.

This statement reflects the perspective of a modern geologist. It reflects a guiding paradigm that asserts validity for the principle of uniformitarianism. We shall return to a more nearly complete discussion of this view shortly, but simply stated, it asserts that the earth has an exceedingly long history during which complex geologic processes such as erosion, mountain building, and rock genesis have proceeded in accordance with fundamental laws (e.g., those of chemistry and physics).

The scientific revolution that gave rise to uniformitarianism was as intellectually labored as the American Revolution was hard-fought with the weapons of war. Let us briefly digress to review how this exceedingly important scientific revolution came about.

I.3
THE BEGINNING OF MODERN GEOLOGY

The well-known, nineteenth-century American scholar Henry Adams wrote, "Anarchy is the law of nature, and order is the dream of man." Without entering into the philosophical debate invited by this statement as to whether man discovers or creates order, let us allow it to suggest a relationship that is fundamental to the rise of modern science: *If we are to understand nature, we must search for its orderliness.* All scientific inquiry begins with the *assumption* that there are discoverable orderly interactions going on within the universe. Simply stated, science rests fundamentally on a *faith* in the inductive and empirical processes and their ability to yield valid conclusions; that is to say, predictions about the future can be formulated reliably only from experiences in the past. Inasmuch as we cannot prove what will happen tomorrow, no scientist can ever be certain about his predictions, and hence no law can ever be wholly proved—even though such terminology is frequently applied to scientific assertions. The so-called "law of gravity," for example, is a statement of a kind of relationship that exists between all forms of matter. We can have exceedingly great confidence in the accuracy of this statement, but in a philosophical sense it is clear that we *cannot be certain.* Consider the so-called "hierarchy of scientific confidence" for scientific statements that is depicted in Figure I.3.

The extreme complexity of nature forces investigators to generate **models** to account for the complicated reality being studied. Scientific models are mental constructs of how nature *might* function. The particular models an investigator is likely to formulate

FIGURE I.3   Hierarchy of scientific confidence. The relationship between hypothesis, theory, and law.

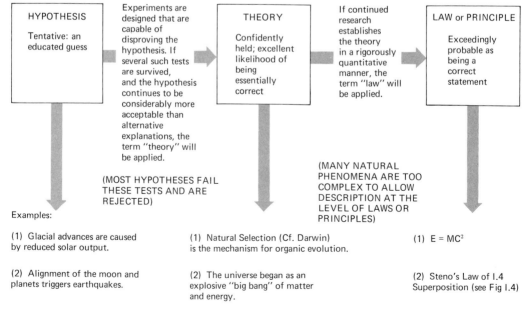

Statements explaining how phenomena are related may evolve through the following stages as experiments are conducted to test them:

HYPOTHESIS	Experiments are designed that are capable of disproving the hypothesis. If several such tests are survived, and the hypothesis continues to be considerably more acceptable than alternative explanations, the term "theory" will be applied.	THEORY	If continued research establishes the theory in a rigorously quantitative manner, the term "law" will be applied.	LAW or PRINCIPLE
Tentative: an educated guess		Confidently held; excellent likelihood of being essentially correct		Exceedingly probable as being a correct statement

(MOST HYPOTHESES FAIL THESE TESTS AND ARE REJECTED)

(MANY NATURAL PHENOMENA ARE TOO COMPLEX TO ALLOW DESCRIPTION AT THE LEVEL OF LAWS OR PRINCIPLES)

Examples:

(1) Glacial advances are caused by reduced solar output.

(1) Natural Selection (Cf. Darwin) is the mechanism for organic evolution.

(1) $E = MC^2$

(2) Alignment of the moon and planets triggers earthquakes.

(2) The universe began as an explosive "big bang" of matter and energy.

(2) Steno's Law of I.4 Superposition (see Fig I.4)

are ultimately controlled by the paradigms of his science. His models may be mathematical, mechanical, or verbal, and typically they take the form of hypotheses, theories, and laws. They serve us by providing suitably simple vehicles for our use in reasoning by analogy. We do not truly know what an atom is like, for example, but we have developed the so-called "atomic theory," which has provided a variety of models that are helpful in gaining greater insights into many fields of science.

To return to the initial point, it is clear that modern science can be nurtured only within an environment in which the notion of order is accepted, thus allowing models to be devised for explaining nature. When did such mind-sets begin to appear with regard to matters of the earth? Although Aristotle and other Greek philosophers thought in terms of order, an early example dealing more explicitly with geological considerations comes from the work of Nicolas Steno, a Danish scholar living in Florence in the seventeenth century. Steno observed exposures of layered rocks throughout the Florentine countryside. Reasoning that they must have formed in the past in much the same manner as the layered deposits he observed being formed from sediments along Mediterranean shores and Italian stream valleys, he formulated three important statements that he suggested could be applied to *all* layered rocks. Today we have such extreme confidence in the correctness of these statements that we refer to them as "laws" (Figure I.4).

FIGURE I.4   Steno's laws.

Blanket-like, without gaps in continuity of deposition

Youngest layer

Layers are horizontal

Oldest layer

LAW OF SUPERPOSITION: Lower layers of sediment must have achieved firmness before subsequent layers could settle upon them, hence for rocks forming by this sedimentary process the layers become progressively younger from bottom to top. (1 is older than 2, 2 is older than 3, etc.)

LAW OF ORIGINAL CONTINUITY: Sedimentary layers were deposited as blanket-like, continuous sheets of material that gradually thin to nothing at their edges, or have been terminated against a solid surface.

LAW OF ORIGINAL HORIZONTALITY: Although bottom layers may irregularly conform to the shape of the surface upon which they are deposited, most layers were deposited parallel to the horizon (horizontal) or very nearly so.

The great historical and philosophical achievement of Steno's work is that (1) order in nature was assumed, (2) comparison of the present and the past (modern sedimentary environments and old layered rocks) was carefully undertaken, and (3) a general statement about *all* layered rocks was formulated. Furthermore, with the advent of such "laws" (then "theories," perhaps), it became possible, indeed necessary, to view the earth as undergoing dynamic change through time—change that could be understood by careful application of Steno's Laws (Figure I.5). Steno was probably the first person who seriously attempted to work out the geologic history of a portion of the earth. His work in the seventeenth century heralded the beginning of an important human undertaking.

(a)

LAW OF SUPERPOSITION: A is the oldest and D is the youngest of these sedimentary layers.

LAW OF ORIGINAL CONTINUITY: Where edges of layers are exposed at the earth's surface, erosion must have occurred to destroy the original continuity (see regions C' on sketch)

LAW OF ORIGINAL HORIZONTALITY: All these layers have been folded since their time of origin, because they began as horizontal strata.

FIGURE I.5   a) Application of Steno's laws: Historical inferences such as sequence of deposition, folding, and erosion can result from Steno's laws. b) Imagine the enthusiasm of Steno if he had been able to see the Grand Canyon! Superposition, original horizontality, and original continuity at their finest. (b: E. A. Hay.)

(b)

BOX I.1

The Structure of Science

The following anecdote is told of the scholar William James.* Whether it is true or not is less important than the comment it makes on various paths in the search for knowledge. Modern science could not begin its development until the **assumption** was made that the workings of nature are characterized by **discoverable** relationships.

After a lecture on cosmology and the structure of the solar system, James was accosted by a little old lady.

"Your theory that the sun is the center of the solar system, and that the earth is a ball that rotates around it, has a very convincing ring to it, Mr. James, but it's wrong. I've got a better theory," said the little old lady.

"And what is that, madam?" inquired James politely.

"That we live on a crust of earth that is on the back of a giant turtle."

Not wishing to demolish this absurd little theory by bringing to bear the masses of scientific evidence he had at his command, James decided gently to dissuade his opponent by making her see some of the inadequacies of her position.

"If your theory is correct, madam," he asked, "what does this turtle stand on?"

"You're a very clever man, Mr. James, and that's a very good question," replied the little old lady, "but I have an answer to it. And it's this: the first turtle stands on the back of a second, far larger, turtle, who stands directly under him."

"But what does this second turtle stand on?" persisted James patiently.

To this, the little old lady crowed triumphantly, "It's no use, Mr. James—it's turtles all the way down."

* U.S. Philosopher, 1842–1910.

With a new paradigm based on orderliness, scholars eventually began to observe and carefully describe rocks exposed all around them at the earth's surface. They found that order could be found there, although it was not everywhere clear what the order was. The earth was found to be complex, and men, whose minds were unaccustomed to such ambiguity and uncertainty, frequently imposed their own order on nature. Such was true of A. G. Werner and his "Neptunism." Well-meaning investigators often succumbed to temptation out of intellectual frustration and ascribed simple solutions (see "turtles all the way down" in Box I.1) to relationships of bewildering complexity. But always they were guided by a belief in *discoverable orderliness*. Albert Einstein's suggestion that God is ingenious, but not malicious, delightfully characterizes the spirit and essence of this most fundamental of all scientific assumptions.

I.4
THE ARRIVAL OF MODERN GEOLOGY

We have recognized that the assumption of orderliness in the universe provides the basis for scientific inquiry. However, the mechanism for achieving this order on earth has never been obvious. Following the time of Steno, an explanation for the evolution of the earth called **catastrophism** became dominant in western Europe. Subsequent challenges to this theory developed under the banner of **uniformitarianism,** and in the late eighteenth and early nineteenth centuries a major scientific revolution took place within the field of geology.

Out of the conflict between catastrophism and uniformitarianism, geology emerged as a modern science, with uniformitarianism as its paradigm. In a sense, there *was* no geology prior to the acquisition of this paradigm. Let us briefly consider the major points of philosophical disagreement between catastrophists and uniformitarians in this revolutionary battle.

Although no one man is ever responsible, by himself, for a major school of thought, the catastrophist Georges Cuvier (Figure I.6) and the uniformitarian James Hutton (Figure I.7) were clearly the leaders of their respective groups. Cuvier, a French scholar of

FIGURE I.6 Georges Cuvier (1769–1832), leader of the school of Catastrophism. (Brown Brothers.)

FIGURE I.7 James Hutton (1729–1797), the "father" of modern geology. (Dover Publications Inc., New York.)

great reputation, argued that the earth had repeatedly undergone incredibly violent upheavals of a sort that could not currently be observed during the normal day-by-day activities of our planet. Cuvier functioned within the intellectual framework, perhaps religiously inspired, that the earth is relatively young (thousands of years old). Consider his statement, excerpted from a treatise written in 1817:

> [Fossil seashells] have therefore once lived in the sea, and been deposited by it; the sea consequently must have rested in the places the deposition has taken place. Hence it is evident that the basin or reservoir containing the sea has undergone some change at least, either in extent, or in situation, or in both. Such is the result of the very first search, and of the most superficial examination. . . . This change was sudden, instantaneous not gradual, and that which is so clearly the case in this last catastrophe is not less true of those which preceded it. The dislocation and overturning of the older strata show without any doubt that the causes which brought them into the position which they now occupy, were sudden and violent.

Theories of sudden catastrophic change such as this were based on rock exposures similar to that depicted in Figure I.8. Cuvier, with Steno's Laws in mind, was particularly concerned with the significance of the surface separating older rocks from younger ones. Such a surface, called an **unconformity**, was judged to have formed suddenly during the same brief interval when the older rocks were undergoing "dislocation and overturning." Such an explanation is unavoidable for someone operating under the assumption that the earth is quite young. It is not, however, the only interpretation.

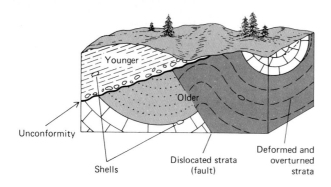

Younger

Older

Unconformity

Shells

Dislocated strata
(fault)

Deformed and
overturned
strata

FIGURE I.8 Block diagram showing an
unconformity and other rock relationships.
See text for discussion.

Let us now consider, in contrast, how it was possible for James
Hutton to view similar rock relationships and be led to significantly
different explanations for their origin. Hutton, a Scot who was
trained in medicine and prospered as an agriculturist, was an avid
student of present-day earth processes. He became profoundly influenced by strong similarities existing between modern and ancient
features of the earth. He observed that sedimentary features in
beach deposits along the coast of Scotland are essentially indistin-
guishable from those seen in hard rocks located in the highlands
many miles from the sea. Sediment-laden streams flowing to the
sea, he proposed, clearly attest to the slow destruction of land. Hutton reasoned that the processes he was observing were capable of
bringing about a sequence of changing geographies whose record
is frozen into rocks of the earth's crust—capable, that is, if these
present-day processes had been able to operate over inconceivably
long periods. So impressed was Hutton by this explanation that he
quickly accepted the conclusion that the earth is truly ancient. Indeed, in 1795 he wrote that, as far as he could determine, for the
earth there is "no vestige of a beginning, no prospect of an end."*

Hutton's analysis of the unconformity separating the older and
younger rock strata in Figure I.8 would surely have been that it
represented a very long period of time during which slow geologic
processes such as folding and faulting (breaking) of layers caused
the marine sediments to rise above sea level and to undergo prolonged erosion until they became essentially featureless. Later subsidence of the region then led to renewed deposition of sediment
burying the eroded surface (Figure I.9). The contrast between this
interpretation and Cuvier's could hardly be more extreme. Hutton
saw the unconformity as documenting a very old earth that had
slowly changed through time by means of presently observable processes; in the words of Archibald Geikie (1905), he was guided by
the view that "the present is the key to the past." That same uncon-

* Theory of the Earth, with Proofs and Illustrations, 1795, 2 vol., Royal Society of Edinburgh.

Deposition of older strata below sea level

Sea level

Passage of time

Folding and dislocation causing elevation above sea level and erosion begins

Passage of time

Surface of deep erosion

Erosion eventually destroys most of the uplifted terrain

Passage of time

Subsidence below sea level initiates new deposition

Unconformity

Sea level

FIGURE I.9   Sequence of events leading to the relationships shown in Figure I.8.

formity and the strata surrounding it, when viewed from the perspective of a different paradigm, led Cuvier to conclude, "Without any doubt . . . the causes which brought them into the position which they now occupy were sudden and violent." Both Hutton and Cuvier recognized orderly changes through time. Their great disagreement concerned the pace at which the changes occurred and the processes responsible for them.

The doctrine of uniformitarianism, with its insistence that the earth has great antiquity and its commitment to the assumption that matter and energy have always interacted in an unchanging and hence "lawful" manner throughout the earth's long history, was thus put forth by James Hutton during the late 1700s. The triumph of this view, however, was not immediate. Catastrophism did not easily suffer defeat, and intellectual battles raged on into the 1830s until, with the publication of Charles Lyell's three-volume *Principles of Geology* (1830–1833), this most important of revolutions in geology was, for all practical purposes, won. Lyell's *Principles* was, in effect, the first textbook in geology (Figure I.10). The fact that such a book could be written was an affirmation that a new paradigm had emerged. It was destined to exert a strong influence on how men would view themselves and the universe. Charles Darwin, for example, carried the first volume of Lyell's *Principles* up the gangplank of the *H.M.S. Beagle* with him in 1831, at the beginning of the five-year voyage during which he developed the initial ideas of a mechanism to account for organic evolution. Darwin later commented: "I feel as if my books came half out of Sir Charles Lyell's brain."

Many new geologic insights have marked the remainder of the nineteenth century and the twentieth century till now. They have all flourished from research founded upon the paradigm of uniformitarianism. However, the term *uniformitarianism* did not, originally at least, have the same meaning for all geologists. There emerged a threefold ambiguity as to whether a person advocating uniformitarianism was (1) suggesting a uniformity of *rate* and *intensity* for geologic events and processes, (2) asserting that presently observable processes are *completely* sufficient to decipher earth history, or (3) simply assuming that matter and energy have always interacted in the same manner. Only the last of these interpretations has been retained as acceptable. The first two attitudes fail to account for the evolution of the earth's sources of energy and its physical and chemical systems. Inasmuch as the energy of the earth is less now than it was in the past, we cannot reasonably expect all geologic processes to have maintained their intensity during several billions of years. We do, however, assume that these processes, whatever their intensities, have continued to act according to uniform laws throughout this long span of time.

FIGURE I.10 a) Charles Lyell (1797–1875), author of the first textbook of geology. b) Title page of "Principles of Geology" (3 volumes), first published 1830–1833. (a: Crown copyright, Geological Survey photograph; b: G. Craven.)

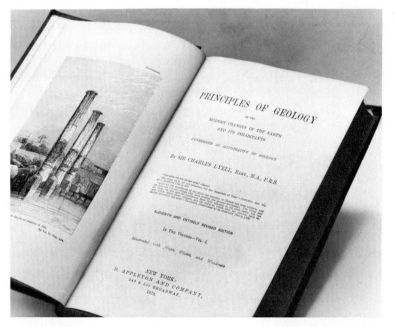

Until recently, geologists continued their investigations of the earth in the spirit of Steno, Hutton, and Lyell but were increasingly frustrated by their failure to discover principles capable of unifying many seemingly unrelated areas of study. Scientists always seek order and simplicity, and for the geologists the earth had long been a very difficult object of study. But during the 1960s, a new revolution in geology began to develop, one that we are still in the midst of today.

Later in this book (in Chapter 1 and Chapter 8) you will encounter discussions of "plate tectonics" as a model describing major rigid "plates" of crustal rock and the interactions that take place between them. Acceptance of this new paradigm represents the revolutionary overthrow of many long-entrenched geologic notions. Our ocean floors, for example, are now considered to be among the youngest major features of the earth, whereas just a few years ago, prior to the development of the plate tectonics model, they were universally acknowledged to represent rocks of great age. Many other examples of dramatic changes could be cited, but at this point it will suffice to recognize that the unprecedented vitality and excitement currently found in the geological sciences are direct consequences of this most recent scientific revolution involving the paradigm of plate tectonics and the new perspectives it has provided. Many previously insoluble problems will become less difficult when now viewed within this framework.

ADDITIONAL READINGS

* ADAMS, F. D.: *The Birth and Development of the Geological Sciences,* The Williams & Wilkins Company, Baltimore, 1938 (Dover Publications paperback edition, 1954). A standard and detailed history of earth studies from classical times through the early nineteenth century.

*ALBRITTON, C. C., Jr. (ed.): *The Fabric of Geology,* Freeman, Cooper & Co., Stanford, Calif., 1963. Advanced essays on the history and philosophy of the geological sciences, with extensive bibliographies.

*GEIKIE, A.: *The Founders of Geology,* Macmillan Publishing Co., Inc., 1905 (Dover Publications paperback edition, 1962). Classic history of geology through the midnineteenth century.

* Available in paperback.

*Fenton, C. L., and M. A. Fenton: *Giants of Geology*, Doubleday & Co., Inc., Garden City, N.Y., 1952. Well-written, popular biographies of influential nineteenth-century geologists.

*Kuhn, T. S.: *The Structure of Scientific Revolutions*, The University of Chicago Press, Chicago, 1962.

Shea, J. H.: "Twelve Fallacies of Uniformitarianism," *Geology*, 10, no. 9 (September 1982), 455–60. An analysis of misleading views about uniformitarianism that are widely held within the geological community.

Stent, G. S.: "Prematurity and Uniqueness in Scientific Discovery," *Scientific American*, December 1972, pp. 84–93.

1

The New Geology – A Basic Model

D

URING THE MIDDLE AND LATE
1960s, a major scientific revolution occurred within the geological sciences. This change in thinking provided geologists with a new model for explaining and investigating the many dynamic processes of the earth. In a sense, this view, called **plate tectonics**, created a new geology, and because of the plate tectonics model, a host of previously ignored, or poorly understood, geological problems were satisfactorily integrated and explained through the application of this new perspective.

PLATE TECTONICS

The plate tectonics model asserts that most dynamic geologic processes such as volcanic eruptions, earthquakes, mountain building, and the like occur because of interactions between the edges of large, slowly moving (centimeters per year), rigid slabs of earth. These slabs are 60–100 km thick and are called **lithosphere** (*litho* = rock, plus *sphere*). They are slowly sliding over a weaker portion of the earth's interior called the **asthenosphere** (*asthen* = weak, plus *sphere*). Figure 1.1 is a side view of the outer portion of the upper earth as the plate tectonics model envisions it. *Tectonics* refers to large-scale movements of the earth, and *plates* are composed

FIGURE 1.1 The lithosphere is rigid and is composed of the entire crust and the upper part of the mantle ("mantle" is the rock beneath the crust). The asthenosphere is more plastic and weaker than the zones above it and below it.

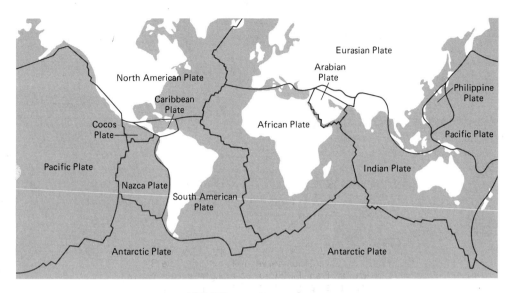

FIGURE 1.2 Twelve major lithospheric plates.

of slabs of lithosphere. As stated earlier, differential movements of these huge plates (there are twelve major plates recognized; see Figure 1.2) are believed to account for most of the earth's dynamic features. Not much earth movement or volcanic activity occurs within the interior of a plate because each plate is rigid, but where one plate is in contact with another plate, geologic "fireworks" result. Plate boundaries are marked by earthquakes and in some cases by volcanic activity.

PLATE BOUNDARIES

Three types of plate boundary exist. The first occurs along oceanic ridge-rise systems where liquid rock wells up from within the asthenosphere and creates new oceanic crust. This is the spreading ridge boundary. This new oceanic crust moves horizontally from both sides of the ridge-rise system and thus is added to the two plates on either side. This plate boundary is where new lithosphere forms (Figure 1.3). These divergent zones, commonly called ridges or rises, (Figure 1.4) are characterized by earthquakes that are relatively small and shallow (less than 60 km deep).

The creation of new crust along plate boundaries must be balanced by the destruction of old crust elsewhere on a moving plate. If this were not so, the earth would be continuously expanding in diameter, and this prospect has no convincing evidence to support

THE NEW GEOLOGY—A BASIC MODEL

Plate B

TRANSFORM FAULT

Plate A

Plate C

Lithosphere   Lithosphere   Lithosphere

Asthenosphere   Asthenosphere

SUBDUCTION ZONE   SPREADING RIDGE

Molten rock formed

FIGURE 1.3   Shown above are three lithospheric plates (separated by yellow lines). There is convergence between Plate A and Plate B and divergence between Plate B and Plate C except along the transform fault where there is horizontal slipping with Plate C moving to the right, and Plate B moving to the left. Plate A is represented as having a fixed position in this drawing; therefore there is convergence between it and Plate B.

FIGURE 1.4   Spreading Ridge. Spreading of Central Iceland where the Midatlantic Ridge extends on shore. (Photo by Sigurdur Thorarinsson.)

FIGURE 1.5 Mountains formed above a subduction zone. Quito, Ecuador. (B. Wuth)

it. It is clear, instead, that many plates are bounded by zones in which rigid lithosphere abruptly descends deep into the asthenosphere, where ultimately it is destroyed by melting. This is the second type of plate boundary. Such regions, called **subduction zones,** (Figure 1.5) are usually marked by deep oceanic trenches and deep-focus earthquakes caused by movements at the margin of the descending plate (Figure 1.3). Melting of the descending slab and adjacent asthenosphere commonly causes volcanism. In such zones, mountain building and intense crumpling of rock layers occur because of the compression at these convergent boundaries.

If crust is created at one side of a moving plate and is destroyed at the other, there must be additional boundaries where compensating motions take place without either plate creation or destruction. This third type of plate boundary is marked by long faults caused by horizontal motions between adjacent plates (Figure 1.3). These faults are now commonly called **transform faults,** (Figure 1.6) a name suggested by the Canadian geophysicist J. Tuzo Wilson in 1965, since they occur where new crust zones (e.g., midocean ridges) abruptly end, and so the fault is where one feature is "transformed" into another.

Consider Figure 1.7(a) and (b), which shows the geometry of the three kinds of plate boundary. If Plate 2 is thrust under Plate 1, there is a **subduction zone** along line AB. CD is simultaneously pulled open, so it is analogous to a **spreading ridge.** Pure horizontal

THE NEW GEOLOGY—A BASIC MODEL

. **FIGURE 1.6** Transform Fault. San Andreas Fault, Carrizo Plain, Central California. (R. E. Wallace, U.S. Geological Survey.)

FIGURE 1.7 Three types of plate boundaries: Plate 2 moves toward the left, while Plate 1 remains stationary. Plates 1 and 2 converge along AB, diverge along CD, and slip horizontally along BC and AD as a result of the movement.

(a)

Before movement of Plate 2 to the left.

(b)

After movement of Plate 2 to the left.

motion, such as characterizes a **transform fault**, takes place along lines BC and AD. These are the basic interactions that occur along lithospheric plate boundaries.

The extent to which this new model of the earth has enabled geologists to understand many previously insoluble problems has been truly remarkable. We are, indeed, in an era of geologic discovery that is unprecedented—an era of "The New Geology." Not all geologic processes can be related to plate tectonics, especially those involving landscape evolution by weathering and erosion, but throughout this book an effort will be made to relate all dynamic geologic processes to plate interactions.

ADDITIONAL READINGS

Chapter 8 will develop plate tectonics to a far greater extent than has been introduced here. After reading that chapter, the readings suggested at its conclusion are recommended.

Basic Building Blocks — Matter and Minerals

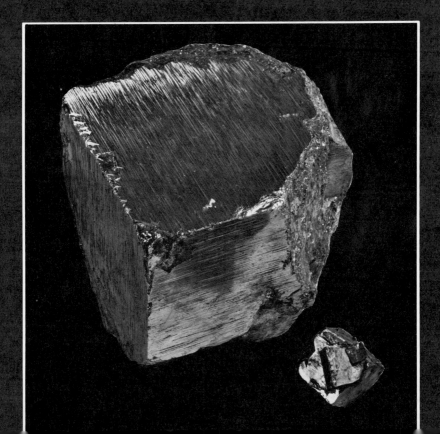

P

HYSICAL GEOLOGY IS CONCERNED
with the origin of earth materials and how they have been changed
through time. It is appropriate, therefore, to begin with an introduction to the materials that make up the solid earth.

Earth materials are traditionally and most conveniently considered on two different scales: (1) The units of smaller scale are **minerals**, natural substances of uniform chemical composition possessing a definite crystalline structure. Each mineral has a combination of composition and structure that characterizes it and no other. About 2,000 different minerals have been found, but only about 20 common ones make up the bulk of the earth. Some examples among these common minerals are mica, quartz, and gypsum. (2) The units of larger scale are **rocks**, usually aggregates of several different minerals that have been brought together by one of many rock-forming processes. Examples are granite, basalt, and sandstone. Unlike minerals, rocks are not rigidly defined by their composition and structure since they may be composed of endlessly varying mixtures of minerals. Nevertheless, only about 20 mineral combinations are really common; these 20 rocks make up most of the solid earth.

Rocks and minerals, like all other substances, or **matter**, in the universe, are composed of elemental particles assembled according to certain fundamental principles. Before we look more closely at the common rocks and minerals, it will be useful to turn to this smaller scale and review some of these principles. In Chapters 3 and 4 we shall discuss the major categories of rocks found on earth and learn how their origins are better understood in the light of plate tectonics.

MATTER

2.1
ELEMENTS AND COMPOUNDS

The simplest forms of matter that normally concern earth scientists are the **elements**, substances that cannot be broken down into other substances by chemical means. There are 88 such elements known to occur naturally; in addition, 15 others have been produced artificially by physicists using atomic reactors and particle accelerators.

These 103 elements are the basic building blocks of *all* matter, living and nonliving, on earth. The interrelationships of the elements are best shown by arranging them into a **periodic table,** which groups together elements with similar physical and chemical characteristics (Figure 2.1). Reviewing the complete periodic table would be a cumbersome introduction to the structure of earth materials were not most of the elements extremely rare in the earth. Indeed, the rocks and minerals of the solid earth are made up almost entirely of only 10 elements—those shown in color in Figure 2.1. Five additional elements, shown in gray in Figure 2.1, are of less importance in the solid earth but are abundant in the water and air. Our primary concern throughout this book will be with these 15 elements that make up the bulk of the earth, although we shall have occasion to investigate several others of special interest.

The properties of the elements are expressed in the periodic table in the following way: the elements become progressively heavier from left to right and from top to bottom. Thus hydrogen (element 1, upper left) is the lightest element and lawrencium (element 103), the heaviest. Note that the most abundant elements are all relatively light; no element heavier than nickel (element 28) is among the 15. The periodic table also associates in vertical "groups" those elements having similar chemical properties. For example, the 6 elements in the extreme right-hand column (group

FIGURE 2.1 Periodic table of the elements. The 10 abundant solid earth elements are shaded in color; the abundant fluid earth elements are shaded in gray. The steplike line separates metals (below) from nonmetals (above). Asterisk denotes a man-made element. Elements 104 and 105 have been tentatively created and identified in the Soviet Union.

VIII) are all very stable, nonreactive gases called the **noble gases.** For the abundant elements of the earth, this columnar grouping shows that sodium and potassium, although differing in weight, have similar chemical properties, as do the pairs magnesium-calcium, carbon-silicon, and oxygen-sulfur. Although it is listed in group I, hydrogen has properties found in no other element.

Pure elements seldom occur in nature; instead, two or more elements are usually found chemically combined in substances called **compounds,** which are usually more stable than pure ("free") elements. Within the solid earth, only carbon, sulfur, copper, and iron are found in any abundance as free elements, and even these four are much more common in compounds such as *calcium carbonate,* a compound of calcium, carbon, and oxygen that makes up ordinary limestone, or *iron disulfide,* the familiar "fool's gold" that is a compound of iron and sulfur. With few exceptions, then, the bulk of the earth is composed of chemical compounds.

Why is it that elements typically have greater stability when in combination than in their pure form? To answer this question we must take a closer look at them and develop a **model** to explain how they function.

2.2
AN ATOMIC MODEL

Our discussions of earth materials will deal primarily with elements and compounds, but in order to understand better the behavior of these materials, we shall now briefly consider the components of the elements themselves and the ways that elements combine to make compounds. The smallest particles of an element that still possess its characteristic properties are called **atoms.** Reactions between unlike atoms form compounds. Just as elements are made up of individual atoms, so are compounds composed of combinations of elements bonded together in definite proportions. Common salt (sodium chloride), for example, is a combination of the elements sodium and chlorine. Strictly speaking, this combination involves particles of each called **ions,** rather than the more familiar "atoms." This distinction will be clarified shortly. That a difference truly exists between atoms and ions can be anticipated, though, by noting the contrast between table salt and its elemental components. If a sample of table salt was separated to yield uncombined sodium and chlorine, the properties of the compound would be lost, for chlorine alone is a poisonous, greenish gas and sodium is a gray, explosively reactive metal.

Until the beginning of this century, scientists believed that

FIGURE 2.2 A schematic representation of the concentric electron shells of the silicon atom. Silicon, with atomic number 14, has 14 electrons distributed in three shells—two in the inner, eight in the middle, and four in the outer shell.

the atoms of the chemical elements were indivisible units of matter. Then, in the early 1900s, a model for the atom emerged that was more helpful to scientists in their efforts to understand how elements interact with each other. Although this model is now known to be oversimplified, it will nevertheless be satisfactory for our purposes.* It proposes a central **nucleus** containing most of the mass of the atom, surrounded by one or more extremely tiny, rapidly moving, and electrically charged particles called **electrons**. Researchers also found that the manner in which the elements combine to make compounds is determined by the number of electrons surrounding the nucleus. Each element has a characteristic number of electrons, ranging from only 1 in hydrogen to 103 in lawrencium. The normal number of electrons corresponds to the **atomic number** of the element (atomic numbers are shown above the element symbols in Figure 2.1).

The positions of the electrons around the nucleus are not random; instead, the rapidly moving electrons occur in concentric, cloudlike clusters called **shells** (Figure 2.2). The innermost shell of a given atom always contains only two electrons (or one in hydrogen), and any additional electrons are arranged in complex cycles of eight to form additional shells. The electron arrangement is important because the manner in which elements combine to form compounds is largely determined by the number of electrons in the *outermost* shell. The number of these outer-shell electrons for the 15 most

---

* It is important to remember that *all* scientific models are mental constructs; they *are not* "truth." It is sensible to use whichever model is simplest, yet appropriate, for whatever task is at hand. Inasmuch as models are *tools* for thinking, we shall always attempt to use the most convenient one, so long as it adequately serves our purpose.

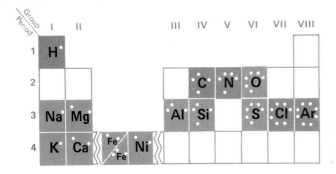

FIGURE 2.3 Electron-dot formulas of the 15 abundant elements. The dots show the number of electrons in the outermost electron shell.

abundant elements is shown arranged around their element symbols in Figure 2.3.

The most stable elements are those with completely filled outer shells containing *eight electrons*. Examples are the previously mentioned noble gases (helium,* neon, argon, krypton, xenon, and radon) occupying group VIII in the periodic table. These gases almost never react with other elements to form compounds. In contrast, the most reactive elements are those that are only one or two electrons short of having a completely filled outer shell—that is, those having one, two, six, or seven electrons in that shell. These elements occur in groups I, II, VI, and VII of the periodic table. As was seen with the noble gases, the presence of eight electrons in the outer shell seems to be a highly stable configuration, so much so that elements not intrinsically possessing that structure react in a variety of ways to achieve it. These are the reactions that give rise to the formation of compounds. In general, elements with one or two electrons in the outer shell tend to react with those having six or seven electrons in the outer shell to form stable compounds having complete outer shells containing eight electrons. Thus two atoms of hydrogen, with one outer electron each, combine with one atom of oxygen, with six outer electrons, to form a single molecule of water (Figure 2.4).

FIGURE 2.4 A schematic representation of the combination of two hydrogen atoms with one oxygen atom to form a molecule of water sharing eight outer shell electrons.

* Helium is an exception, having only two electrons—which nevertheless fill the first shell and thus yield a stable configuration.

There are two models frequently used to describe how the bonding between elements takes place in the formation of compounds.* One model involves forming electrically charged particles called **ions**, usually formed long ago by electrons *moving* away from or onto an atom, and the other model envisions the *sharing* of one atom's electrons with another atom; compounds formed by these different mechanisms are said to possess **ionic** and **covalent** bonds, respectively (Figure 2.5). Why are there two different types? The fundamental answer to this question is, "We do not know," but within the framework of our models there does seem to be an intuitive explanation. Elements that can achieve the stable eight-electron outer-shell configuration by losing or gaining only one or two electrons tend to do just that, thus forming ions capable of bonding by electrical attraction with oppositely charged ions. On the other hand, elements that require the transfer of several electrons to become ions tend not to do so; instead, they tend to form covalent bonds. Carbon and silicon, for example, would each require the movement of four electrons to form ions. Apparently it is more efficient for them to achieve a stable configuration by sharing the electrons of other atoms than by moving so many of their own.

You may be thinking, "How do we know that such differences really exist?" Observing a grain of table salt and a grain of sugar, for example, what is the evidence supporting the assertion that salt is ionically bonded and that sugar is covalently bonded? Because no one can directly see electrons, circumstantial evidence must be

FIGURE 2.5   (a) Ionic bonding (electron transfer). (b) Covalent bonding (electron sharing).

Table salt: NaCl

Na^{+1} ion
(1 electron transferred away, leaving outer shell with 8)

10 electrons total

18 electrons total

Electrical attraction

Cl^{-1} ion
(1 electron gained, thus filling outer shell with 8)

+1 CHARGE   −1 CHARGE

(a)

Methane: CH_4

Hydrogen atom (1 electron only)

Carbon atom (4 electrons in outer shell +4 shared electrons from hydrogen)

(b)

*There are several other bonding models of lesser geologic significance not being considered here.

Table salt in water

Battery

Sugar in water

Battery

Ions in solution
(Electricity flows)

Molecules (neutral) in solution
(No vehicle to carry electricity)

FIGURE 2.6 Ions versus molecules in solution. The electrically charged ions in solution facilitate the flow of electricity; neutral molecules cannot.

used in generating these two different models for chemical bonding. For example, a simple yet convincing test for salt and sugar involves dissolving both in separate beakers of water and observing the effects of attempting to pass an electrical current through each (Figure 2.6): the current flows through the salt water, but the sugar water fails to transmit any electricity. Our models for the bonding within each compound are wholly consistent with these observations: the flow of electricity is essentially the bumping along of electrons, requiring the presence of electrically charged particles (ions), whereas the presence of neutral molecules of covalently bonded sugar would not provide a suitable medium for electron movement. It is evidence of this sort, derived from observable properties of elements and compounds, that has led to the formulation of different models for chemical bonding.

The number of electrons gained, lost, or shared by an element when it forms an ion or bonds covalently determines the **oxidation number** of that element. By convention, elements that tend to *receive* electrons during the process of forming compounds are given negative oxidation numbers, whereas those that tend to *donate* electrons are given positive numbers. All compounds contain elements having both positive and negative oxidation numbers.

The **empirical formula** for a compound gives the simplest proportion in which its elements combine. One can deduce such a formula by remembering that the sum of all positive oxidation numbers must equal the sum of all negative oxidation numbers. Consider the following examples:

EXAMPLE 1: (Mineral Quartz)

$$\text{Silicon} + 2 \text{ Oxygen} = SiO_2$$
$$Si^{+4} \qquad 2 \times O^{-2}$$
$$\left(\begin{array}{c}\text{total positive} \\ \text{charge is 4}\end{array}\right) = \left(\begin{array}{c}\text{total negative} \\ \text{charge is 4}\end{array}\right)$$

FIGURE 2.7 The normal oxidation numbers of the 15 abundant elements.

EXAMPLE 2: (Mineral Corundum)

$$2 \text{ Aluminum} + 3 \text{ Oxygen} = Al_2O_3$$
$$2 \times Al^{+3} \qquad 3 \times O^{-2}$$
$$\left(\begin{array}{c}\text{total positive} \\ \text{charge is 6}\end{array}\right) = \left(\begin{array}{c}\text{total negative} \\ \text{charge is 6}\end{array}\right)$$

The normal oxidation numbers of the 15 most abundant elements are shown in Figure 2.7. Note that some elements may have more than one oxidation number, depending on how the electrons are gained, lost, or shared in forming a particular compound.

2.4
THE ATOMIC NUCLEUS

Although the atom's pattern of electrons determines most of an element's *chemical* properties, many *physical* properties, including the element's weight, are determined not by the electrons but by the massive nucleus around which the almost weightless electrons move. Atomic nuclei are themselves composed of two principal kinds of particles: **protons** and **neutrons**. Protons carry a positive electrical charge; each atom has the same number of protons as electrons because the positively charged protons in the nucleus serve to balance the negative electrical charges of the surrounding electrons. Thus the atomic number of an element corresponds not only to the number of electrons in that element but also to the number of protons.

Neutrons, in contrast, have no electrical charge and may be thought of as single particles, each composed of both a proton and an electron that balance each other in charge but are grossly unequal in weight. The much larger proton contributes almost all the mass of the neutron. The important point about neutrons is that in a random sample of atoms of a single element, the individual atoms may have *differing numbers of neutrons* in their nuclei, whereas each atom will have the same *fixed number of protons and surrounding electrons* (Figure 2.8). Because an element may have atoms

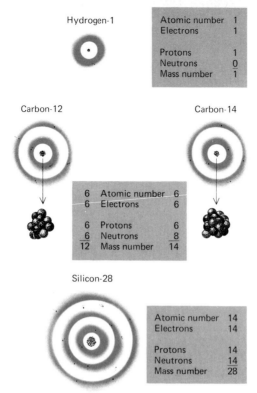

Hydrogen-1

Atomic number	1
Electrons	1
Protons	1
Neutrons	0
Mass number	1

Carbon-12   Carbon-14

6	Atomic number	6
6	Electrons	6
6	Protons	6
6	Neutrons	8
12	Mass number	14

Silicon-28

Atomic number	14
Electrons	14
Protons	14
Neutrons	14
Mass number	28

FIGURE 2.8 Schematic representations of four nuclides: hydrogen-1, carbon-12, carbon-14, and silicon-28.

with differing numbers of (heavy) neutrons, each element occurs in differing weight configurations called **nuclides.** Nuclides of a single element differ in number of neutrons and in weight but not in ordinary chemical properties.

In principle, any element might have any number of neutrons in its nucleus, thus leading to an infinite number of nuclides. In fact, however, most nuclides are *unstable*; that is, the nuclear forces of attraction are insufficient to hold the neutrons together. In these circumstances the neutrons "decay" by breaking into separate electrons, protons, or other particles; this decay process is called **radioactivity.** Many thousands of nuclides are known, but only about 270 are stable, an average of less than 3 stable nuclides per element. All other nuclides are radioactive and tend to decay at rates that are constant for a particular nuclide but vary greatly between nuclides. For most of these nuclides the decay rate is so rapid that they do not occur naturally on earth (any that were present early in earth history having long since decayed) but must be created artificially in nuclear reactors and particle accelerators.

Because almost all the weight of an atom comes from its neutrons and protons, nuclides are distinguished by the total number of *both* types of particles in the nucleus. This total is known as the **mass number** of the nuclide. All the important naturally occur-

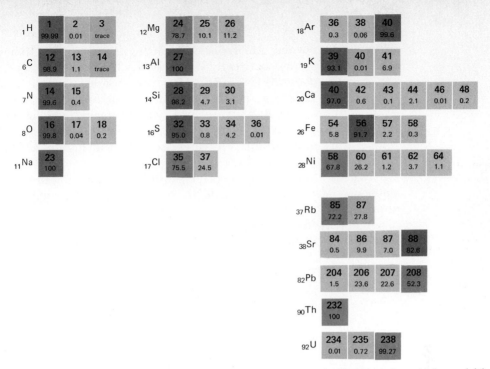

FIGURE 2.9 Natural nuclides of the 15 common elements and of 5 additional elements (lower right) important in earth chronology (see Chapter 5). Radioactive nuclides are shown in color. The lower numbers of each box show the percentage abundance of each nuclide in natural mixtures of the element; darker shading indicates dominant nuclides. (Data from Wedepohl, "Handbook of Geochemistry," vol. 1, 1969.)

ring nuclides and their mass numbers are shown in Figure 2.9. Most elements occur in nature not as pure nuclides but as relatively uniform mixtures containing all the natural nuclides of that element. The proportions of each nuclide in these mixtures are also shown in Figure 2.9.

2.5
GASES, LIQUIDS, AND SOLIDS

Let us now turn from the structure of atoms and ions to a more general consideration of the three *states* or *phases*—gaseous, liquid, and solid—in which matter can occur. Most elements and compounds can exist in each of the three phases, depending on the physical conditions, particularly temperature and pressure, to which they are subjected. At room temperature and normal atmospheric pressure, 90 of the 103 elements are solids, 11 are gases, and only 2 (bromine and mercury) are liquids. With changing temperature and pressure, however, the elements, and compounds made up of them, may pass from one state to another. The most familiar example is water: At normal atmospheric pressure, it is a solid ice below 0°C (32°F), a liquid between 0 and 100°C (32 and 212°F), and a gas steam above 100°C (212°F). Most people are aware of these temperature effects on water, but less familiar are the effects of changes in pressure. At high pressures, water remains liquid at temperatures as great as 371°C (700°F). The combined effects of both temperature and pressure on water are shown in Figure 2.10, an example of a **phase diagram**.

At the atomic level, the principal differences among the three states of matter relate to the *degree of ordering* of the constituent atoms or ions. In typical solids, the atoms or ions have a very regular arrangement; most commonly they are joined in rigid geometrical frameworks (Figure 2.11). Such complete frameworks seldom exist

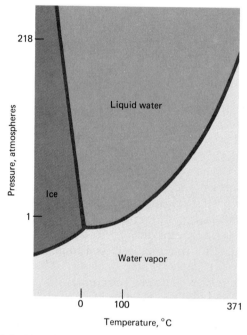

FIGURE 2.10 Phase diagram for water, showing the relation of the gaseous, liquid and solid phases to pressure and temperature (not to scale).

FIGURE. 2.11 Solid, liquid, and gaseous states: a schematic representation of the degree of atomic ordering in the three states of matter.

Solid (crystalline space lattice)   Liquid   Gas

in liquids, although the atoms are still held in close associations. In gases the atoms (or molecules, in the case of gaseous compounds) are completely separated from each other and move about freely. Many processes important to an understanding of the earth are concerned with transformations among these three states. Liquid-gas transitions are particularly crucial in the interaction of the ocean and atmosphere, whereas liquid-solid transitions, and the resulting solid state, are of primary importance in the minerals that make up the solid earth.

PROPERTIES OF MINERALS

2.6
MINERAL STRUCTURE

Naturally occurring inorganic solids of fixed chemical composition are called **minerals**. There are, however, some materials that superficially seem to be minerals, such as glass and opal, that in a precise sense do not qualify because they lack the internal geometric regularity required of matter to be classified as solid. Glass, for example, has the slightly disordered structure of a liquid and may best be thought of as a supercooled liquid rather than a true solid (Figure 2.11). Matter having internal orderliness is said to be **crystalline**, and all minerals are by definition crystalline. An individual crystal is characterized by an extensive three-dimensional pattern of repeated atoms or ions called a **crystalline space lattice** (Figure 2.11). Most solid substances found in nature are aggregates of many such individual crystals. Inasmuch as we cannot directly look into an individual crystal and see its crystalline space lattice, you might legitimately ask, "How is it known that such regularity exists?" The evidence for internal orderliness is largely circumstantial but compelling. It derives from four major properties of minerals:

Crystals are characteristically bounded by flat surfaces, called *crystal faces*, which are large-scale reflections of the internal arrangement of the atoms in the crystal. Long before the principles of atomic structure were understood, study of the arrangement of faces in natural crystals showed that crystals can be divided into six basic groups, each with a characteristic symmetry of the faces (Figure 2.12). These six groups of crystals, each of which can be divided into additional subgroups, provided the principal clues to the structure of solid matter. As early as 1669, Steno recognized that even though the arrangement of faces sometimes varies for a given mineral, *the angles between corresponding faces of a mineral remain constant*. This statement has become known as the *law of constancy*

1. CRYSTAL FORM

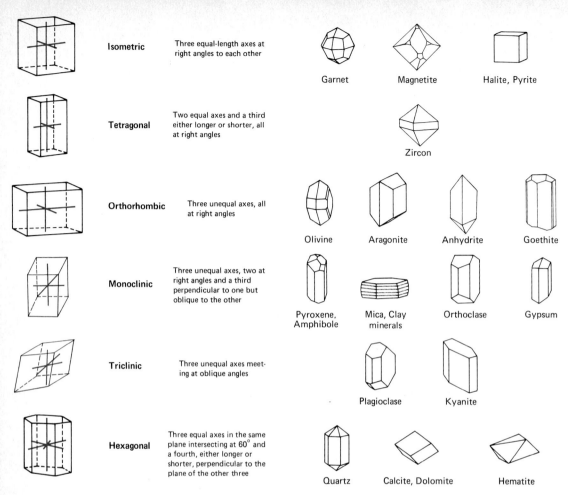

Isometric	Three equal-length axes at right angles to each other	Garnet Magnetite Halite, Pyrite
Tetragonal	Two equal axes and a third either longer or shorter, all at right angles	Zircon
Orthorhombic	Three unequal axes, all at right angles	Olivine Aragonite Anhydrite Goethite
Monoclinic	Three unequal axes, two at right angles and a third perpendicular to one but oblique to the other	Pyroxene, Amphibole Mica, Clay minerals Orthoclase Gypsum
Triclinic	Three unequal axes meeting at oblique angles	Plagioclase Kyanite
Hexagonal	Three equal axes in the same plane intersecting at 60° and a fourth, either longer or shorter, perpendicular to the plane of the other three	Quartz Calcite, Dolomite Hematite

FIGURE 2.12 The six basic systems of crystal symmetry. Drawings at left show the simplest crystal form of each system, with crystallographic axes in color. At right are typical crystal forms of the common minerals in each system.

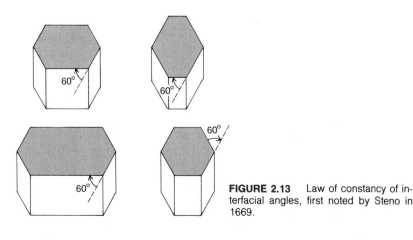

FIGURE 2.13 Law of constancy of interfacial angles, first noted by Steno in 1669.

of interfacial angles (Figure 2.13). Such external regularity could almost certainly not exist except as an effect of an internally regular crystalline space lattice.

Many crystals fracture in a manner that yields smooth planar surfaces that develop only at fixed orientations with respect to their external form (Figure 2.14). It has long been concluded that there must be some internal control for this remarkably reproducible phenomenon. Our model suggests that there are internal planes within many crystals across which the bonding forces are weaker than across planes in other directions. It is only natural, therefore, that these weaker planes yield to fracturing more readily than stronger planes, thus producing the phenomenon of **cleavage**.

2. CLEAVAGE

FIGURE 2.14   Cleavage of mica. (Walter R. Fleischer.)

Ordinary light may be thought of as vibrating in many different planes, as diagrammatically indicated for the nonpolarized light in Figure 2.15 before it enters the calcite crystal. The nonpolarized light undergoes a remarkable change as it passes through the crystal. Instead of one nonpolarized light ray emerging from the other side, two separated rays emerge, each having been caused to vibrate in only one plane (hence *plane-polarized*). Furthermore, the two planes of polarization are exactly 90 degrees from one another. Many minerals affect light in this manner, and with calcite the amount of this **double refraction** is so great that instruments are not necessary for its detection (Figure 2.16). This same experiment meets with failure when glass, or some other material lacking an orderly crystalline space lattice, is used.

3. POLARIZATION AND DOUBLE REFRACTION

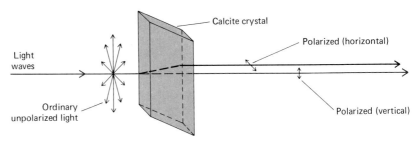

FIGURE 2.15 Polarization of light by a mineral. See text for discussion.

FIGURE 2.16 Calcite rhomb showing double refraction. (D. Ester.)

4. X-RAY PATTERNS   The most recently discovered evidence of internal regularity in crystals has also proved to be the most useful in constructing precise models of their three-dimensional framework. In 1912, it was discovered that crystals alter X-ray beams passing through them in such a way that it becomes possible to determine precisely the internal arrangement of the atoms or ions (Figure 2.17). This X-ray technique quickly supplanted older methods of measuring crystal faces and became the principal tool for studying the structure of crystalline solids. X-ray methods now also serve as a quick and reliable means of identifying even the smallest grains of a crystalline substance, for each element or compound has a distinctive pattern of X-ray transmission.

X-ray studies of atomic structure, combined with other lines of evidence, have shown that the arrangement of atoms and ions in crystals is largely determined by two properties: the *size* and *oxidation number* of the constituent atoms. In order to visualize how these properties affect crystal structure, it is helpful to think of individual atoms or ions as small spheres that become packed together to form crystals. These spheres tend to arrange themselves so that positive and negative oxidation numbers are balanced and

FIGURE 2.17 X-ray determination of crystal structure. The X-ray pattern shown indicates a hexagonal arrangement of the internal ions.

Photographic film

Crystal

Lead shield   X-ray source

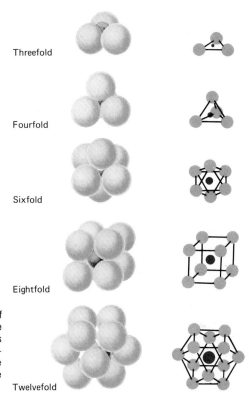

Threefold

Fourfold

Sixfold

Eightfold

FIGURE 2.18 Five types of ionic coordination. As the positive and negative (color and gray) ions become more similar in size, additional negative (gray) ions can be packed around a single positive (color) ion.

Twelvefold

so that there is a minimum distance between the spheres. When the positive and negative spheres differ greatly in size, a triangular packing arrangement is favored in which each element bonds with three adjacent atoms of opposite charge, giving rise to what is known as *threefold* coordination (Figure 2.18). As the difference in size between positive and negative elements decreases, *fourfold, sixfold*, and *eightfold* coordinations are favored. Finally, when the size of the positive and negative spheres is equal, a *twelvefold* coordination with a maximum density of closely packed spheres occurs. Figure 2.19 summarizes the normal oxidation numbers and comparative sizes of the ions that are common in rock-forming minerals. Sizes of *ions*, rather than *atoms*, have been shown in Figure 2.19

Negative

S^{-2} Cl^{-1} O^{-2} OH^{-1}

Positive

K^{+1} Ca^{+2} Na^{+1} $Fe^{+2,+3}$ Mg^{+2} Al^{+3} Si^{+4} S^{+6} C^{+4}

FIGURE 2.19 Oxidation numbers and relative sizes of ions found in common rock-forming minerals.

because the majority of common minerals may be most conveniently treated "as if" they were the products of ionic bonding. This is not precisely true, but whatever the truth is, it is too complex for us to model easily; this simpler model nicely serves our present purposes.

2.7
MINERAL COMPOSITION

As noted earlier, the relative abundances of the 103 chemical elements are such that only 10 elements make up most of the earth's minerals. This composition has been established by chemical analyses of the minerals exposed at the earth's surface in combination with less direct evidence about the materials of the earth's vast interior. The darker bars of Figure 2.20 present a modern estimate of the relative abundances of the elements most common in the entire solid earth. Note that only 8 elements constitute over 99 percent of the total earth; all the other 80 naturally occurring elements combine to make up less than 1 percent. Of these 8 elements, only 4—iron, oxygen, silicon, and magnesium—constitute over 90 percent of the solid earth.

It is now possible to apply some of the chemical principles discussed earlier to predict the *combinations* of elements present in the minerals of the solid earth. Refer again to Figure 2.19, which shows the normal oxidation numbers and ionic sizes of the principal elements. The only really abundant element with a *negative* oxidation number is oxygen. This means that in most compounds making up the solid earth, oxygen supplies the negative charge, and the other elements supply the balancing positive charges. Note also the very large size of the oxygen ion relative to all the common positive ions (except potassium). This leads us to predict that minerals are, *by volume*, mostly composed of large spheres of ionic oxygen interspersed with smaller, positively charged ions of other elements. The

FIGURE 2.20 Abundances of elements (weight percent) in the whole earth and in the surficial crust. (Data from Mason, "Principles of Geochemistry," 1966.)

character of this oxygen-positive ion interaction provides a useful means of classifying many of the 2,000 minerals that have so far been discovered in the rocks of the solid earth (Figure 2.21).

In the simplest case, oxygen combines directly with various positive ions to give oxide minerals such as *hematite* (iron oxide, Fe_2O_3). More commonly, the positive ions combine not with oxygen alone but with combinations of oxygen and additional positively charged atoms that function together as a unit in carrying the negative charge of the mineral. These combinations, called **ion groups,** have an overbalance of negative charges and thus form compounds just as if they were single, negatively charged elements. Three such atom groups are of great importance in minerals: the **silicate group,** in which oxygen combines in various proportions with silicon; the **sulfate group,** in which four oxygen ions combine with one sulfur ion; and the **carbonate group,** in which three oxygen ions combine with one carbon.*

---

* Carbon is not one of the most abundant elements of the solid earth, although it makes up a small but significant fraction of the atmosphere. Even though it composes much less than 1 percent of the crust, carbon is locally concentrated into accumulations of carbonate minerals that are of great importance in earth chemistry.

MINERAL GROUP		MINERAL	GENERALIZED CHEMICAL COMPOSITION — Positive ions						Negative ions Group of ions
			Sodium	Magnesium	Aluminum	Potassium	Calcium	Iron	
Silicates	Isolated tetrahedra	Olivine		Mg				Fe	SiO_4^{-4}
		Aluminum silicates			Al				
		Garnets		Mg	Al		Ca	Fe	
	Chain	Pyroxenes	Na	Mg	Al		Ca	Fe	SiO_4^{-4}
		Amphiboles	Na	Mg	Al		Ca	Fe	$(OH)^{-1}$
	Sheet	Micas		Mg	Al	K		Fe	SiO_4^{-4}
		Clay minerals			Al	K			$(OH)^{-1}$
	Framework	Quartz	[Si only]						SiO_4^{-4}
		Orthoclase feldspar Microcline feldspar			Al	K			
		Plagioclase feldspar	Na		Al		Ca		
Carbonates		Calcite					Ca		$(CO_3)^{-2}$
		Aragonite					Ca		
		Dolomite		Mg			Ca		
Sulfates		Gypsum					Ca		$(SO_4)^{-2}$
		Anhydrite					Ca		
Oxides		Hematite						Fe	O^{-2}, $(OH)^{-1}$
		Goethite						Fe	
		Magnetite						Fe	
		Aluminum oxides			Al				
Halide		Halite	Na						Cl^{-1}
Sulfide		Pyrite						Fe	S^{-2}

FIGURE 2.21 Classification and generalized chemical composition of the principal rock-forming minerals.

Sulfur is one of the few common elements that can have either a positive or negative oxidation number (see Figures 2.7 and 2.19). When it combines with oxygen in the sulfate atom group, its oxidation number is positive. With a negative oxidation number it provides the sole negative charge in **sulfide** minerals.

The relatively rare element chlorine occurs concentrated as the sole negative ion in the mineral *halite* (sodium chloride, NaCl).

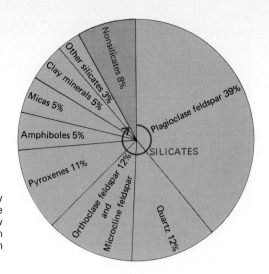

FIGURE 2.22 Percentage (by volume) of common minerals in the earth's crust. (Data from Ronov and Yoroshevsky, "American Geophysical Union Monograph 13," 1969.)

Minerals in which chlorine or other closely related elements provide the only negative charge are called **halides.**

The six principal kinds of negative chemical charges define six principal groups of rock-forming minerals: silicates, carbonates, sulfates, oxides, halides, and sulfides (Figure 2.21). A seventh mineral group can be added for those few elements—primarily carbon, iron, nickel, and sulfur—that may occur not only as compounds but also as free, uncombined elements. Such relatively rare minerals are called **native elements.** These seven mineral groups contain most of the 2,000 known minerals, of which only about 20 are really common in the solid earth (see Figure 2.22); the others are very rare and restricted in occurrence. These common rock-forming minerals are those that we shall consider here and be referring to in later chapters.

2.8

PHYSICAL PROPERTIES OF MINERALS AS A MEANS BY WHICH TO IDENTIFY THEM

We have seen that the packing pattern, bonding, and chemical composition of the atoms or ions that compose a mineral determine which mineral is formed. It follows that certain physical properties of the mineral, such as its hardness, cleavage, density, and its color-related characteristics, might serve to identify it because these properties reflect the unique chemical composition and lattice structure possessed by each different mineral. See Box 2.1.

BOX 2.1

Common Rock-Forming Minerals
(showing physical properties used in their identification)

MINERAL	COLOR	HARDNESS	CLEAVAGE DIRECTIONS	SPECIFIC GRAVITY
Quartz	light	7	none	2.65
Orthoclase* (feldspar)	light (some- times pink)	6	2 @ 90°	2.6
Plagioclase (feldspar)	light	6	2 @ 90° (w/striations)	2.6 to 2.7
Muscovite (mica)	light	2–2½	1	2.8 to 3.0
Biotite (mica)	black	2½–3	1	2.8 to 3.2
Hornblende (amphibole)	dark green– black	5–6	2 @ 56°–124°	2.9 to 3.2
Augite (pyroxene)	black	5–6	2 @ 90°	3.2 to 3.6
Olivine	pale green– black	6½–7	none	3.3 to 4.4
Calcite	usually light	3	3 @ 75°–105°	2.7
Halite	light	2½	3 @ 90°	2.1
Gypsum	light	2	3:1 perfect and 2 poor	2.3

* Orthoclase and microcline are similar in appearance and abundance, and both have the same chemical composition—$KAlSi_3O_8$.

INCREASING HARDNESS

1. Talc (very soft)
2. Gypsum
3. Calcite
4. Fluorite
5. Apatite
6. Orthoclase
7. Quartz
8. Topaz
9. Corundum
10. Diamond (very hard)

FIGURE 2.23   Mohs Hardness Scale for Minerals. Common minerals are listed in an ascending order of hardness. Higher-numbered minerals are able to scratch all lower-numbered minerals.

The degree to which a mineral surface resists being scratched is called its **hardness**. Like other physical properties of minerals, hardness is a function of crystal structure. Stronger bonding forces between atoms or ions result in greater hardness. Greater hardness means that there is greater difficulty in separating the atoms or ions. Figure 2.23 illustrates the Mohs Hardness Scale. It lists a series of minerals that have increasing hardnesses as the numerical scale is ascended. Most of the minerals are separated from the adjacent ones by about the same difference in hardness, except that diamond (number 10) is dramatically harder than corundum (number 9).

HARDNESS

If, when broken, a mineral yields parallel plane smooth surfaces that can be repeated by further breaking along parallel planes, it is said to possess **cleavage** (Figure 2.24). As mentioned earlier, the

CLEAVAGE

FIGURE 2.24   Cleavage in minerals.

(a)

Two directions at 90° (as in feldspar).

(b)

One direction (as in mica).

(c)

Two directions at oblique angles (as in amphibole).

(d)

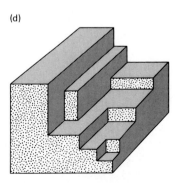

Three directions at 90° (as in halite).

property of cleavage provides evidence for the orderliness of crystalline structure because cleavage is controlled by weakness in the bonding forces that hold parallel atomic planes together. This weakness results from either weaker types of bonds or greater lattice spacing between the bonds in the direction perpendicular to the cleavage planes. In some minerals, it results from a combination of the two factors.

Many minerals do not show any cleavage, and comparatively few display it excellently; but if it can be recognized, it serves as an outstanding basis for mineral identification. One, two, three, four, or six different orientations of cleavage planes are known to exist in different minerals. Diamond, for example has four (4) directions, whereas quartz has none. It is apparent that cleavage is not a function simply of hardness since diamond is considerably harder than quartz. There are certain lattice planes within diamond across which there is weaker bonding than in other directions, even though *all* the bonds are very strong. The existence of *weaker planes* causes diamond to cleave, yet the great hardness of diamond exists because all the individual bonds within its structure are very strong. The individual bonds in quartz are not as strong as diamond; but the bonding strength across all directions of lattice planes within quartz is nearly uniform; thus there is no tendency to produce cleavage.

DENSITY OR
SPECIFIC
GRAVITY

Density is expressed as the mass of a mineral per a given volume, such as 5.02 grams per cubic centimeter as being the density of pyrite (fool's gold). Usually it is convenient to describe this physical property in terms of **specific gravity** rather than **density**. Both terms reflect the same property, however. The specific gravity of a mineral is a numerical expression of the ratio between the weight of the mineral and the weight of an equal volume of water. It is expressed by a number without units. For example, we said that pyrite has a density of 5.02 grams/cubic centimeter—thus its specific gravity is simply 5.02. That is, any chunk of the mineral pyrite would weigh 5.02 times the weight of the same volume of water.

When attempting to identify a mineral, follow the good common practice of "hefting" it. That is, bounce it in your hand, and considering its size, make an estimate of its specific gravity. The accuracy with which this can be done greatly increases with experience, but the beginner will find it useful even when only a broad distinction can be made.

PROPERTIES
DEPENDING
ON LIGHT

Minerals are described in terms of color, luster, and streak. These properties tend to be more subjective than are hardness, cleavage, and specific gravity and therefore are less useful in mineral identification. However, in some identifications, they are very important. *Color* is highly variable for some minerals, but usually a distinction

BASIC BUILDING BLOCKS—MATTER AND MINERALS

between dark- (green to black) and light- (any pale color) colored minerals is reliable. *Luster* describes the manner in which light is reflected. Metallic, glassy, waxy, and greasy are some of the adjectives used to describe luster. Some minerals have a different color when finely powdered. This color is called the mineral's *streak*.

2.9
SILICATE MINERALS

Of the principal mineral groups, the **silicates** are by far the most important because they make up about 92 percent of the earth's crust (Figure 2.22). In addition to being an extremely abundant element, silicon also has unique chemical properties that permit it to link with oxygen to form large structural networks of atoms. Silicon has an oxidation number of $+4$ and a very small ionic size (Figure 2.19); a silicon ion is always surrounded in crystal structures by four much larger oxygen ions in a fourfold coordination that resembles a geometric tetrahedron (Figure 2.25). This structural unit, the silicon-oxygen **tetrahedron,** is the *fundamental building block* of all silicate minerals. We shall continue our discussion of this important mineral group by treating these tetrahedra as large ionic units possessing a negative charge of -4 each. Inasmuch as minerals are without charge, we must consider the various ways these negatively charged tetrahedra can be bonded together to yield electrically neutral crystalline space lattices.

In the simplest case, these silicon-oxygen tetrahedra occur as isolated units, bound together only by positive metallic ions. More commonly, however, they are linked so that more complex structures—chains, sheets, or completely interlocking frameworks—are formed; these are illustrated in Figure 2.26. These structural differences define four principal groups of silicate minerals: *silicates with isolated tetrahedra, chain silicates, sheet silicates*, and *framework silicates*.* The minerals within each of these groups may be further

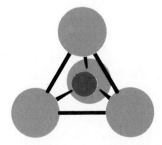

FIGURE 2.25   The silicon-oxygen tetrahedron.

* Several minor groups of silicates, whose minerals are relatively uncommon, have been omitted.

classified by the positive ions that combine with the negative silicon-oxygen tetrahedral groups. These are principally ions of sodium, magnesium, aluminum, potassium, calcium, and iron, the dominant positive elements (other than silicon) found in the earth's crust.

In the first group, the ratio of silicon to oxygen ions is $1:4$ (SiO_4) because none of the oxygen ions is shared among adjacent silicon ions (Figure 2.26). The basic oxidation number of the silicon-oxygen group is -4 since the oxidation number of the silicon is $+4$, and that of each of the four oxygen ions is -2. This large excess negative charge serves to bind a high proportion of other positive ions into the structure so that the charges are balanced. Three important mineral subgroups have this structure: the **olivines** in which magnesium and iron provide the principal additional positive ions; the **aluminum silicates,** in which aluminum is the principal positive ion; and the **garnets,** which have various complex combinations of positive ions, principally magnesium, aluminum, calcium, and iron (Figure 2.27).

FIGURE 2.26   Linking patterns of silicon-oxygen tetrahedra in silicate minerals. (a) Isolated tetrahedra; no sharing of O. (b) Single chain; each tetrahedron shares two O's. (c) Double chain; adjacent tetrahedra share two or three O's (alternating). (d) Sheet; each tetrahedron shares three O's. (e) Framework; each tetrahedron shares all four O's. A single tetrahedral unit is outlined in dark color on each pattern.

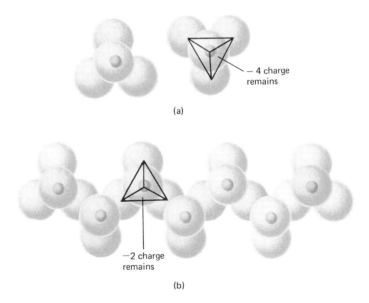

— 4 charge
remains

(a)

—2 charge
remains

(b)

FIGURE 2.26 continued

—Oxygen ion

—Silicon ion

either − 2 or − 1
charge remains

(c)

− 1 charge
remains

(d)

No charge
remains

(e)

(a)

(b)

(c)

(d)

Either
Fe^{+2} or
Mg^{+2}

Si

Mg

Fe

O

FIGURE 2.27   Isolated tetrahedra silicate minerals. (a) Olivine. (b) Aluminum silicate. (c) Garnet. (d) Diagrammatic structure of olivine. Isomorphism: Fe^{+2} and Mg^{+2} ions can substitute for each other within this space lattice in any proportion because they have the same charge and nearly the same size. (a-c: Yale Peabody Museum.)

CHAIN SILICATES   In chain silicates, oxygen ions are shared between silicon ions in such a way that long silicon-oxygen chains of two kinds are formed. In one, each silicon ion shares two of its four oxygen ions with adjacent silicon ions; this is the *single-chain structure*. The principal minerals with this structure are the **pyroxenes** (Figure 2.28), important rock-forming minerals that can contain all the common positive ions except potassium, which doesn't fit into the chain structure due to its large ionic size. The other group of chain silicates has a

(a)

(b)

FIGURE 2.28 Chain silicate minerals, (a) Pyroxene. (b) Amphibole. (c) Diagrammatic structure of a calcium- and magnesium-bearing pyroxene, showing chains held together by Ca^{++}, Mg^{++}.

(c)

double-chain structure in which adjacent silicon ions alternately share two and three of their oxygen ions. The principal double-chain silicates are the **amphiboles** (Figure 2.28). Like the closely related pyroxenes, these may contain various combinations of all the common positive atoms. Because of their structure, amphiboles and pyroxenes tend to crystallize as elongate minerals whose external shape reflects their internal chainlike arrangement.

In sheet silicates, each silicon ion shares three of its oxygen ions to form a sheetlike, two-dimensional network. Because of this arrangement, minerals with this structure tend to split into thin parallel sheets. The micas, one of two important groups of sheet silicates,

SHEET SILICATES

(a)

(b)

(c)

FIGURE 2.29   Sheet silicate minerals. (a) Mica. (b) Clay mineral [earthy mass about 2 cm (¾ in.) across; the extremely tiny individual crystals are not visible]. (c) Diagramatic structure of a mica. The large potassium ions fit between the structural sheets of silicon, oxygen, and aluminum. Note that cleavage occurs only between the sheets of silicon-oxygen tetradedra.

are common examples (Figure 2.29). Micas all contain aluminum ions, some of which replace some silicon ions in the structural tetrahedra. They are also characterized by potassium ions whose large size permits them to fit *between* the sheetlike layers of silicon-aluminum-oxygen tetrahedra [Figure 2.29(c)]. In addition, some micas contain iron and magnesium. The other important group of sheet silicates, the **clay minerals**, are similar but differ in structural detail. Clay minerals never occur as large crystals but are usually found in earthy masses of extremely tiny crystalline particles—particles that are usually so small that they can be seen only with an electron microscope. Both the clay materials and micas have water-derived oxygen-hydrogen (OH) ionic groups in their structures in addition to the principal oxygen-silicon groups.

FRAMEWORK SILICATES   In the last group, every silicon ion shares each of its four oxygen ions with adjacent silicon ions to give a three-dimensional network with a ratio of one silicon for every two oxygens (SiO_2). They are thus the most silicon-rich of the silicate minerals. Note that the basic charge of the SiO_2 is neutral since silicon's oxidation number of +4 is balanced by the two oxygen ions, each of which has an oxidation number of −2. Framework silicates have a very stable structural arrangement and are by far the most abundant of all the minerals in the earth's crust. The two principal minerals of this type are **quartz**, which is composed *only* of silicon and oxygen, and the **feldspars**, a group of minerals in which sodium, aluminum, potassium, and calcium occur in the framework in varying combinations and proportions (Figure 2.30). The bulk of the earth's crust is composed of feldspar (51 percent) and quartz (12 percent) as seen in Figure 2.22.

Because the basic electrical charge on tetrahedra in framework silicates is neutral, we need to explain how additional positive ions— such as sodium, aluminum, potassium, and calcium—can occur in the structure of the feldspars. The reason for this is related to the presence of aluminum, which is unique among all the common elements in being able to substitute for silicon in some of the silicon-oxygen tetrahedra. This is possible because the small size of the aluminum ion is close to that of silicon (see Figure 2.19). Aluminum, however, has an oxidation number of +3, whereas silicon's is +4;

(a)

(b)

FIGURE 2.30   Framework silicate minerals. (a) Quartz. (b) Orthoclase feldspar. (c) Diagrammatic structure of orthoclase feldspar. The unbalanced charges caused by the substitution of aluminum for some silicon ions serve to hold potassium in the structure. (a,b: Yale Peabody Museum.)

(c)

thus when an aluminum ion substitutes for a silicon ion, it leaves an unbalanced negative charge that serves to bind other positive ions into the structure [Figure 2.30(c)]. Two groups of feldspars are defined by these extra ions: in **orthoclase** feldspar and **microcline** feldspar, potassium is the dominant additional ion; in **plagioclase** feldspar, varying proportions of sodium and calcium dominate. The presence of these ions explains why the feldspars have cleavage, whereas quartz, a pure SiO_2 framework silicate, does not: planes of weakness occur where the metallic ions are located.

A summary of the compositions of all the major silicate minerals is given in Figure 2.21. Note again the predominance of only a few elements in the ionic structure of these common minerals; these elements are the principal constituents of the earth's crust.

Perhaps the most important aspect of our study of different silicate minerals is the recognition that physical properties of a mineral are manifestations of its crystalline space lattice structure and its chemical composition. Consider, for example, the properties of *color* and *density* for the olivine mineral group. As shown diagrammatically in Figure 2.27(d), olivine has a structure of isolated silicon-oxygen tetrahedra ionically bonded together by +2 ions of either iron or magnesium. Because iron and magnesium ions both have a +2 change and are approximately the same size (see Figure 2.19), they may substitute for each other in any proportion within the lattice structure of olivine. Olivine is said to be an **isomorphic** (*iso* = equal, *morphic* = form) mineral because of this. Olivine may be a pure iron silicate (Fe_2SiO_4), or a pure magnesium silicate (Mg_2SiO_4), or any mixture of iron and magnesium in between—but always with the same lattice structure and hence isomorphic. What differences would you predict between the iron-rich olivine and the magnesium-rich variety? Remembering that the *only* difference between them is compositional, we might expect iron ions with a mass number of 56 to impart a greater density than mass number-24 magnesium ions (see Figure 2.9). Indeed, such is the case: Fe_2SiO_4 weighs 4.4 grams per cubic centimeter, and Mg_2SiO_4 only 3.3 grams. What about color? Here again the presence of iron seems to be important. The iron-rich variety is black, whereas the magnesium-rich olivine is a pale green. A similar contrast exists in the mica group of silicates: biotite (iron-bearing mica) is black, whereas muscovite, devoid of iron, is colorless.

Cleavage is another physical property that can easily be related to a mineral's space lattice pattern. The one perfect direction of cleavage characterizing the micas, for example, results from the weak bonding between tough sheets of silicon-oxygen tetrahedra [see Figure 2.14 and 2.29(c)]. The ionic bonding between adjacent sheets is not particularly strong because the sheets themselves do

Ions bonding
chains together

approximately 90°

Pyroxene
(single chain)

56°

Amphibole
(double chain)

FIGURE 2.31 Cleavage differences for chain silicates. Weakest planes are between chains of tetrahedra, therefore wider chains (amphibole) have different cleavage angles from narrower chains (pyroxene).

not possess a great deal of negative charge to be satisfied—only −1 per tetrahedron.

Both types of chain silicates provide another instructive comparison. They both display two directions of cleavage parallel to their chains of tetrahedra because the weakest parts of their structure are where positive ions are bonding the chains together. But pyroxenes and amphiboles differ in the angles between their two cleavage directions. Figure 2.31 provides an explanation for this quantitative difference.

These examples should serve to clarify an important generalization: The physical properties displayed by a mineral are reflections of its chemical composition (atoms or ions present) and its pattern of packing (crystalline space lattice) at the atomic level.

2.10
NONSILICATE MINERALS

Although only 8 percent of the earth's crust is composed of minerals that lack the characteristic silicon-oxygen tetrahedra of the silicates, several of these nonsilicate minerals are common enough in certain geologic settings to require consideration.

In carbonate and sulfate minerals, the negative charges are provided by ionic groups of oxygen combined with either carbon or sulfur,

CARBONATES AND SULFATES

(a)

(b)

(c)

FIGURE 2.32 Carbonate minerals. (a) Calcite. (b) Dolomite. (c) Diagrammatic structure of aragonite. Each carbon atom is linked to three oxygen atoms. (a,b: Yale Peabody Museum.)

rather than with silicon as in the silicates. Carbon, like silicon, has a normal oxidation number of +4; unlike silicon, however, it combines with oxygen in only one arrangement in forming carbonate minerals. Because of the extremely small size of the carbon, it has only three attached oxygen ions arranged in a triangular, threefold coordination (see Figures 2.18 and 2.32).

There are three common carbonate minerals. Two of these, **calcite** and **aragonite**, have the same chemical composition, in which the only positive ion is calcium ($CaCO_3$). The two minerals differ only in crystal structure (minerals that differ only in structure but not in chemical composition are termed *polymorphs* of each other). In calcite, the ions are arranged with hexagonal symmetry; in aragonite, the ions have orthorhombic symmetry (see Figures 2.12 and 2.32). The other important carbonate mineral, **dolomite** [$CaMg(CO_3)_2$], is similar to calcite except that its crystal structure contains varying amounts of magnesium in addition to calcium.

FIGURE 2.33 Sulfate minerals. (a) Gypsum. (b) Diagrammatic structure of anhydrite. Each sulfur atom is linked to four oxygen atoms. (a: Yale Peabody Museum.)

In sulfate minerals, four oxygen ions combine with one positive sulfur ion to form tetrahedral atomic groups with an overall oxidation number of −2 (Figure 2.33). There are only two common sulfate minerals, and both have calcium as the only additional positive ion: **gypsum** ($CaSO_4 \cdot 2H_2O$) has water bound into the crystal structure, whereas **anhydrite** ($CaSO_4$) lacks water and has a different structural arrangement.

OXIDES

A few minerals have oxygen *alone* as the negative ion, rather than oxygen combined into ion groups with silicon, carbon, or sulfur. The most important such minerals are the **iron oxides.** Iron is one of several elements that may exist with either of two different oxidation numbers, depending on how the electrons in the outer shell combine with other elements. For iron these oxidation numbers are +2 and +3; because of them, iron combines directly with oxygen in a variety of arrangements. In one, the iron has an oxidation number of +3 and forms either the mineral **hematite** (Fe_2O_3) or the mineral **goethite** [$FeO(OH)$], which also contains an oxygen-hydrogen ionic group (from water) in its crystal structure (Figure 2.34). In addition, iron of both oxidation numbers mixes and combines with oxygen in the ratio of Fe_3O_4 to make the important iron oxide mineral **magnetite.**

A second important group of oxide minerals contains aluminum as the only positive element. Like the silicon-bearing clay minerals, these **aluminum oxides** occur mostly as earthy masses in which the individual crystals are so tiny that they can be seen only under an electron microscope.

(a)

(b)

(c)

FIGURE 2.34 Oxide minerals. (a) Hematite. (b) Goethite. (c) Diagrammatic structure of magnetite. (a,b: Yale Peabody Museum.)

HALIDES AND SULFIDES

Two other common minerals that need to be considered are the only ones made up of compounds that lack oxygen in their structure. In halite (NaCl), the negative charge is carried by the relatively rare element chlorine, with sodium as the positive ion (Figure 2.35). The other important oxygen-free mineral is pyrite (FeS_2), in which sulfur supplies the negative charge and iron the positive (Figure 2.35). Although pyrite (iron disulfide) is the only *common* mineral in the group, many *rare* sulfide minerals are of great economic importance as ore minerals for lead, copper, and zinc.

NATIVE ELEMENTS

The final group of nonsilicate minerals comprises the elements that are *not* combined into compounds but occur instead as uncombined "native" elements (Figure 2.36). Such elements are rare in the earth's crust, although some—particularly gold, silver, copper, sulfur, and carbon (as either *graphite* or the high-pressure polymorph *dia-*

(a)

(b)

FIGURE 2.35 Halide and sulfide minerals. (a) Halite. (b) Pyrite. (c) Structure model of halite. (a,b: Yale Peabody Museum.)

Cl   Na

(c)

FIGURE 2.36 Native element mineral. Diamond (carbon). (De Beers Consolidated Mines.)

mond)—are found in local concentrations that are of great economic importance. Uncombined iron, although very rare in the crust, is believed to be present in large quantities deep within the interior of the earth, where it occurs mixed with nickel and other uncombined metallic elements.

SUMMARY OUTLINE

MATTER

2.1 Elements and compounds: The bulk of the solid earth is composed of only 10 elements chemically combined in compounds.

2.2 An atomic model: An element is most stable when it has eight electrons in its outer shell (helium is an exception, having only two).

2.3 Bonding to form compounds: Ionic bonding (electron transfer) and covalent bonding (electron sharing) are models widely used to explain the formation of most compounds.

2.4 The atomic nucleus: Atomic nuclei are composed of protons and neutrons, the sum of which equals an element's atomic weight.

2.5 Gases, liquids, and solids: Transformations among these three fundamental states of matter continuously occur among the elements and compounds making up the earth's rocks, water, and air.

PROPERTIES OF MINERALS

2.6 Mineral structure: Minerals have internal orderliness, as indicated by their crystal form, cleavage, and their ability to polarize light and produce X-ray patterns.

2.7 Mineral composition: Most of the earth's solid crust is composed of crystalline minerals dominated by oxygen-silicon groups; a small but significant proportion of crustal minerals lack silicon; only a very few common minerals lack oxygen.

2.8 Physical properties of minerals: Minerals can be identified by using their hardness, cleavage, density, color, luster, and streak as diagnostic properties.

MINERAL DIVERSITY

2.9 Silicate minerals: Adjacent silicon-oxygen tetrahedra share oxygen ions in differing ratios to make four principal groups: framework, sheet, and chain silicates, and silicates with isolated tetrahedra; the physical properties of silicate minerals derive from these groups and their chemical composition.

2.10 Nonsilicate minerals: The most important mineral groups that lack silicon are carbonate, sulfate, and oxide minerals, all of which contain oxygen; and halide and sulfide minerals, which lack oxygen.

ADDITIONAL READINGS

DESAUTELS, P. E.: *The Mineral Kingdom*, Grosset & Dunlap, Inc., New York, 1968. A popular introduction to gems, minerals, and mineral collecting, with sumptuous illustrations.

DIETRICH, R. V., and B. J. SKINNER: *Rocks and Rock Minerals*, John Wiley & Sons, Inc., New York, 1980. An authoritative summary of rock-forming minerals.

*ERNST, W. G.: *Earth Materials*, Prentice-Hall, Inc., Englewood Cliffs, N. J., 1969. A comprehensive introduction to minerals and rocks.

MASON, B.: *Principles of Geochemistry*, John Wiley & Sons, Inc., New York, 1966. A clearly written and accessible introduction to all aspects of the chemistry of the earth.

MASON, B., and L. G. BERRY: *Elements of Mineralogy*, W. H. Freeman & Company, Publishers, San Francisco, 1968. An outstanding intermediate text on minerals.

*TUREKIAN, K. K.: *Chemistry of the Earth*, Holt, Rinehart and Winston, New York, 1972. A brief but authoritative introduction.

VANDERS, I., and P. F. KERR: *Mineral Recognition*, John Wiley & Sons, Inc., New York, 1967. A guide to mineral identification, with many fine color photographs.

*ZIM, H. S., and P. R. SHAFFER: *Rocks and Minerals*, Golden Press, New York, 1957. An excellent elementary guide to mineral and rock identification.

* Available in paperback.

Igneous and Metamorphic Processes

N GENERAL, ROCKS ARE AGGRE-
gates of several minerals; that is, rock-forming processes do
not ordinarily completely segregate different minerals but, instead,
lead to characteristic associations of minerals: Granite, for example,
is a rock made up primarily of three minerals: mica, quartz, and
feldspar. Under certain circumstances, rocks composed of only one
mineral may be formed. Ordinary limestone is such a rock; it is
composed mostly of the mineral calcite.

There are three universally recognized classes of rocks, each
of which has a different origin: **igneous** rocks, which form by crystallization from a hot molten mass called magma; **sedimentary** rocks,
which form on the earth's surface when fragmentary particles or
dissolved substances from preexisting rocks are transported and deposited by water, ice, or wind; and **metamorphic** rocks, which are
made up of either igneous, sedimentary, or other metamorphic rocks
that have been profoundly modified by high temperatures and pressures.

We can directly observe only the first two of these three rock
types in the making. Modern volcanic (igneous) and sedimentary
processes can be seen at the earth's surface, but for those rocks
requiring extreme conditions of temperature and pressure to form
(metamorphic rocks), we can only reason by analogy from laboratory
experiments and field relationships. In this chapter we shall begin
with observations of volcanic rocks and then consider how crustal
materials of the earth respond when subjected to the elevated temperatures and pressures existing at depths of tens or even hundreds
of kilometers beneath the surface. In the next chapter we shall return
to consider sedimentary rocks.

IGNEOUS ROCK APPEARANCES

3.1
IGNEOUS TEXTURES

When molten magmas erupt onto the earth's surface, two factors
contribute to their rapid crystallization. These are: (1) the temperature of the surface environment, which is dramatically lower (even

FIGURE 3.1 Obsidian: volcanic glass resulting from eruption and quick cooling of magma. (Robert Navias.)

on a hot day) than the temperature of the magma and the crustal interior from which it came; and (2) the reduced (atmospheric) pressure at the earth's surface, which allows any gases dissolved in the magma to effervesce, thus cooling it even more. Sometimes these cooling effects are so rapid that the silicon-oxygen tetrahedra and other ionic constituents of the magma are frozen into relatively rigid positions before they achieve orderly crystalline space lattice orientations. Volcanic glass such as obsidian (Figure 3.1) is formed when this occurs.

FIGURE 3.2 (a) Photo of volcanic eruption. (b) Porphyritic texture. Note large phenocysts within a fine-grained groundmass. (a: R. S. Fiske, U.S. Geological Survey; b: D. Ester.)

(a)

(b)

IGNEOUS AND METAMORPHIC PROCESSES

More frequently, however, a magma erupting onto the earth's surface forms crystalline assemblages primarily consisting of two or three silicate minerals. Most of the crystals are quite small and form a **groundmass**; but there may be much larger crystals, called **phenocrysts** (*pheno* = apparent, *cryst* = crystals), scattered throughout the rock (Figure 3.2). We refer to this crystalline relationship as **porphyritic texture**. Like *all* rock textures (the relationships among the grains composing a rock), porphyritic textures provide valuable clues to the genesis (mode of origin) of the rock.

As an example, consider the following interpretation for the porphyritic texture shown in Figure 3.3. Imagine a completely liquid magma, formed at a depth of several kilometers, beginning an ascent toward the earth's surface (Figure 3.3, position 1). As this magma rises through somewhat cooler and lower-pressure environments, a few crystals, usually of only one or two mineral types, begin to grow. These are typically minerals of high melting points, so the bulk of the magma remains liquid throughout its movement toward eventual eruption (Figure 3.3, position 2). Immediately prior to eruption, the condition of the magma is typically that depicted at position 2: a few phenocrysts surrounded by liquid silicate material. Upon exposure to the earth's surface, the liquid phase of this magma undergoes rapid crystallization. Because the silicate liquid is extremely

FIGURE 3.3 Formation of porphyritic texture. Changes in magma as it solidifies from a melt during the process of eruption.

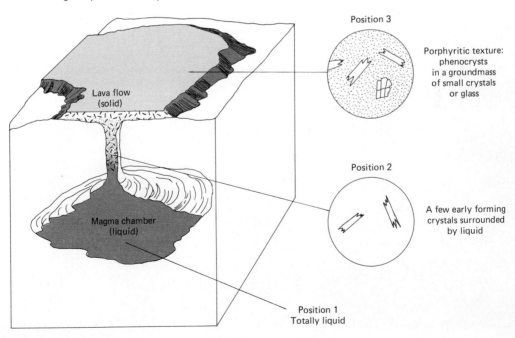

Position 3

Porphyritic texture: phenocrysts in a groundmass of small crystals or glass

Lava flow (solid)

Position 2

A few early forming crystals surrounded by liquid

Magma chamber (liquid)

Position 1
Totally liquid

viscous (thick), the ions within it cannot move great distances, so they become organized into *many small crystals*, thus forming the fine-grained groundmass that typifies volcanic rocks (Figure 3.3, position 3).

This analysis argues that, since (1) the formation of porphyritic texture requires an *increased* rate of crystal growth at a time when most of the magma is still liquid; and since (2) modern lava flows are observed to have undergone such an increase upon eruption, and they frequently possess porphyritic texture; therefore, (3) any rock having porphyritic texture and a fine-grained groundmass probably formed from a magma on the earth's surface. Thus, porphyritic texture is genetically significant as an indicator of volcanic or extrusive igneous origin. Although some very old rocks may show no indication of volcanic forms—indeed, they may even be observed as stream-worn pebbles—if their texture is *fine-grained* and *porphyritic*, we will nevertheless conclude that their ultimate origin was an extrusive igneous process. Under some conditions the phenocrysts are too few or too small to be apparent, in which case the very small crystal size of the rock will still serve as evidence of rapid crystallization and hence of an extrusive origin.

Now comes the time for some geological detective work. Consider the rock material shown in Figure 3.4. This rock seems to have originated by crystallization of a silicate magma. But where? Surely not at the earth's surface! Such large crystals, all approximately the same size, suggest two characteristics of crystallization that are distinctly different from what happens for volcanic rocks:

(a)

FIGURE 3.4 Plutonic rocks. (a) Vast region of coarse-grained igneous rock exposed at earth's surface. Sierra Nevada. (b) Photomicrograph of granular texture; rock from terrain in Figure 3.4a. (a: E. A. Hay; b: D. Ester.)

(b)

(1) the large size indicates rather slow growth, and (2) the size equality suggests a more or less constant rate of growth. Because geologists have not discovered any place on earth where such coarse-grained silicate rocks having this granular texture (intergrowth of equal-sized crystals) are forming, we must conclude that their origin takes place in some region not accessible to direct observation. Where might

FIGURE 3.5 Events to be inferred from the exposure of plutonic rocks. (a) Crystallization of plutonic rocks at depth. (b) Uplifting that causes erosion. (c) Erosion eventually exposes plutonic rock.

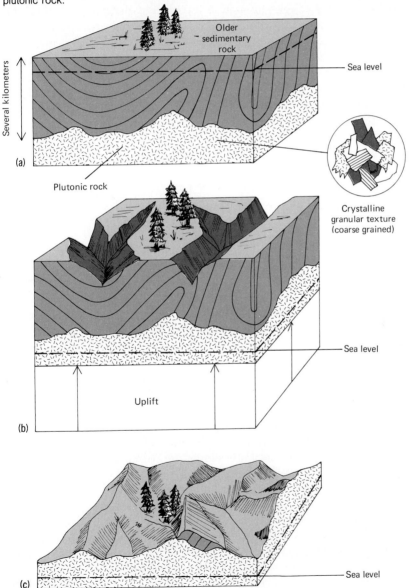

magma crystallize slowly and at a constant rate? What if magma that was formed at depth within the earth did not migrate to the surface but simply moved into another deep, but somewhat cooler, environment? In such a setting it could slowly crystallize over a very long interval of time, eventually becoming solid rock. Surely its texture would be *coarse-grained* because the crystals would have a long time to grow, and *crystalline granular* because they would all grow at a constant rate [Figure 3.5(a)]. Indeed, the logic of this analysis is so attractive that we have come to believe that this texture indicates intrusive igneous—or, as it is often called, **plutonic**—origin.

One important problem still surrounds our interpretation of plutonic rocks. If they originate deep within the earth's crust, why do we frequently observe them at the surface? If our inferences about their site of origin are correct, then their widespread exposure at the surface, particularly in mountainous regions, demands another geologic inference of no less significance: that is, deep erosion must have stripped away huge volumes of rock from above them. *Whenever exposures of plutonic rocks are encountered, we infer conditions of crustal uplifting and subsequent deep erosion in the geologic past* [see Figure 3.5(b) and (c)]. How else could these rocks become exposed at the surface of the earth?

3.2
CLASSIFICATION OF IGNEOUS ROCKS

Igneous rocks fall naturally into two broad categories on the basis of their textures and the different modes of origin their textures suggest: (1) glassy, fine-grained granular, and fine-grained porphyritic textures indicate volcanic origin, and (2) coarse-grained granular texture suggests plutonic origin. The description and classification of igneous rocks would thus be very simple if their variability was limited to only these textures. It turns out, however, that one additional variable of great importance must be taken into consideration: *mineral composition*. Some igneous rocks, for example, contain quartz; others do not. And some are rich in dark silicate minerals, whereas others contain mostly light-colored feldspars. A host of other variations could be cited. How should we respond to this complexity that nature has forced upon us?

Geologists have reacted in a manner consistent with the pattern of all scientific activity: they have developed systems of *classification* to subdivide the entire spectrum of igneous rocks into a relatively few categories. This is simply the process of imposing *order* on nature, and it is absolutely necessary before further understanding can proceed. Any system of classification must be concerned with *similarities* and *differences*, and all systems are characterized by some degree of compromise to determine which factors should have the greater emphasis. What should be the goal in designing a system of rock classification? We might separate large rocks from small rocks, or light-colored rocks from dark-colored ones, or pretty rocks from ugly rocks, or we might apply a host of other criteria. Should we arbitrarily select *any* rock characteristic, or are there logical guidelines that should be followed? We have already discussed the one rock characteristic, texture, that geologists have seized upon as possessing particular significance. Why? Recall the contrasting inferences made concerning igneous rocks of fine-grained porphyritic and coarse-grained granular texture. We concluded that they had solidified—that is, originated—in different environments. Texture was used, in other words, as a criterion for the mode of origin of rocks. For this reason, all systems of rock classification begin with a consideration of texture. It serves to provide an important insight into how individual rocks originated.

For igneous rock classification, then, the properties of texture and mineral composition are the basis for assigning different names. The organization of these rocks is particularly important because igneous rocks are so abundant: they make up about two-thirds of the earth's crust. During our planet's long history, most parts of the crust have at some time been heated to form a molten liquid and subsequently cooled to crystallize as igneous rocks (Figure 3.6). As might be predicted from our earlier discussions of the most abundant elements and minerals, the rocks produced by these meltings and coolings are composed almost entirely of a few common silicate minerals—feldspars, quartz, micas, amphiboles, pyroxenes, and olivines. Not all these minerals occur together in a single igneous rock,

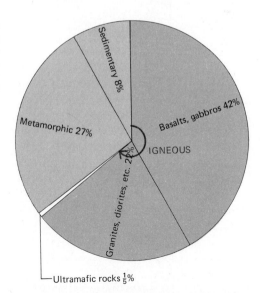

FIGURE 3.6 Abundances of the principal rock types in the earth's crust. Igneous basalts and granites are the dominant crustal rocks. (Data from Ronov and Yoroshevsky, American Geophysical Union Monograph 13, 1969.)

Sedimentary 8%

Basalts, gabbros 42%

Metamorphic 27%

IGNEOUS

Granites, diorites, etc. 2%

Ultramafic rocks $\frac{1}{5}$%

for when magmas crystallize, only certain combinations of minerals are formed. These combinations are the basis for the classification of igneous rocks shown in Figure 3.7. Note that the varying compositions of igneous rocks form a gradational series: from silicon-rich granites, composed mostly of quartz and orthoclase feldspar, at one end of the scale, to magnesium- and iron-rich gabbros and ultramafic rocks, composed largely of pyroxenes and olivines, at the other end. (Recall that pyroxenes and olivines both have iron and magnesium as their dominant positive ions, whereas neither iron nor magnesium occurs in quartz or feldspars.) The silicon-rich granites and granodiorites are commonly referred to as **silicic** igneous rocks, whereas the iron- and magnesium-rich gabbros and ultramafic rocks are called **mafic** igneous rocks.

Silicic and mafic igneous rocks differ not only in mineral composition but also in certain gross physical characteristics such as color

FIGURE 3.7   Classification of the common igneous rocks by mineral composition. The graph in the center shows the proportions of common minerals occurring in each rock type. On either side of the graph are enlarged drawings of the rock types.

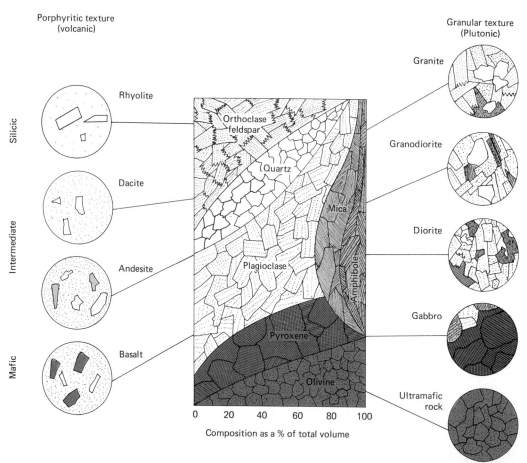

and density. Silicic rocks are typically light in color—white, pink, or light gray—as in the familiar granites used as building stone [Figure 3.8(a)]. Mafic rocks, on the other hand, are usually very dark in color—dark gray, dark green, or even black—because of the predominance of dark-colored pyroxenes and olivines [Figure 3.8(b)]. Mafic rocks are also denser than silicic rocks. This density difference has important implications for the distribution and origin of igneous rocks because the light-colored silicic rocks (particularly granite) make up most of the earth's continents, whereas the ocean basins are primarily basalt (a dense igneous rock), and probably much of the earth's interior is composed of denser mafic rocks.

Figure 3.6 also indicates which silicate structures are dominant in silicic and mafic rocks. In silicic rocks, the framework structures of quartz and feldspars prevail, with only minor amounts of minerals with sheet or chain structures (some micas and amphiboles). In contrast, the silicon-poor mafic rocks are dominated by chain structures (pyroxenes) and isolated tetrahedral structures (olivines). The ratio of silicon to other elements is much lower in these structures than in the framework structures, and this accounts for the relative paucity of silicon in mafic rocks.

FIGURE 3.8 Exposures of igneous rocks. (a) Granite exposed in a massive dome in the mountains of central California. (b) Basalt exposed along the Snake River in southeastern Washington. (a: Josef Muench; b: U.S. Geological Survey.)

(a)

(b)

IGNEOUS ROCK ORIGINS

As with all scientific investigations, we shall begin this search for igneous rock origins by describing observable processes and their products—namely, volcanoes and the landforms they create. This will help us in formulating the important questions that need answering.

3.3
VOLCANOES AND VOLCANIC LANDFORMS

Much of what is known about volcanoes comes from studies of oceanic islands and continental margins where volcanic rocks can be observed above sea level. Such studies have provided a wealth of data on the composition both of volcanic rocks themselves and of the magmatic liquids and gases from which they form. In general, volcanoes associated with oceanic islands as well as some found along the continental margins are composed of basalt, just as are the volcanic rocks sampled from the ocean floor. In many regions, however, volcanic outpourings near continental margins are *not* mafic basalt but are, instead, more silicic andesites, the fine-grained volcanic equivalent of diorite (see Figure 3.6). Because of differences in their fluidity, basaltic and andesitic lavas produce somewhat different landscapes at the earth's surface. The fluidity of a magma is largely determined by its silicon content—the more silicon, the thicker and more viscous the magma. This is because the silicon-oxygen tetrahedra are bulky structures, and thus a greater proportion of them in a magma obstructs its movement, causing it to be less fluid.

Basaltic lavas are, as a general rule, the most fluid. Even they, however, exhibit variations of fluidity, depending principally on the amount of gas (mostly H_2O and CO_2) dissolved in the magma as it erupts. As an example of the influence of gas content, contrast the appearance and fluidity differences shown between the two Hawaiian basalt flows in Figure 3.9. The upper photograph depicts the ropy, gas-rich, more fluid variety called **pahoehoe.** Flows of pahoehoe basalt typically evolve, through loss of their gases, into the blocky, more viscous flows called "aa" shown in the lower photograph. There are many vesicles (gas-bubble holes) in a hand specimen of pahoehoe.

Very fluid lavas are not likely to form conelike landforms. This is the reason why the classic volcanoes of the world such as Mount Fuji in Japan or Mount Rainier in Washington State (Figure 3.10) are not basaltic in composition. For such a conelike volcano to form, eruptions must remain localized at a single position, and the outpour-

(a)

(b)

FIGURE 3.9   Lava flows. (a) Pahoehoe flow. (b) Aa flow. (a, b: G. A. MacDonald.)

FIGURE 3.10   Composite volcano, Mt. Fuji. (W. C. Ernst.)

IGNEOUS AND METAMORPHIC PROCESSES   77

FIGURE 3.11   Devil's Postpile in California. Note the excellent polygonal columns. (E. A. Hay.)

ings must be sufficiently viscous to build up a conelike feature surrounding the central vent. Basalts, on the other hand, are frequently observed as great sheetlike flows, as shown in Figure 3.8(b). A closer look at these *flood* or *plateau* basalts, as they are often called, often reveals an internal pattern of vertical fractures called **columnar jointing** (Figure 3.11). How might these remarkable columns have formed? Let us once again apply two important techniques of geo-

FIGURE 3.12   Development of polygonal shrinkage cracks. (a) Modern mudcracks. (b) Top of Devil's Postpile. (a: N. T. Hall; b: E. A. Hay.)

(b)

(a)

IGNEOUS AND METAMORPHIC PROCESSES

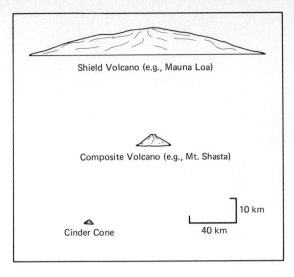

FIGURE 3.13 Relative sizes of volcanoes.

logic investigation: allowing the present to serve as the key to the past, and reasoning by analogy. The pattern that most of us have seen developed by mud as it dries out and shrinks (Figure 3.12) is so like the polygonal basalt that a similar origin is suggested. In the case of basalt, contraction results from cooling rather than from loss of moisture, but the same polygonal pattern is developed in both mud and basalt as a result of the reduction of volume.

If fluid basalt flows continue to erupt from the same general region for long periods of time, a volcano having a broad, low, domal form develops. Its form reflects the lava's tendency to flow great distances before solidifying. These large landforms are called **shield volcanoes**. They are the only volcanoes surfacing from deep ocean basins; they are also to be found on continents. The Hawaiian Islands form a chain of such shield volcanoes that have achieved truly gigantic dimensions. Compare the sizes of various other volcanic landforms shown in Figure 3.13 to Mauna Loa, the largest of the Hawaiian volcanoes.

In addition to shield volcanoes, there are other volcanic types, each reflecting differences in eruptive styles, which in turn are primarily controlled by the chemical composition and gas content of the erupting lava. **Composite volcanoes** [Figure 3.14(a)] consist of interlayered flows (typically andesite) and fragmental ejecta. The fragmental material consists of fine ash, forming a rock called **tuff**, and larger angular blocks, called **breccia**. This **pyroclastic debris** (*pyro* = fire, *clastic* = broken) results from periodic eruptions of great explosive violence caused by abnormal build-up of gases. Pyroclastic debris interlayered with the normally more viscous (com-

(a) Flows and pyroclastics (typically andesite)

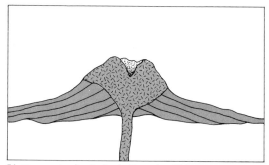

(b) Viscous plug (typically dacite or rhyolite)

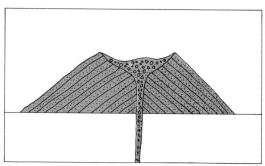

(c) Vesiculating but fluid (typically basalt)

(d) Steam blast by H_2O penetrating the volcanic "plumbing" (typically basalt)

FIGURE 3.14 Types of volcanoes. (a) Composite cone (Mayon). (b) Dome volcano (Lassen). (c) Cinder cone (Sunset crater). (d) Maar volcano. (a: Gardner Collection, Harvard University; b: E. A. Hay; c: Tad Nichols; d: NASA.)

FIGURE 3.15 Eruption of Mt. St. Helens, Washington, May, 1980. (U.S. Geological Survey.)

pared to basalt) andesite flows yields steep-sided volcanoes with concave upward slopes. The explosive eruptions of Mount St. Helens in 1980 are a dramatic example of the extreme devastation that occurs when gas pressure beneath such a volcano becomes unusually great (Figure 3.15). Although these eruptions seemed catastrophic to us, they are typical of the ongoing geologic processes within regions such as the High Cascades of the Pacific Northwest.

Often during the later stages of a series of eruptions the rising magma becomes more viscous. This can be accomplished either by depletion of gas content or by enrichment of silicon content in the magma. Very viscous magma (typically dacite or rhyolite) pushed up into the throat of a central vent may not have sufficient fluidity to flow at all. Instead, it will rise upward and perhaps bulge outward in the manner of an almost-solid plug. Landforms of this origin are referred to as *volcanic domes* or *plug domes* [Figure 3.14(b)].

Rapidly effervescing gas-rich mobile magmas (typically basalt) often erupt explosively. The resultant landform is a **cinder cone** [Figure 3.14(c)]. **Maar volcanoes** [Figure 3.14(d)] are similar to cinder cones but differ in that they have a large explosion crater. The explosions are caused by steam action generated when large volumes of ground water come into contact with hot magma at depths of a few hundred feet.

There is one additional landform of volcanic origin deserving of mention: the **caldera.** Calderas are roughly circular collapse depressions that form around the central summit of volcanoes. Collapse is almost certainly caused by the relatively rapid removal of the magma chamber, thereby leaving the massive summit of a volcano without sufficient support. Crater Lake in Oregon, shown in Figure 3.16, is one of the best known calderas in the world. Indian lore of that region appears to establish its development in very recent, but prehistorical, time.

(a)

(b)

FIGURE 3.16 (a) Crater Lake, Oregon, a recently formed caldera. (b) Sequence of events that formed Crater Lake caldera. (a: John S. Shelton; b: after H. Williams.)

Any discussion of the origin of magmas must account for the dominance of basalt among igneous rocks. Indeed, about 40 percent of the entire crust of the earth is basalt, and the oceanic portion of the crust is almost entirely basalt. Basalt is clearly the most common magma formed by volcanic processes. The question is, "What is the source of the magma and what mechanism produced it?" Analysis of earthquake shock waves indicates that magmas are generated below the crust and within the mantle. The principal mantle region for this process is the asthenosphere, where the rock is nearer to melting (and hence more plastic) than other mantle rock located either above or below the asthenosphere.

But if the basaltic rocks that make up most of the oceanic crust originate within the asthenosphere, then we are faced with a fundamental problem because the asthenosphere is composed of materials that are denser than the overlying basaltic crust. Thus the crustal basalts appear to have originated, in some manner, from more dense underlying rocks. Many lines of evidence suggest that the upper mantle consists largely of olivine and pyroxene and thus is similar in composition to **ultramafic** rocks that are rarely exposed at the earth's surface. If the upper mantle is composed of more dense silicon-poor ultramafic materials, then how can their melting give rise to basaltic magmas that are less dense and contain more silicon? The most probable answer relates to simple melting-point differences. Because feldspar melts at a lower temperature than either olivine or pyroxene, heating only slightly beyond the melting temperature of feldspar might cause a partial melting of ultramafic mantle rocks that contain only small amounts of feldspar (Figure 3.17). This partial melting, in turn, could form local concentrations of silicon-enriched basaltic magmas surrounded by still-solid olivine and pyroxene. This has been demonstrated experimentally in the

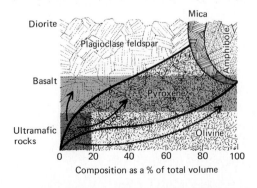

FIGURE 3.17 Partial melting of ultramafic rocks to create basalt. The small amount of feldspar in ultramafics has a lower melting point than either pyroxene or olivine. Heating sufficient only to melt this feldspar plus a small portion of the pyroxene and olivine (dark color) could produce a magma of basaltic composition (light color in diagram).

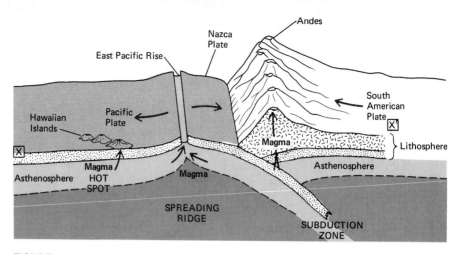

FIGURE 3.18   Three settings for magma production: Spreading Ridges, Subduction Zones, and Hot Spots. Cross section view along line x-x′ shown of Figure 3.13.

laboratory. Basaltic fluids are the first to be formed by the partial melting of ultramafic rock. Most geologists now believe that basalts originate in this way.

It seems likely, then, that the ultimate origin of basaltic magma is partial melting of the asthenosphere. There seem to be, however, three different settings within which magma derived from the asthenosphere occurs. These are diagrammatically shown in Figures 3.18 and 3.19. The side view (cross section) in Figure 3.18 is drawn along line X–X′ of Figure 3.19. It extends from near the Hawaiian Islands in the mid-Pacific to the Andes in South America:

FIGURE 3.19   The arrows indicate the direction of relative plate movement (for plates shown along x-x′).

As lithospheric plates separate, pressure is reduced on the ultramafic rock of the underlying asthenosphere. This rock material slowly rises to fill the cracks produced at the trailing edges of lithosphere, and the lowering of pressure on the rising asthenosphere induces partial melting, in turn producing basaltic magmas that rise toward the surface, eventually erupting near the axis of the spreading ridge. Vast volumes of basalt have been added in this fashion to the earth's lithosphere throughout history. Almost all oceanic crust has formed through this mechanism.

One of the basic tenets of plate tectonics is that the principal tectonic and volcanic processes occur at plate boundaries, but **hot spot** volcanism provides a significant exception to this generality. A number of centers of volcanism exist well within a plate, such as Hawaii within the Pacific Plate, yet these are, and have long been, active sites of eruption of basaltic lava. It is believed that these centers of eruption are located above hot spots anchored in the asthenosphere beneath the moving lithosphere. Plumes of magma rise through the lithosphere to erupt on the surface, but the volcanic rocks are then carried away in the direction of plate movement, much as a plume of rising smoke is carried along in the direction of air movement. The Hawaiian Islands farther away from the currently forming big island of Hawaii are progressively older. This suggests that the Pacific Plate is moving toward the northwest, which is a conclusion well supported by several other lines of evidence. For example, earthquake activity is associated only with regions of current volcanism, and islands to the northwest are quiet with respect to both earthquakes and volcanic eruptions. They are smaller, too, because as they move farther away from the hot spot, the lithosphere contracts due to cooling, and subsides, causing the ocean floor to become deeper. A ridge of submerged volcanic material extends northwestward from the Hawaiian Islands and bends northward into another submerged line of extinct volcanoes called the Emperor Seamount Chain (Figure 3.19). This entire chain of basaltic material, extending from the North Pacific near Siberia to the active volcanoes on the big island of Hawaii, traces the path of the Pacific Plate in its northwestward movement over the Hawaiian hot spot during the last 75 million years or so. To the southeast along this chain, the rocks become younger, and the ocean floor becomes shallower.

The convergence of two plates results in subduction of one beneath the other. The subducted plate is warmed as it descends, and upon reaching a depth zone of 100–200 km, partial melting of the basaltic lithosphere, the adjacent asthenosphere, and perhaps some of the more silicic sediments attached to the lithosphere generates basaltic and also somewhat more silicic andesitic magma.* If an oceanic plate overlies the subducting plate, as when two plates of oceanic lithosphere are converging, an island arc of basaltic and andesitic volcanoes is formed above the subduction zone. The Philippines are such an island arc. If, on the other hand, an oceanic plate converges against a continental one, the oceanic lithosphere descends because it consists of denser (more mafic) rock material. As the basaltic and andesitic magma rises, it now must travel through silicic rock composing the continental lithosphere above. Contamination and assimilation can make the rising magma more silicic than basalt or andesite, thus causing occasional eruptions of dacite and rhyolite. Great volumes of andesite, coupled with these more silicic eruptions, cause the formation of arcuate chains of volcanic mountains above subduction zones where oceanic lithosphere dives beneath continental lithosphere. The Andes of South America are a fine example of this process in action today (Figure 3.18). The High Cascades of northern California, Oregon, Washington, and British Columbia are another region having this same kind of geologic setting. Recent eruptions of Mount St. Helens are dramatic testimony for the ongoing generation of magma at converging plate margins.

EXPERIMENTAL LABORATORY STUDIES   We have seen how partial melting of the asthenosphere explains the huge volumes of basaltic magma that developed throughout earth history, and how partial melting of subducted basaltic lithosphere can yield andesite, which in turn can become even more silicic through assimilation as it rises through continental crust. This does not explain, however, the origin of vast volumes of silicic magmas necessary to form the framework of continental lithosphere. Continents are composed primarily of granite and metamorphic equivalents to granite. Extensive study of continental igneous rocks has shown also that rock compositions exist that are intermediate between mafic basalt (gabbro) and the silicic extreme of granite (rhyolite). How have rocks in this spectrum originated? Why are some rocks dominated by silicon-rich minerals and others by magnesium- and iron-rich minerals? Why can certain combinations of minerals coexist in the same rock while other combinations never occur? Under what conditions of temperature and pressure do the common igneous rocks originate? Many clues to such questions have been provided by careful field and laboratory studies of natural igneous rocks, but perhaps the most important clues have come from laboratory studies of silicate melts—artificial, man-made "magmas" heated and cooled under varying conditions in an attempt to simulate the

* Andesite, rather than basalt, can be formed by partial melting of the oceanic lithosphere and its water-rich veneer of sediments.

natural settings in which igneous rocks form. Such studies were begun over 60 years ago by pioneering workers, particularly N. L. Bowen, at the Geophysical Laboratory of the Carnegie Institution in Washington, D.C. This laboratory, still one of the leaders in this work, is augmented today by many university and government laboratories that are also engaged in experimental studies of igneous rock origins.

Laboratory experiments can seldom *precisely* duplicate natural conditions because most natural magmas have from six to ten or more chemical constituents, which is too many for accurate, controlled laboratory analysis. Instead, most laboratory experiments are confined to simpler systems containing only two to four elements or compounds. These studies have shown that solid minerals do not crystallize all at once from the liquid as a magma cools but instead go through complex series of interactions with the liquid magma; that is, certain minerals crystallize at high temperatures but become unstable and react with the magmatic liquid to give still other minerals as the temperature drops.

From his experimental studies, combined with observations on natural igneous rocks, Bowen in 1922 proposed the following theory to account for the varying compositions of igneous rocks. If a mafic magma (rich in magnesium and iron) crystallizes directly, it will form gabbroic or ultramafic rocks made up of calcium feldspar, pyroxene, and olivine. But if, as crystallization begins, the first-formed crystals of olivine, pyroxene, and calcium feldspar are somehow separated from the remaining liquid (for example, by sinking to the bottom of a chamber filled with the liquid magma), then the remaining magma will become progressively more silicon-rich. If the separation of iron and magnesium minerals continues long enough, the remaining silicon-rich liquid magma will crystallize as a granite made up largely of quartz and potassium feldspar.

Bowen recognized that there is a sequence of different minerals formed in a magma as it cools; he showed that two such sequences of minerals—one for feldspars, the other for olivines, pyroxenes, amphiboles, and micas—coexist in magmas as temperatures are lowered (Figure 3.20). These two series correspond, in a general way, to the changing compositions of igneous rocks shown in Figure 3.6. These findings led Bowen to postulate that all igneous rocks form from "primary" magmas of mafic composition. Silicic rocks originate when these mafic magmas change composition, or "evolve," as early-formed, silicon-poor crystals are separated from the main magmatic mass. This is a mechanism called *magmatic differentiation*. Field studies of igneous rocks have shown that such magmatic differentiation does indeed occur, and there are other lines of evidence suggesting that many silicic igneous rocks did originate from mafic materials but in a more complex manner than visualized by Bowen.

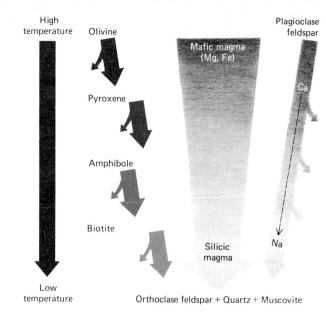

High
temperature

Olivine

Pyroxene

Amphibole

Biotite

Mafic magma
(Mg, Fe)

Plagioclase
feldspar

Ca

Na

Silicic
magma

Low
temperature

Orthoclase feldspar + Quartz + Muscovite

FIGURE 3.20 Changing composition of magma, based on Bowen's work. If crystals of olivine, pyroxene, and calcium-rich plagioclase are removed (small arrows) from a cooling mafic magma, the remaining melt becomes more silicic in composition. Crystallization of amphiboles, micas, and ultimately, orthoclase feldspars and quartz results from this silicon enrichment. These changes correspond to the changing compositions of the principal igneous rocks. (Figure 3.6).

3.5
PLUTONIC ROCK MASSES

Earlier in this chapter we inferred that coarse-grained silicate rocks have probably crystallized in the plutonic environment deep within the crust. Were it not for profound erosion, we would never see such **plutons** (the general name given to any intrusive body). But we do, in fact, see them abundantly, and they display a variety of sizes, shapes, and relationships to the older material they intruded (so-called country rock). Broad categories of plutonic rocks include those that are either **concordant** or **discordant** in their mode of emplacement (Figure 3.21).

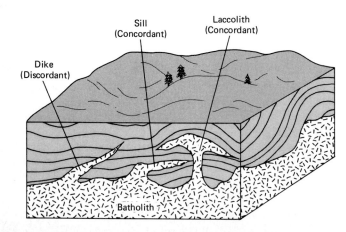

Dike
(Discordant)

Sill
(Concordant)

Laccolith
(Concordant)

Batholith

FIGURE 3.21 Reconstruction of the appearance of plutonic rock bodies prior to their exposure by erosion. Note both concordant and discordant bodies.

Concordant intrusives are emplaced essentially parallel to layering in the older rock through which the igneous material is injected. There is only one common type of concordant intrusive—a sill [Figure 3.22(a)]. Some sills are mistaken for flows of lava since in both, the igneous rocks are parallel to sediments that lie below and above them. **Laccoliths** (*lacco* = cistern, *lith* = rock) are concordant intrusives that are considerably less common than sills. They differ from sills in that laccoliths arch up the overlying sedimentary rock layers, and thereby take on a mushroomlike appearance (Figure 3.21).

Discordant intrusives cut across the layering of the older country rock. When a discordant intrusion is of relatively small scale—that is, its dimensions are measured in meters rather than kilometers—the term **dike** is used [Figure 3.22(b)]. Very extensive exposures of plutonic rock, on the other hand, are referred to as **batholiths**

(a)

(b)

FIGURE 3.22 Small igneous intrusive bodies. (a) Sill of light colored igneous rock parallel to the layering in dark shades. (b) Dike of dark colored igneous rock discordant to sandstone layers. (a, b: E. A. Hay.)

(*batho* = deep, *lith* = rock). Batholiths result from massive emplacements of magma in the deep regions of the earth's crust (perhaps several kilometers deep). Only after extensive erosion, however, do the plutonic rocks that formed by crystallizing slowly in this deep setting become exposed at the earth's surface. The exposure of batholiths, then, immediately tells us a story of great significance: that the region has undergone a long history of uplift and erosion. Sometimes plutonic rocks are exposed over an area of several square kilometers but not extensively enough to merit the term *batholith*. These smaller terranes of exposed intrusive rock are called **stocks**. All batholiths, and most stocks, are composite in nature. That is, they consist of many different kinds and ages of coarse-grained, granular-textured, igneous rocks that have intruded into each other during the geologic past, before subsequent erosion exposed them at the surface of the earth. It seems likely that most stocks will enlarge downward to batholiths, which will be exposed after erosion strips away more and more of the country rock. Occasionally fragments or large remnants of country rock are engulfed, or surrounded, by plutonic rock. On a regional scale this gives rise to **roof pendants**, as shown in Figure 3.23. On a much smaller scale, incorporation of old rock material by intruding magma forms **xenoliths** (*xeno* = foreign, *lith* = rock) of the sort shown in Figure 3.24.

Detailed mapping of plutonic rocks has shown that they are primarily granitic—that is, they are much more silicic than most volcanic rocks. There is evidence for at least two different origins for this granitic material that composes the bulk of continental rock (Figure 3.25). In some areas, the boundaries between large granite masses and the surrounding rocks are very sharp and distinct, suggesting that liquid granitic magma was squeezed into the surrounding rocks to make the granitic mass. In contrast, many areas show a complete gradation between granitic masses and surrounding metamorphic rocks, which suggests that the granite formed from

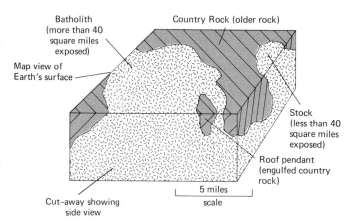

Batholith
(more than 40
square miles
exposed)

Country Rock (older rock)

Map view of
Earth's surface

Stock
(less than 40
square miles
exposed)

Roof pendant
(engulfed country
rock)

5 miles

scale

Cut–away showing
side view

FIGURE 3.23 Distinction between batholiths and stocks; batholiths are plutonic masses exposed over an area greater than 40 square miles. (Note roof pendants are remnants of engulfed "country rock.")

IGNEOUS AND METAMORPHIC PROCESSES

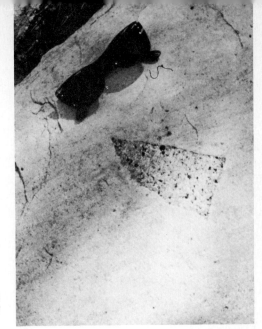

FIGURE 3.24 Xenoliths (foreign rocks) are fragments of older rock that have been incorporated within younger igneous material. (E. A. Hay.)

(a) Magmatic origin

(b) In-place origin

FIGURE 3.25 Cross sections of rocks suggesting different origins of granite. In (a) the granite apparently crystallized from a molten magma that moved upward from deeper levels. In (b) the granite appears to have formed by in-place melting of pre-existing rocks without any appreciable movement of liquid magma.

a kind of "in-place melting" of preexisting rocks without any appreciable movement of liquid magma.* Typically, such regions of gradation between metamorphics and granites show a zone of rocks composed of thin bands of granite alternating with thin bands of metamorphic rock as occurs between the areas of "pure" granite and

* The question of the actual degree of "melting" that takes place in the formation of granites by this means has been much debated by geologists. Some believe that complete fusion takes place, but others feel that true granites may form from rearrangement of crystal structures in a solid or partially solid state. This suggests a *metamorphic* origin for some granites, and is referred to as *granitization*. This problem has not yet been resolved, but it is less important for our purposes than the still more fundamental question of the *place* of origin of the granitic materials.

IGNEOUS AND METAMORPHIC PROCESSES

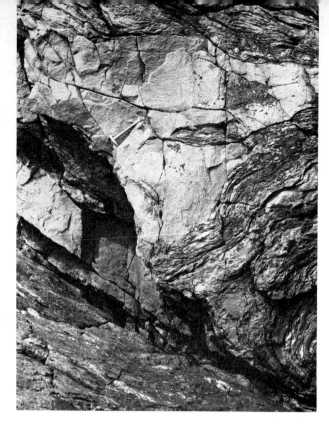

FIGURE 3.26 Migmatite showing a small mass of granite (light color) surrounded by granitic gneiss (dark color). The hammer resting on the granite provides the scale. (Geological Survey of Great Britain.)

"pure" metamorphic rock (Figure 3.26). Such mixed granitic rocks, called **migmatites,** indicate that the granites formed where the melting was most intense but that in the surrounding areas, temperatures did not exceed the melting range of preexisting minerals and only metamorphic rocks were produced.

Many geologists have favorably noted the advantages of the concepts of *in-place melting* and *granitization* in regard to the so-called room problem. The problem is simply this: Where did the material (country rock) go that occupied the pluton's space prior to its intrusion? In many but not all areas of granitic rock, field mapping provides evidence for shouldering aside of country rock and forceful emplacement of molten material. For those regions where migmatites are common and evidence for large-scale magmatic movement is lacking, the room problem is obviated by a model calling for granitization or in-place melting.

Because of the abundance of migmatites and transitional granitic masses in the oldest cores of continents, most geologists now believe that much of the granite seen in the continents today was formed by local melting of preexisting continental rocks rather than by upward movement of liquid magma from deep levels of the earth's interior. Note, however, that if most of the continental crust has originated from melting of earlier crustal rocks, we are still faced with the fundamental question of *how* the silicon, sodium, potassium, and other elements characteristic of granite became concentrated in continental masses in the first place. Our discussion of magmatic differentiation of magmas (Section 3.4) produced within subduction zones suggests a likely mechanism for achieving this concentration of the lighter elements.

METAMORPHIC ROCKS

At the beginning of this chapter we concluded that some rock types could not be directly observed in the process of formation. Metamorphic (*meta* = change, *morphic* = form) rocks fall into this category. Let us again use the approach of evaluating a rock's texture under the assumption that it will provide a clue about the rock's origin. Figure 3.27 shows an example of a rock with foliated texture, wherein the minerals are oriented in nearly parallel sheetlike planes. Nowhere has anyone observed such a texture in the making. Furthermore, many of the minerals common to rocks having a foliated texture—such as garnet, muscovite, and various aluminum silicates—are comparatively rare among volcanic, plutonic, and sedimentary rocks. Two rather striking differences are thus apparent between the rock in Figure 3.27 and those with which we are more familiar: (1) the texture shows preferred (not random) directions of crystal growth, and (2) the mineral assemblage is different from well-known igneous associations such as quartz, feldspar, pyroxene, etc., or sedimentary suites comprising sandstones, shales, and the like.

It appears that these metamorphic rocks must have originated at some depth within the earth. Perhaps they are really nothing more than a special group of igneous (grown-from-a-melt) rocks and do not deserve special classification. But how can we explain the

FIGURE 3.27 Hand specimen of schist showing foliated texture. (Yale Peabody Museum.)

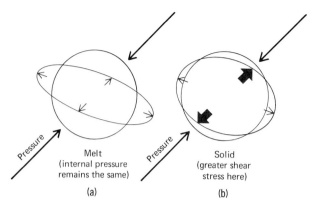

FIGURE 3.28 Application of directed pressure on liquids and solids. (a) Directed pressure on a liquid causes the liquid mass to change shape, thereby maintaining an approximately equal internal pressure throughout. (b) Solids do not readily flow, so greater shear stresses can be generated in some directions as compared to others.

remarkable foliations by growth from a melt? The parallelism of crystal growth suggests the existence of directed pressures in the environment of growth, but since liquids have no rigidity, they flow. It is essentially impossible, therefore, to attain great pressure differences of a directional nature within liquids (Figure 3.28). Solids, on the other hand, *can* have directions of greater shear stress developed within them. The unique mineral assemblages of these rocks provide an additional basis for rejecting their igneous origin. Recall the work of N. L. Bowen (Section 3.4) regarding the products of crystallization from a silicate melt. Minerals such as garnet and the aluminum silicates—andalusite, kyanite, and sillimanite—are never formed in the laboratory from normal silicate melts and are extremely rare in naturally occurring igneous rocks.

Thus the circumstantial evidence against the igneous origin of what we call metamorphic rocks seems compelling. But what other alternative is there? Difficult though it may be to visualize, consider this possibility: Some preexisting rock (igneous, sedimentary, or even metamorphic) may be subjected to conditions of significantly increased *temperature* and *pressure*, and perhaps new *chemically active fluids*, for a long period of time. This new environment, no doubt at considerable depth, imposes nonequilibrium conditions on the minerals and texture of the preexisting rock. That is to say, the minerals are no longer stable (comfortable) in their new environment, so their lattice structures are slowly reorganized in a manner to achieve a more stable configuration (Figure 3.29). The process of doing this is called **ionic diffusion**. It is greatly facilitated by elevated temperatures. Metamorphic rocks are thus seen as rocks having formed in response to new environments of increased temperature, pressure, and sometimes the availability of new ions.

As you might expect, there are a great many variations in the intensity of metamorphism to which a rock might be subjected. The upper extreme is melting, at which point, metamorphism gives way to igneous processes. Laboratory investigations of the effects

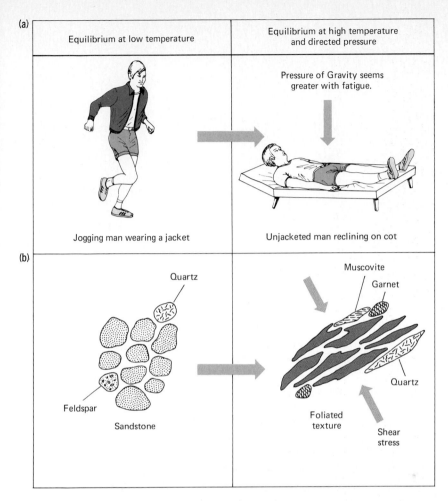

FIGURE 3.29 The achievement of equilibrium for (a) a man and (b) a rock. Rock metamorphism results as mineral assemblages achieve new equilibria.

of elevated temperatures and pressures on mineral change have provided instructive tools with which to evaluate the intensity of natural metamorphic environments. Figure 3.30 shows, for example, the experimentally determined stability fields for the aluminum silicate (Al_2SiO_5) polymorphs (*poly* = many, *morph* = form). Andalusite, kyanite, and sillimanite have the same composition but different lattice structures: each mineral is a different form of Al_2SiO_5, and thus is a different polymorph. The lattice structure for each is determined by the conditions of temperature and pressure at which it is most stable. When one or another of these minerals is in a metamorphic rock, we are thus afforded some specific insight into the conditions of its formation.

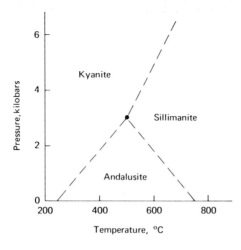

FIGURE 3.30 Aluminum silicates derived from different metamorphic conditions. (After W. S. Fyfe, "Chemical Geology," vol. 2, p. 74, 1967.)

3.7
CLASSIFICATION OF METAMORPHIC ROCKS

It is often possible to distinguish between three broad genetic categories of metamorphic rocks. **Contact metamorphism** results from increased temperature effects imposed on an older rock near its contact with a younger plutonic mass. **Regional metamorphism** occurs over broad areas in response to strong deformational pressures as well as significant increases in temperature. **Dynamic metamorphism** involves mineral changes wherein strong shearing deformation is the dominant factor. Regional and contact metamorphism are by far the most significant of these categories, accounting for the great majority of metamorphic rocks.

Metamorphic rocks are more varied and complex than igneous and sedimentary rocks, and many names and classification schemes have been proposed for them. Figure 3.31 shows a simple, widely used classification that is based not so much on mineral composition, as were the previous classifications of igneous rocks, but on the different textures of the resulting metamorphic rock. As the minerals of preexisting rocks recrystallize during dynamic metamorphism, they commonly become oriented in parallel, sheetlike planes, yielding foliated texture. The basis of classification for these rocks depends on the coarseness of the foliation. **Slates** are so fine-grained that only a distinct luster on some surfaces serves as evidence of parallel grains. **Schists** are coarser-grained and are frequently rich in micas and amphiboles or other sheetlike or needlelike crystals that make the foliation obvious. More coarsely foliated varieties, called **gneisses,** are banded by segregated regions of different minerals. These types of foliation can result from the metamorphism of many kinds of

Quartzite

Schist

Marble

Gneiss

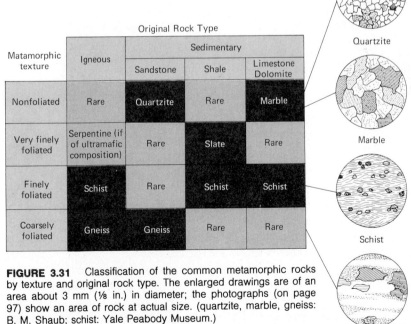

Matamorphic texture	Original Rock Type			
	Igneous	Sedimentary		
		Sandstone	Shale	Limestone Dolomite
Nonfoliated	Rare	Quartzite	Rare	Marble
Very finely foliated	Serpentine (if of ultramafic composition)	Rare	Slate	Rare
Finely foliated	Schist	Rare	Schist	Schist
Coarsely foliated	Gneiss	Gneiss	Rare	Rare

Quartzite

Marble

Schist

Gneiss

FIGURE 3.31 Classification of the common metamorphic rocks by texture and original rock type. The enlarged drawings are of an area about 3 mm (⅛ in.) in diameter; the photographs (on page 97) show an area of rock at actual size. (quartzite, marble, gneiss: B. M. Shaub; schist: Yale Peabody Museum.)

97

(a)

(b)

FIGURE 3.32 Typical exposures of metamorphic rocks. (a) Schist exposed along sea cliffs in western Scotland. (b) Gneiss exposed along a stream in northern Arizona. (a: Geological Survey of Great Britain; b: John S. Shelton.)

igneous and sedimentary rocks. In addition, a few metamorphic rocks lack a foliated arrangement of the constituent minerals. The most common such rocks are **quartzites** and **marbles**, which form from the metamorphism of sedimentary sandstones and carbonate rocks, respectively (Figure 3.31).

By far the most abundant metamorphic rocks are gneisses, most of which are similar to ordinary granite in composition and are thus called *granitic* gneisses (Figure 3.32). It has been estimated that such gneisses account for about 80 percent of all metamorphic rocks, schists for about 15 percent, and quartzites and marbles for only about 5 percent.

Classifications of metamorphic rocks based on mineral composition are more complex than the textural classification of Figure 3.31 because different minerals may be formed from the same original rock by differing metamorphic temperatures and pressures. Figure 3.33 shows how increasing temperatures and pressures lead to progressive changes in mineral components during metamorphosis of a sedimentary shale. Similar "zones" of mineral change have been defined for the progressive metamorphism of other common sedimentary and igneous rocks.

FIGURE 3.33   Changes in the mineral components of shale when metamorphosed to schist at increasing temperatures and pressures. The clay minerals are first altered to quartz and mica, some of which then converts to garnet and, finally, to aluminum silicate minerals. The presence of these key minerals can be used to identify "zones" of increasing metamorphism in the schists. The map shows the progressive metamorphic zones as exposed in schists of upper Michigan. (After Ernst, "Earth Materials," 1969; generalized from James.)

SUMMARY OUTLINE

IGNEOUS ROCK APPEARANCES

3.1 *Igneous textures*: Volcanic rocks are typically fine-grained and porphyritic in texture, whereas plutonic rocks have coarse-grained, granular textures.

3.2 *Classification of igneous rocks*: Igneous rock classification is based primarily on the properties of texture and mineral composition.

IGNEOUS ROCK ORIGINS

3.3 *Volcanoes and volcanic landforms*: Different volcanic landforms result from variations in eruptive style, which are strongly influenced by differences in composition and gas content of the erupting lava.

3.4 *The origin of magmas*: Laboratory experiments with artificial silicate melts have suggested that some granite rocks originate from the chemical evolution of basaltic magmas; oceanic basalt magmas appear to result from partial melting of ultramafic rocks from the asthenosphere. The three principal sites of magma generation are spreading ridges, subduction zones, and hot spots. Melting of preexisting rocks may also produce magmas.

3.5 *Plutonic rock masses*: Plutonic rock masses have crystallized at great depth, and may be either concordant or discordant in their mode of emplacement.

METAMORPHIC ROCKS

3.6 *Metamorphism*: When preexisting rocks are subjected to high temperature and pressure in the presence of chemically active fluids, metamorphism is likely to occur.

3.7 *Classification of metamorphic rocks*: Gneisses and schists are the most abundant foliated metamorphic rocks; quartzites and marbles are the most common nonfoliated ones.

ADDITIONAL READINGS

DECKER, R., and B. DECKER: "The Eruptions of Mt. St. Helens," *Scientific American*, March 1981.

*"Earthquakes and Volcanoes," * *Scientific American*, W. H. Freeman & Company, Publishers, San Francisco, 1980.

MACDONALD, G. A.: *Volcanoes*, Prentice-Hall, Inc., Englewood Cliffs, N.J., 1972. A clearly written, nontechnical intermediate text.

*OAKESHOTT, G. B.: *Volcanoes and Earthquakes: Geologic Violence*, McGraw-Hill Book Company, New York, 1976. A general introductory treatment.

PECK, D. L., T. L. WRIGHT, and R. W. DECKER: "The Lava Lakes of Kilauea," *Scientific American*, October 1979.

* Available in paperback.

*Rinehart, C. D., and W. C. Smith: *Earthquakes and Young Volcanoes along the Eastern Sierra Nevada*, Wm. Kaufmann, Inc., Los Altos, Calif., 1982. Excellent photographs of this volcanically active region.

*Zim, H. S., and P. R. Shaffer: *Rocks and Minerals*, Golden Press, New York, 1957. An excellent elementary guide to mineral and rock identification.

Yosemite, Kings Canyon, and Sequoia National Parks

IGNEOUS ACTIVITY DURING MESOZOIC AND CENOZOIC TIME IN THE SIERRA NEVADA REGION OF CALIFORNIA

The geologic evolution of any region involves many different processes: creating rocks, mountain-building activity, and wearing away of rocks are but a few. In this section we will look at past igneous activity responsible for the bedrock framework of the modern-day Sierra Nevada (Figure 3.34).

Later in this text, other elements such as uplifting, stream erosion, and glacial sculpturing involved in the total development of this important mountain range will be studied to establish a comprehensive picture of the evolution of Yosemite National Park and its nearby Sierra Nevada environs.

The earliest rock record in this region dates back several hundred million years—to the Paleozoic era. At that time, sediments were deposited in a marine environment at the flooded western margin of the North American continent. Today only a few remnants of these very old rocks remain—most of them have been eroded away following uplifts that occurred long ago.

Coarse-grained igneous rocks are dominant in the Yosemite region and elsewhere throughout the Sierra Nevada. We learned earlier in Chapter 3, however, that granitic batholiths do not form at the earth's surface but are exposed at the surface only following great uplift and erosion. To trace the heritage of this batholith, then, our story begins about 225 million years ago during the early part of the Mesozoic era. The geologic setting was like that shown in Figure 3.35. An oceanic plate (Farallon Plate) was undergoing east-west convergence with a continental plate (North American Plate). As in the Aleutians or the Japanese Islands, a volcanic island arc system developed above the descending slab of oceanic crust where it reached a depth of 100–200 km in the subduction zone. Partial melting of the oceanic crust and some of the sedimentary material that was on it took place in this subduction zone when high temperatures were reached beyond a depth of about 100 km. In the Sierra Nevada region, this condition began early in the Mesozoic era (about 200 m.y. ago),* but magma generation and its emplacement didn't

* m.y. is abbreviation for a million years.

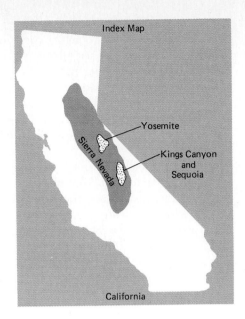

Index Map

Yosemite

Kings Canyon
and
Sequoia

Sierra Nevada

California

FIGURE 3.34 The Sierra Nevada and three national parks located within the mountain range.

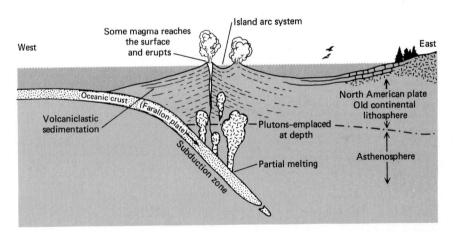

Island arc system

Some magma reaches
the surface
and erupts

West

East

Oceanic crust

North American plate
Old continental
lithosphere

Volcaniclastic
sedimentation

(Farallon plate)

Plutons-emplaced
at depth

Subduction zone

Partial melting

Asthenosphere

FIGURE 3.35 Relatively smooth subduction during early Mesozoic time (225–150 million years ago).

reach truly batholithic volumes until the Cretaceous period later in the era (about 120–80 m.y. ago). As shown in Figure 3.35, some of the magma generated by partial melting made an ascent to the surface and erupted to form the island arc. The bulk of the magma, however, did not reach the surface but instead migrated through the asthenosphere, assimilating some of it, as well as some of the continental crust, and finally the magma crystallized at some depth as coarse-grained granitic plutons of rock having crystalline granular textures. Above the plutons, both the volcanic rocks (flows, tuffs, breccias) and the sedimentary rocks derived from them (primarily shales) composed the island arc system. These units are referred to today as the Logtown Ridge-Mariposa complex. They have been intensely deformed, metamorphosed, and intruded by younger granites since the time of their formation about 150 million years ago.

Strong deformation of the Logtown Ridge-Mariposa complex gave rise to the Ancestral Sierra Nevada late in the Jurassic period (approximately 140–150 million years ago, Figure 3.36). Perhaps relatively smooth subduction of the Farallon Plate that had been going on for tens of millions of years "stuck," thereby causing strong compression deforming the volcanic rocks and the volcaniclastic sediments composing the Logtown Ridge-Mariposa complex. The rocks were strongly folded and uplifted to maximum elevations of approximately 15,000 feet above sea level. Faulting of these rocks was also extensive at this time. This mountain-building episode is called the Nevadan Orogeny.

Erosion of the folded and faulted rocks of the high-standing Ancestral Sierra Nevada became a dominant geologic activity in this region for a long time following the Nevadan Orogeny. Because subduction resumed after strong deformation concluded, emplacement of plutonic rocks in the root region of the Ancestral Sierra continued throughout the remainder of the Mesozoic era. In fact, the greatest volume of granitic rock composing the batholith crystallized during this interval. These granites were not exposed at the surface, however, until millions of years passed and stream erosion

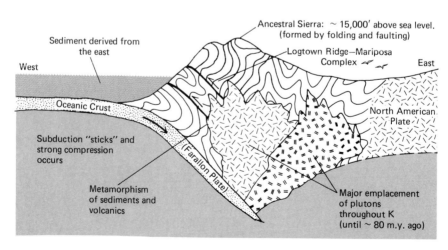

FIGURE 3.36 Subduction "sticks" and strong compression occurs during mid-Mesozoic time (150–140 million years ago).

IGNEOUS AND METAMORPHIC PROCESSES

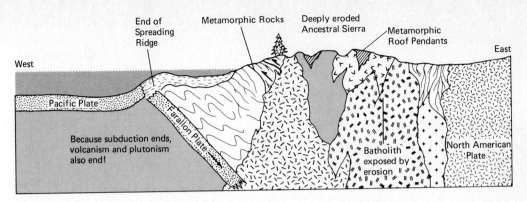

FIGURE 3.37 Subduction ceases because Pacific Plate *is not* moving toward the North American continent. San Andreas Fault is born during mid-to late Cenozoic time (30–5 million years ago).

swept away the overlying blankets of deformed sedimentary, volcanic, and metamorphic rock. By mid-Cenozoic time (about 30 million years ago), large expanses of granitic terrane were at the earth's surface. Metamorphic rocks were exposed in the western region of the Sierra, and a few metamorphic pendants were in the central and eastern portions of the range, but granitics were dominant (see Figure 3.37); the batholith had come into existence.

Large-scale magmatism ceased in the Sierra Nevada during this same mid-to-late-Cenozoic time interval because the Farallon Plate (the plate that had been undergoing subduction) was then fully consumed beneath the North American Plate. Thus there was no longer a deep subducting plate capable of yielding magma by partial melting, so emplacement of plutons at depth and voluminous volcanic eruptions at the surface terminated in both the Sierra and the Basin and Range province of Nevada and western Utah.

The disappearance of the Farallon Plate also allowed the San Andreas Fault to come into being. As the Farallon Plate disappeared, the Pacific Plate came into collision contact with the North American Plate for the first time. The motion between these two plates was (and still is) a shearing motion, giving rise to the transform fault boundary called the San Andreas Fault. One view is that this new sense of movement was largely responsible for the uplift of the modern Sierra Nevada and therefore of the downcutting by streams and glaciers that sculptured impressive landscapes such as those of Yosemite, Kings Canyon, and Sequoia National Parks. We will describe this mountain building in a later section. Before it began, however, the igneous and metamorphic rock framework for the Sierra Nevada was completely formed and widely exposed at the surface of the earth.

4

Sedimentary Processes

T HE SILICATE MINERALS OF
igneous and metamorphic rocks normally form at high temperatures
and pressures and are generally unstable when exposed to the lower
temperatures and pressures of the earth's surface. There the chemical action of air and water tends to break down the common igneous
minerals and to convert them into other minerals that are stable
under surface conditions. This process, known as **weathering**, provides the raw materials for sedimentary rocks, which are merely
the products of rock weathering transported and deposited by the
action of water, wind, or ice. Sedimentary rocks thus originate from
the interaction of the minerals of the solid earth with the waters
and atmosphere of the fluid earth. Sedimentary rocks constitute
only about 8 percent of the earth's crust, yet they are of great importance as the primary documents for understanding the earth's history because they lend themselves so well to comparisons with modern processes of sedimentation, and because they cover more than
70 percent of the land surface on continents.

SEDIMENTS AND SEDIMENTARY ROCKS

Particles accumulating as sediments today have two principal
sources: some originate and are transported as *solid* particles derived
from weathering of the land—accumulations of such particles are
called **detrital sediments**; others originate when the *dissolved* materials derived from weathering are precipitated from the waters of
streams, lakes, or the ocean—accumulations of these precipitated
particles are known as **chemical sediments**. Let us briefly contrast
the rock textures resulting from these two processes (Figure 4.1).
Clastic texture refers to fragmental accumulations. Whenever
weathered bits of mineral or rock are carried from a source area
to an environment of deposition, they undergo abrasion. The effect
of this wearing-away process is both to round the individual grains
and to reduce them in size. A necessary consequence of rounding
is that the grains, when deposited, cannot pack together in a manner
that fills up the total rock volume; hence detrital sediments typically
display a texture having rounded grains and original pore spaces
among them. Whenever we observe clastic texture in a rock, we
are well assured that it originated by a sedimentary process.

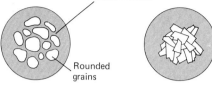

Pore spaces (voids); typically filled by chemically precipitated cementing material such as calcite or silica

Rounded grains

Clastic texture (detrital sediment)

Granular texture (chemical sediment)

FIGURE 4.1 Sedimentary rock textures.

Quite in contrast to detrital deposits, chemical sediments display a **granular texture,** not unlike that seen in plutonic rocks. Confusion between the two is not likely, however, because the sedimentary rocks having this texture are composed of low-temperature nonsilicate materials of the sort that can precipitate from surface waters.

4.1
DETRITAL SEDIMENTS

Complete weathering of igneous rocks normally leads to two kinds of solid particles: **clay minerals,** extremely fine-grained sheet silicates produced by the alteration of feldspars and other igneous minerals; and **quartz** *particles*, which resist weathering and accumulate relatively unchanged from the original igneous rock. Because clay minerals and quartz grains are the dominant particles produced by weathering, it is not surprising that they are the principal constituents of most accumulations of detrital sediments.

Accumulations dominated by clay-sized particles are called **muds,** and those dominated by larger particles are called **sands.** Muds are usually further subdivided by color, which normally ranges from very light gray to black; in general, the darker the color, the more fine-grained organic matter the mud contains. Sands, in turn, are classified by the size of their fragments, which may range from tiny grains of *silt* less than one-sixteenth millimeter in diameter to large *pebbles* many centimeters in diameter (Figure 4.2). When such large fragments predominate, the accumulation is given the name **gravel** rather than "sand."

Sediments composed largely of either clay particles or sand particles of a single size are known as **well-sorted sediments.** Mixtures of clay and sand particles of various size are called **poorly sorted sediments** (Figure 4.3). The degree of sorting of detrital sediments provides a useful index to the conditions under which they were deposited. Because moving fluids of differing velocities erode, trans-

FIGURE 4.2 Grain sizes of detrital sand particles. True scale photographs. (Fundamental Photographs.)

Sand   fine   medium   coarse   very coarse

FIGURE 4.3 A poorly sorted sediment, made up of sand and pebble particles of varying size. Exaggerated scale. (Fundamental Photographs.)

port, and deposit particles of differing sizes (Figure 4.4), well-sorted sediments normally result from slow accumulation and long exposure to varying velocities of flow. Poorly sorted sediments, on the other hand, indicate rapid accumulation and little exposure to such velocity variations.

Detritral sediments are converted to rocks by the processes of *cementation* and *compaction*. Cementation is the binding of the individual detrital grains to each other by a chemically precipitated material filling the pore spaces that originally existed among the fragments. Calcite and silica are the most common cements, although iron oxides are also found. All of these materials precipitate out of water, either from the original water filling the voids or from waters that percolate through the sediment following deposition

SEDIMENTARY PROCESSES   **109**

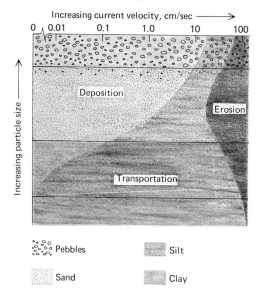

Increasing current velocity, cm/sec ⟶

0 0.01   0.1   1.0   10   100

Increasing particle size ⟶

Deposition

Erosion

Transportation

Pebbles   Silt

Sand   Clay

FIGURE 4.4 Approximate velocities of water flow for erosion, transportation and deposition of detrital particles of different sizes (100 cm/sec = about 2 mi/hr). (Modified from Turekian, "Oceans," 1968, after Heezen and Hollister.)

and burial. Compaction is an effective agent of rock formation only when the sediment is composed largely of very small fragments. The weight of overlying material can then cause the sediments to bond together into solid rock.

Chemical sediments, on the other hand, are converted to rock by recrystallization of the originally precipitated material. This process produces the granular texture shown in Figure 4.1.

4.2
CHEMICAL SEDIMENTS

In contrast to the solid products of weathering that accumulate as detrital sediments, chemical sediments are derived from the more soluble elements—particularly calcium, magnesium, sodium, potassium, and silicon—that are transported to lakes and the ocean in solution. This material does not remain indefinitely in solution; instead, much of it is *precipitated* as solid particles that accumulate to form chemical sediments. Today, much of this precipitation results from the life processes of water-dwelling plants and animals, many of which can concentrate even those dissolved elements that are present in very small quantities. Such organism-produced sediments are known as **biogenic chemical sediments.** Less commonly, the dissolved materials may become so concentrated by evaporation—for example, in desert lakes or tropical lagoons—that they spontaneously precipitate without the intervention of living organisms. Accumula-

(a)

(b)

(c)

FIGURE 4.5 Biogenic and nonbiogenic chemical sediments. (a) Biogenic calcium carbonate sand made up largely of shell fragments. (b,c) Nonbiogenic calcium carbonate sand. The surface of the sand particles is shown in b; c shows the internal structure of concentric precipitated spheres. (a-c: Courtesy of the Library Services Department, The American Museum of Natural History. Photos: Norman D. Newell.)

tions of such materials are called **nonbiogenic chemical sediments**.

By far the most common chemical sediments forming today are biogenic accumulations of calcium carbonate deposited by marine animals and plants [Figure 4.5(a)]. Many animals living in the ocean secrete hard, mineralized shells composed largely of the two calcium carbonate minerals calcite and aragonite. Corals, snails, clams, sea urchins, starfish, and crabs are a few familiar examples, but there are numerous others. The greatest volume of marine chemical sediment is derived from the remains of microscopic organisms called *coccoliths* and *foraminifera* (Figure 4.6). This sediment, called *calcareous ooze*, covers nearly one-half of the world's ocean floor. In addition, many simple seaweedlike marine plants also precipitate calcium carbonate from ocean water. Over large areas of the ocean floor, areas where there is little influx of detrital sand

(a)
(b)

FIGURE 4.6 Calcareous ooze constituents: a) Coccolith; b) Foraminifera. (Reprinted with permission from Eicher and McAlester, History of the Earth, © 1980 by Prentice-Hall, Inc., Englewood Cliffs, New Jersey.)

and clay to dilute the carbonate minerals, relatively pure concentrations of calcium carbonate shells and shell fragments are accumulating today.

Occasionally the evaporation of water from lakes, bays, and lagoons proceeds so far that even the most soluble dissolved elements—sodium, magnesium, and potassium—are deposited as unusual sulfate minerals and as common salt, sodium chloride (Figure 4.7). The deposition of these very soluble elements requires an almost complete evaporation of the water in which they are dissolved and leads to the accumulation of **evaporite sediments**.

Biogenic calcium carbonate deposits and nonbiogenic evaporites are the most common chemical sediments forming today, but two less common chemical sediments also deserve mention. The first is *silica*, a compound of silicon and oxygen with the same composition as quartz but often lacking its stable, regular crystal structure. Quartz, as we have seen, is extremely resistant to weathering; in contrast, the silicon in more complex silicate minerals is far less stable, and these minerals contribute large amounts of dissolved silica to streams and the ocean as they are weathered. Most water-

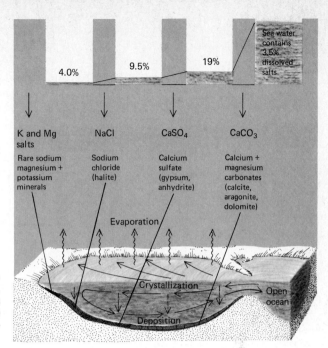

FIGURE 4.7 Sequence of mineral precipitation in evaporating ocean water. Evaporation of some lake water produces different minerals and sequences because of differing proportions of dissolved elements.

dwelling organisms that secrete shells or other hard parts construct them of calcium carbonate, but a few use this dissolved silica instead. By far the most important silica extractors today are *diatoms*, microscopic plants that are abundant in both the ocean and in lakes, and *radiolarians*, microscopic animals that live primarily in the ocean. Both secrete tiny, glasslike skeletons of silica that are accumulating on some parts of the ocean floor to form sedimentary silica deposits (Figure 4.8).

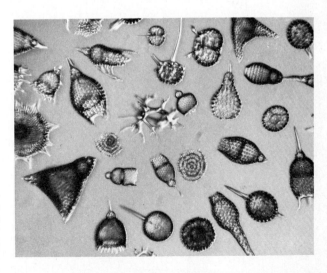

FIGURE 4.8 Skeletons of radiolara magnified 140 times. The remains of these microscopic animals accumulate in enormous quantities on some parts of the ocean floor to form biogenic silica deposits. (Eric V. Grave.)

The second less common type of chemical sediment also results from the activities of animals and plants, but in this sediment it is not the hard, mineralized skeletons that accumulate but the soft organic materials themselves. Some organic matter from the decay of animals and plants is found in almost all present-day sediments, but such materials usually make up only a small fraction of the total volume. Less commonly, local conditions permit the accumulation of sediments with much higher amounts of organic matter. On land, deposits of *peat* may form when plant remains accumulate in acid waters which act as a preservative to prevent decay. Peat deposits often contain as much as 90 percent organic materials; the remaining 10 percent is usually detrital sand or clay. Likewise, on portions of the ocean floor, organic materials that are produced by animals and plants in the sunlit surface waters may sink and accumulate, along with clay and sand, to make up a significant fraction of the bottom sediments. Both of these types of organic-rich chemical sediment have a significance far out of proportion to their small volume for, when buried and altered in sedimentary rocks, peat deposits become coal, and the organic matter in marine muds becomes petroleum.

4.3
CLASSIFICATION OF SEDIMENTARY ROCKS

About 99 percent of all sedimentary rocks fall into one of four integrating groups: sandstones, shales, carbonate rocks, or evaporites (Figures 4.9, 4.10, 4.11). Sandstones, as the name implies, are rocks made up of particles of sand compressed and cemented to form rock. Most of the sand particles are composed largely of quartz, because, of all the common minerals, only quartz is stable and resists further breakdown to far smaller particles when exposed to weathering at the earth's surface. Under special circumstances, however, other minerals, particularly feldspars, may also be important constituents of sandstones. A sandstone composed mostly of feldspar and quartz is known as an arkose. When particles significantly larger than sand, such as pebbles or cobbles, are abundant in a sedimentary rock, the term conglomerate is applied to it; if the large particles are angular, rather than rounded, the rock is called breccia.

Shales are rocks made up of clay mineral particles that are too small to be distinguished except under the extreme magnification of an electron microscope. Clay minerals are the stable silicate phases formed at the earth's surface by weathering of most kinds of igneous silicate minerals, especially feldspars. Because feldspars are the most common minerals in igneous rocks, clay minerals resulting from the weathering of feldspars are also the most common sedimentary

Limestone

Sandstone

Shale

FIGURE 4.9 Classification of the common sedimentary rocks by mineral composition. All gradations exist between pure sandstones, shales, and limestones—dolomites, which are shown in enlarged drawings at the points of the triangular diagram. The enlargements are of an area about 3 mm (1/8 in.) in diameter. (Limestone: B. M. Shaub; sandstone, shale: Yale Peabody Museum.)

minerals. It has been estimated that about half of the earth's sedimentary rocks are clay-rich shales, almost one-quarter sandstones and conglomerates, and about one-quarter carbonate rocks and evaporites.

Carbonate rocks, as the name implies, are those composed of carbonate minerals, principally calcite and dolomite. The two common carbonate rocks are **limestone**, composed predominantly of calcite, and **dolomite**, composed principally of the mineral dolomite (this is one of the few cases where the same name applies to a rock and a specific mineral). These carbonate rocks form when dissolved calcium and magnesium ions, derived from the weathering of preexisting rocks and combined with the carbonate radical (CO_3^{-2}), are precipitated either directly from the waters of lakes and oceans or indirectly by the action of organisms in making shells and skeletons, many of which are composed of calcium carbonate.

Evaporites are relatively uncommon chemical sedimentary

(a)

(b)

(c)

FIGURE 4.10 Typical exposures of sedimentary rocks. (a) Sandstone exposed in a road cut in western Texas. (b) Shale exposed along a stream bank in eastern New York. (c) Evaporite exposed in a road cut in southern Utah. (b: New York State Geological Survey; c: U.S. Geological Survey.)

FIGURE 4.11 Gradational relationship of evaporite to the three more common sedimentary rock types shown in Figure 4.9. Areas of photograph and enlargement same as Figure 4.9. (Photograph: Yale Peabody Museum.)

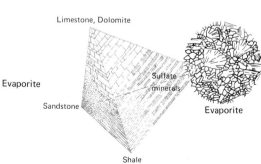

Limestone, Dolomite

Evaporite

Sulfate minerals

Sandstone

Evaporite

Shale

SEDIMENTARY PROCESSES

FIGURE 4.12 Bedded chert from California. (E. A. Hay.)

rocks that form when the dissolved materials of lake or ocean waters become highly concentrated through evaporation. Under such circumstances, dolomite, gypsum, anhydrite, and halite are the principal minerals deposited. Evaporite rocks usually contain two or more of these minerals.

Sedimentary rocks commonly occur as pure, unmixed sandstones, shales, carbonates, or evaporites, but all gradations exist among these major types. Sandstones, for example, may contain clay or carbonate minerals, giving rise, respectively, to "muddy" or "calcareous" sandstones. Some of these intermediate compositions can be conveniently described by the terms shown in Figure 4.9.

At least one other chemical sediment (**chert**) deserves inclusion in our system of classification. Chert consists of layers of exceedingly fine-grained quartz (Figure 4.12), which typically have a porcelain-like surface. It seems likely that tiny silica-secreting organisms (Figure 4.8) are the principal contributors to these deposits.

4.4
SEDIMENTARY STRUCTURES

In addition to the sedimentary properties of particle size and composition, special features of layering can also be instructive about a rock's origin. Like detrital sand and clay, the precipitated grains of chemical sediments are usually transported by moving fluids before they finally come to rest in sedimentary accumulations. For this reason, both chemical and detrital sedimentary deposits normally show patterns of superimposed layers formed as they are sorted and deposited by fluid motions. These layers, and related features formed at the time of sediment deposition, are called **physical sedimentary structures.** An additional structural pattern is found in sediments that accumulate in aquatic environments where bottom-dwelling animals and plants are abundant, as they are on the floors of most lakes and shallow seas. Under these conditions, the sediments are often reworked, burrowed, and otherwise modified by the organisms to produce **biogenic sedimentary structures.**

The most important physical sedimentary structure is the characteristic layering, called **bedding** or **stratification,** found in almost all sediment accumulations (Figure 4.13). Bedding results from the fact that thick sediment accumulations rarely form from a single massive deposition of particles; instead, many small depositional increments are required. A single stream flood or moving ocean current normally transports and deposits only a relatively thin sheet of particles. These sheets seldom exceed a few centimeters in thickness, and it thus requires many of them to form thick accumulations of sediment. Usually each thin increment, or *bed*, shows slight differences in particle size and arrangement that distinguish it from adjacent increments; these slight differences give sediment accumulations their characteristic bedded structure.

In the simplest case, the boundaries of individual beds in a sediment accumulation are horizontal, and adjacent beds are distinguished by slight differences in color or particle size. Such **parallel bedding** is common in sedimentary accumulations, but since it can form under a variety of conditions, it gives relatively few clues to the original fluid motions that deposited the sediment (Figure 4.14).

Parallel bedding

Cross bedding

Graded bedding

FIGURE 4.13 The principal kinds of sedimentary bedding.

SEDIMENTARY PROCESSES

(a)

(b)

FIGURE 4.14 Parallel bedding in modern beach sand of eastern Scotland (a) and in ancient lime-stones of southern Utah (b). (a: Geological Survey of Great Britain; b: Tad Nichols.)

(a)

(b)

FIGURE 4.15 Cross bedding in modern muds and silts of eastern England (a) and in ancient sandstone of northern Arizona (b). (a: Geological Survey of Great Britain; b: Tad Nichols.)

SEDIMENTARY PROCESSES

More useful in such interpretations are two equally common but less regular types of bedding—**cross bedding** and **graded bedding**.

Cross bedding is formed when the fluid motions of sediment deposition cause wavelike undulations on the surface of the sediment. Such sedimentary wave forms are known as *ripples* and are common in accumulations of sand-sized sedimentary particles. When a rippled surface is partly eroded before a new layer is deposited on it, the individual layers have various angular relations to each other (Figure 4.15). Such bedding, called **cross bedding**, may provide important clues to the nature of the depositing fluid. For example, cross bedding formed by wind action usually shows individual beds inclined at a somewhat steeper angle than does cross bedding formed by moving water. In addition, laboratory studies of sediment rippling show that different patterns of cross bedding form under differing conditions of fluid flow. Thus it is sometimes possible to infer the approximate velocity, direction, and other features of the depositing fluid motion from patterns of cross bedding (Figure 4.16).

Frequently the rippled surfaces of noneroded sedimentary layers are buried by successive pulses of deposition, thus preserving what are called *ripple marks* (Figure 4.17). These, too, are indicators of fluid motions in the depositional environment.

So long as sedimentary rocks remain in their originally deposited flat-lying orientation, we have no difficulty determining which layers are older and which layers are younger (remember Steno's

FIGURE 4.16 Type of bedding as a function of sediment size and fluid velocity.

FIGURE 4.17 Ripple marks. Close-up view of mud deposits in a 1 m (3 ft) cross section along the Colorado River in western Arizona. (Tad Nichols.)

Law of Superposition, Figure I.4). What if, however, the layers have been steeply tilted as shown in Figure 4.18? In such a position, features of cross bedding and ripple marks are useful in determining which is the top side and which is the bottom side of a sedimentary sequence. Figure 4.18(a) and (b) shows how these sedimentary structures can be applied. Each kind of sedimentary structure has a distinctive appearance on its top side and its bottom side when depos-

(a)

(b)

FIGURE 4.18 These two figures show the use of cross bedding and ripple marks to distinguish the top side of a sedimentary layer from the bottom side, even after it has been tilted steeply. (a) Steeply inclined layers of sandstone and shale. (b) Archlike and troughlike folding. (a: E. H. Bailey, U.S. Geological Survey.)

Bottom of Bed   Top of Bed

FIGURE 4.19 Graded bedding (upward decrease in particle size) as seen in a pebble-sized sandstone. (F. J. Pettijohn.)

ited (see Figures 4.15 and 4.17), and this distinction will be apparent later, even though the strata have been strongly folded or tilted away from their original horizontality. As we continue in this chapter, we shall note other features of sedimentary rocks that also are useful in this manner.

Another bedding type that gives important clues to the depositing fluid is **graded bedding,** in which each individual bed shows a progressive decrease in particle size upward through the bed (Figure 4.19). In most sedimentary deposits, *adjacent* beds may show slight size differences, but normally the particle size *within* an individual bed, deposited as a single event, remains constant. Graded beds are an exception and require a depositing mechanism that, in a single event, deposits progressively smaller particles. Field observations and laboratory experiments indicate that graded beds form when dense, sediment-laden currents are introduced into relatively still water. When this occurs, the current abruptly loses velocity, depositing first the larger and heavier particles and then the finer and lighter in a gradational sequence. Such debris-laden currents, called **turbidity currents,** are common where sediment-carrying streams flow into lakes or the ocean; they also occur on the steep slopes of submerged scarps and canyons when large, unstable sediment accumulations break away and slide downward into deeper water (Figure 4.20).

Because of their high concentration of dense sediment particles, turbidity currents normally have a much higher overall density than the surrounding water; they thus move downward under the influence of gravity at high velocities and cover large areas before they are finally dissipated by friction. Their high velocities and densities also commonly cause them to erode or *scour* the previous bottom sediment before dissipating and depositing their own sediment load. This erosion usually forms distinctive channels, scratches, and gouges in the underlying sediment, which, along with graded bedding, are characteristic structures of sediments deposited by turbidity currents. Because they are both formed and buried by a single sedimentary event, these erosional features are difficult to observe in present-day sediments, but they are a common feature of ancient sedimentary rocks. There, the scratches, grooves, and channels are most often preserved as impressions on the base of the overlying

FIGURE 4.20 Origin of graded bedding from sediment slumping and turbidity current flow.

bed, and for this reason they are known as **sole markings** (Figure 4.21). They, too, allow us to distinguish the top side of bedding from the bottom side, just as ripple marks and cross bedding do.

FIGURE 4.21 Sole markings, caused by turbidity current scour, exposed on the base of a sandstone. (W. Hiller.)

(b)

(c)

FIGURE 4.22 Biogenic structures (a,b). (a) Surface tracks and trails made by bottom-dwelling animals on muds of the deep-ocean floor. (b) X-ray cross section of burrows made within lagoonal muds by burrowing animals. Some of the animals' shells can be clearly seen. (c) An accumulation of animal shells becoming buried in beach sands. (a: D. M. Owen; b,c: Donald C. Rhoads.)

Parallel bedding, cross bedding, ripple marks, graded bedding, and sole markings are the most important physical sedimentary structures; equally common are various biogenic sedimentary structures formed in the sediments shortly after deposition by living animals and plants. The two principal kinds are: tracks and trails produced by animals on the *surface* of the sediment, and burrows and borings produced by animals and plant roots *within* the sediment (Figure 4.22). Both of these types of biogenic structure can provide some important clues to the original depositional environment of the sediment.

In addition to such structural traces of organic activity, animal shells and other hard parts of animals and plants are also commonly found in sedimentary accumulations (Figure 4.22). We have already seen that many chemical sediments, particularly calcium carbonate and silica accumulations, are formed almost entirely from the shells and hard parts of animals and plants. In addition, most detrital sediments also contain scattered animal and plant remains. Usually these biologic remains persist, as **fossils**, when the sediment is altered to sedimentary rocks, providing invaluable clues to the original depositional environment of the sediment.

Both detrital and chemical sediments are accumulating on the earth today under a host of different environmental conditions—near polar glaciers and around tropical coral reefs, in valleys far above sea level, and in the deepest ocean basins. The principal goal in studies of these present-day sediments is to determine the characteristic associations of compositions, grain sizes, and structures that are forming under each environment so that this knowledge can be used to interpret the environments preserved in ancient sedimentary rocks.

The most important environmental distinction in both present-day and ancient sediments is between those that accumulate on land as **terrestrial sediments** and those that are deposited on the ocean floor as **marine sediments**. In this section we shall review the characteristic patterns of sediment accumulating today in a variety of terrestrial environments before moving on to consider the much larger volumes of sediment accumulating on the ocean floor.

4.5
FLUVIAL ENVIRONMENTS

The sedimentary environments formed by continuously flowing streams in tropical and temperate regions are known as **fluvial environments**; because of their relative accessibility, these are the most thoroughly studied and best understood of all present-day sediment accumulations. Sand and clay carried by streams during floods are normally deposited downstream as the flood subsides, only to be transported and deposited again during the next flood. The deposition of fluvial sediments, called **alluvium**, is therefore usually only a temporary stop in a journey that leads ultimately to the ocean. Nevertheless, in certain regions, such as low-lying areas where the land surface is rapidly sinking as a result of earth-moving forces, the alluvium deposited by one flood may be buried *without erosion* by deposits of the next flood, and thus be removed indefinitely from the possibility of further transportation toward the ocean. Under such conditions, fluvial sediments hundreds of meters thick may accumulate and, ultimately, be preserved as sedimentary rocks.

Studies of present-day fluvial sediments show that they usually consist of two strikingly different kinds of detrital particles: thick layers of well-sorted sand or gravel alternate with layers of poorly sorted mixtures of finer sand and mud. In addition to differences in grain size and sorting, the alternating sand and mud layers usually

FIGURE 4.23 Characteristic fluvial sediments.

show a sharp contrast in sedimentary structures. The sands usually show abundant cross bedding, indicating that they were deposited by swift horizontal fluid motions that strongly rippled the sediment surface; in contrast, the muds usually show a dominance of parallel bedding, indicating vertical settling in relatively still water (Figures 4.23 and 4.24).

Extensive studies of modern stream deposition have shown that these alternating sand and mud layers tend to form simultaneously, but in different horizontal and vertical positions. During floods, the highest velocities of water movement tend to occur in the deepest parts of the stream channel; there the heaviest, coarsest particles are concentrated and moved by bouncing, sliding, and rolling along the bottom. The finer particles, on the other hand, are widely dispersed in suspension throughout the moving water that covers the entire floodplain (Figure 4.23). As a result, the coarse and fine particles are spatially separated. The coarse particles accumulate as **channel deposits**—thick masses of well-sorted sand and gravel that are rippled and cross-bedded by rapid channel flow. As the river channel slowly shifts its position, these channel deposits become covered by finer-grained **overbank deposits**—clays and fine sands that are spread in suspension over the entire floodplain and deposited there as the floodwaters recede (Figures 4.23 and 4.24). Unlike the channel deposits, these overbank deposits may accumulate in a variety of subenvironments such as swamps, marshes, or temporary lakes. This horizontal and vertical alternation of channel sands and overbank muds is the characteristic pattern of fluvial sediments.

There are features of these fluvial sediments that are useful for determining the top side and the bottom side of a sedimentary sequence. Sometimes an individual channel will be cut into sediments and then filled with course fragments of rock when the current that cut the channel slows down (Figure 4.25). Since channels are usually concave upward in shape, this form may be used later to recognize the top side of the sedimentary deposits. Overbank

(a)

(c)

SEDIMENTARY PROCESSES

(b)

(d)

(e)

FIGURE 4.24 Fluvial sediments. (a) Channel sands and gravels exposed along a stream in northern Scotland. (b) Close-up view of cross-bedded channel sands exposed in a small trench along a stream in western Indiana. (c) Flooding and deposition of overbank sediments along the Missouri River in western Iowa. The normal river channel can be seen at the right. (d) Close-up view of overbank mud deposits in a 1 m (3 ft) cross section along the Colorado River in western Arizona. (e) Ancient channel sands (light color) and overbank muds (dark color) preserved in sedimentary rocks exposed in southern Connecticut. (a: Geological Survey of Great Britain; b: P. E. Potter; c: U.S. Department of Agriculture; d: Tad Nichols.)

(a)

(b)

FIGURE 4.25 (a) Stream channel filled with light colored sandstone cut into dark colored shale. Central Colorado. (b) Stream channel that has been steeply tilted. Tick Canyon, California. (E. A. Hay.)

SEDIMENTARY PROCESSES   **129**

(a)

(b)

FIGURE 4.26 (a) Development of polygonal shrinkage cracks. Modern mudcracks. (b) Mudcracks preserved in very old rocks found in the Grand Canyon, Arizona. (a: N. T. Hall; b: W. R. Cotton.)

deposits are typically fine-grained, so when flooding recedes and they become exposed to the atmosphere, water dries out of the clays and they contract in volume, giving rise to mud cracks near the surface of the sedimentary layer (Figure 4.26). If these mud cracks become covered by younger deposits, they may be used later to tell the top side from the bottom side of the sedimentary rock sequence.

All fluvial sediments are composed predominantly of detrital sedimentary particles. The only chemical sediments normally associated with fluvial environments are organic materials; these are rare in channel deposits, but they may occur in abundance in some overbank muds, particularly those deposited in marshes and swamps. In such environments, the muds are commonly very dark gray or black because of abundant fine-grained plant debris. In addition, larger plant fragments, such as leaves, stems, or even logs, sometimes are found in such deposits. Occasionally these larger plant fragments may accumulate in such high concentrations that they overshadow the muds to form peat, but peat occurs in only a small fraction of present-day fluvial sediments. Most contain relatively few animal and plant remains because such material quickly decays when exposed to the air between periods of flood.

Much of the sediment accumulating today in desert regions is deposited by streams just as are the fluvial sediments of temperate and tropical areas. These desert sediments differ markedly from those of humid regions, however, because temporary desert streams provide little opportunity for separating the sedimentary particles into distinctive channel and overbank deposits. Most desert streams flow only during infrequent periods of heavy rainfall, and even then they flow only over relatively short distances—usually from desert highlands down to the surrounding lowlands, where they quickly disappear by evaporation and absorption into the dry, porous soil. Under such conditions the sedimentary debris moved by the streams tends to be concentrated at the base of the highlands in wedge-shaped alluvial fans (Figures 4.27 and 4.28). Because there are no permanent streams to transport alluvial fan deposits farther toward the ocean, they can accumulate to great thicknesses as older fan deposits are buried by younger ones.

Alluvial fan deposits are almost all composed of a poorly sorted mixture of detrital particles ranging in size from the finest clay to extremely coarse gravel. They commonly contain abundant feldspar fragments, along with the more typical quartz and clay particles, because the relative lack of chemical weathering and the rapid burial of the sediments prevent much of the eroded feldspar from weathering to clay minerals. Cross bedding may be present, but in general these poorly sorted detrital mixtures show few distinctive sedimentary structures.

In addition to alluvial fan deposits, two less common but very distinctive kinds of sediments also accumulate in desert regions. These are evaporites and eolian sediments. The chemical evaporites are formed in temporary lakes that sometimes occur on the floors of desert basins (Figures 4.27 and 4.28). These lakes are filled during the infrequent periods of heavy rainfall as ephemeral streams flow

FIGURE 4.27 Characteristic sediments of desert regions.

(a)

(c)

(b)

(d)

FIGURE 4.28 Desert sediments. (a) Cross section of poorly sorted sediments of a small alluvial fan in southern California. (b) Desert evaporite deposits, Death Valley, California. (c) Cross bedding in desert dune sands of southern California, exposed in a small trench. (d) Ancient alluvial fan deposits (above) and dune sands (below) preserved in sedimentary rocks exposed in southeastern Utah. (a,c: John S. Shelton; b,d: U.S. Geological Survey.)

from desert highlands into the surrounding lowlands. Between rainfalls, the waters are partially or completely lost to the atmosphere by evaporation; when this occurs, the dissolved elements in the lake water are deposited as chemical evaporites. Evaporites deposited in different desert lakes show a wide range of chemical compositions because of differences in the dissolved elements transported to the lakes by local streams. Calcium and sodium evaporite minerals, such as calcite, gypsum, and halite, are the most common deposits, but some evaporites have high concentrations of unusual minerals containing such rare elements as boron and lithium.

Desert basins where evaporation is intense provide the only major setting where *non*biogenic chemical sediments accumulate above sea level. Biogenic chemical sediments almost never occur in desert environments, both because plants and animals are scarce and because the lack of water and high temperatures lead to rapid decay of the small amounts of organic matter present.

In addition to alluvial fan and evaporite deposits, a third type of sediment may occur in desert environments. This is the **eolian** sediments that originate when the sands and clays of alluvial fans are further transported and deposited by wind action (Figures 4.27 and 4.28). Fan deposits normally lack a protective cover of vegetation and are therefore continually subject to varying velocities of wind flow that tend to sort them into different size groups just as does the flowing water of fluvial environments. During periods of high winds, fine silt and clay particles are transported in suspension as *dust storms* and may be carried long distances, often even beyond the desert into more humid environments, before the wind subsides.

Sand particles, in contrast, are usually too heavy for suspension transport by wind; instead, they are bounced and rolled along the desert floor to be concentrated as dunes on the windward side of desert basins. There they may be covered and preserved by later alluvial fan deposition. Wind-deposited sand accumulations show many of the characteristics of fluvial channel sands in that they are well sorted and show strong cross bedding and surface rippling caused by the rapid horizontal flow of the depositing fluid. Certain details of eolian cross bedding differ, however, from those of water-deposited sands. In particular, the angular bedding is commonly much steeper in wind deposits, and this, combined with the associated alluvial fan and evaporite sediments, normally makes it possible to recognize ancient desert sands.

4.7
GLACIAL ENVIRONMENTS

Sediments accumulating today in glacial environments show many of the same characteristics as desert alluvial fan deposits, and the two types of deposits are often difficult to distinguish in ancient sediments. Like desert alluvium, most glacial deposits are unsorted mixtures of clay, sand, and gravel, which lack distinctive sedimentary structures. Whereas alluvial fan deposits typically have crude layering, glacial deposits may lack stratification completely. Because glacial environments, like deserts, normally lack a dense cover of vegetation, wind action locally may sort the surficial glacial deposits into eolian sand dunes similar to those of desert regions. Unlike desert sediments, however, those of glacial regions rarely show evaporite deposits, which normally originate only in warm climates. As in desert environments, organic matter and animal and plant remains are rare in glacial deposits. The most characteristic feature of glacial sediments is the presence of pebbles that have been scratched and abraded by moving against solid bedrock while frozen into the flowing ice; such **striated pebbles** are the surest criterion for the recognition of ancient glacial deposits (Figure 4.29).

FIGURE 4.29   Ancient glacial sediments exposed in southwest Africa, showing striated pebbles scratched by moving in ice. (J. W. Hälbich.)

MARINE SEDIMENTARY PATTERNS

Most sediment accumulation takes place on the ocean floor in various marine environments. In present-day marine sediments, a primary distinction can be made between those deposited under relatively shallow water on the submerged continental shelves and those accumulating beyond the continents in the deep-ocean basins (Figure 4.30). Continental shelf sediments tend to accumulate both more

FIGURE 4.30   Present-day continental shelves, the submerged margins of the continents where most sediment accumulation takes place. (Compiled from various sources.)

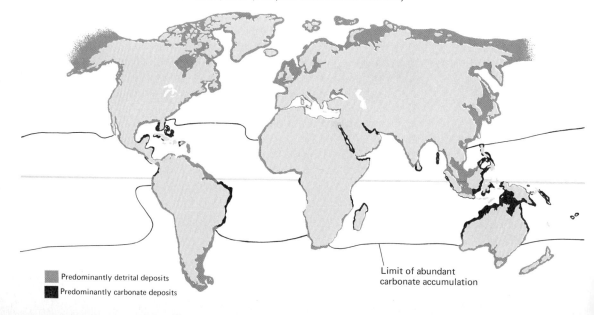

Predominantly detrital deposits
Predominantly carbonate deposits

Limit of abundant carbonate accumulation

rapidly, and by somewhat different processes, than do those of the deep oceans. Shelf and deep-ocean environments resemble each other, however, in that each has some large areas where land-derived sands and muds are accumulating as detrital sediments, and each has other large areas dominated by chemical accumulations, which, for brevity, are usually referred to as *carbonate* sediments because they are dominated by biogenic calcium carbonate. We shall consider both detrital and carbonate accumulations of the continental shelves before examining the somewhat different detrital and carbonate accumulations of the deep-ocean basins.

4.8
DETRITAL SHELF ENVIRONMENTS

Most of the sand and mud delivered to the oceans by streams is deposited on the submerged shelves that surround the continents. These shelves today have an average width of about 80 km (50 miles) and slope gradually seaward to an average water depth of about 200 m (600 ft); beyond them lie the steeper slopes of the continental margins that lead to the deep-ocean basins (Figure 4.30). Because the ocean floor on the shallow, near-shore parts of these shelves is subjected to much more intense wave and current motions than is the deeper shelf, we might predict that large sedimentary particles should be sorted and concentrated on these high-energy near-shore bottoms as accumulations of sand and gravel. Conversely, only finer silt and mud particles should reach the outer shelf region where relatively little wave and current energy is available to transport larger particles [Figure 4.31(a)]. At the end of this chapter we shall consider these patterns of detrital particle size as exposed in very old (about 500 million years) rocks at Grand Canyon, Arizona.

FIGURE 4.31 Predicted and actual patterns of sediment distribution on the continental shelves. The relatively recent expansions and contractions of continental ice sheets have caused repeated migrations of the shoreline and deposition of shallow-water sediment over much of the shelves. The more regular "predicted" pattern of offshore size decrease occurs in many ancient sediments.

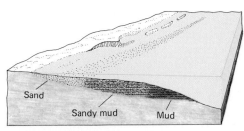

(a) Predicted shelf sediment pattern

(b) Actual shelf sediment pattern

They enable us to discover land and sea relationships as they existed at that time, and they tell us how regions of erosion and deposition changed through time with respect to each other.

Studies of sedimentary rocks have shown that this offshore decrease in particle size *was* common in ancient marine sediments, for they normally show a concentration of sand and gravel in nearshore regions that grades seaward into finer silt and mud deposits. This pattern does *not* occur, however, on the continental shelves today. Instead, studies of modern shelf sediments (made by sampling or photographing the bottom from ships or, in shallow water, by diving with scuba gear) have shown that well-sorted *sand* is the dominant sediment over much of the present-day shelves [Figure 4.31(b)]. Furthermore, sand is particularly abundant on the outermost shelf, where it should be rare or absent. In addition, mud accumulations are far more common today in shallow, near-shore settings than would be predicted from the distribution of wave and current energy.

We have already anticipated the reasons for this anomalous pattern, that is, the relatively recent changes in sea level caused by the expansions and contractions of large continental ice sheets. These sea-level changes led to many oscillations of the shoreline back and forth across the continental shelves (Figure 4.32). As a result, much of the sediment exposed today on even the outermost parts of the shelves was deposited in high-energy near-shore environments at times when the sea level stood much lower. Indeed, large

FIGURE 4.32 Fluctuation of the Atlantic shoreline of the United States. Fifteen thousand years ago enough ocean water was locked up in large continental ice sheets to drop sea level about 200 m (660 ft) and shift the shoreline to the edges of the present continental shelf. If the present Greenland and Antarctica ice sheets were to melt, sea level would rise and the shelves would expand approximately the line marked "future?".

areas of the present shelves appear to be covered with materials deposited above sea level in fluvial or, on polar shelves, glacial environments. Most present-day shelf sediments, therefore, do not reflect their present environments but, instead, are *relict* sediments of earlier environmental patterns.

Too little time has elapsed since the most recent melting of continental ice sheets, and the consequent rise of sea level, to allow sediments now being delivered to the shelves to reach an equilibrium with their environments. Presumably, if sea level were to remain at its present position long enough (an unlikely event, as we shall see in Chapter 10), fine muds now accumulating near shore would be slowly transported seaward to cover the near-shore sands that now dominate the shelf, leading to the expected offshore decrease in grain size. In the meantime, only a few large rivers that carry huge volumes of mud and sand are able to deposit these materials beyond the shore region by building out broad **deltas** onto the continental shelves. In contrast, the lower reaches of most streams have been "drowned" by rising sea level to create elongate, lagoon-like bodies of water known as **estuaries**. Most of the sediment carried by these streams is accumulating in these coastal estuaries, which must be filled before delta build-out and transport of particles onto the shelf can begin.

A characteristic feature of offshore detrital shelf sediments in those few deltaic areas where they are being deposited today is the frequent occurrence of small-scale alternations of parallel-bedded muddy and sandy layers, each usually from a few millimeters to a meter thick (Figure 4.33). These alternating layers are also very common in ancient shelf sediments, but their exact origin is

FIGURE 4.33 Detrital shelf sediments. (a) Accumulation of oyster shells and (b) vertical biogenic burrowed structures preserved in ancient shelf sediments exposed in western South Dakota. (c) Ancient organic-rich shelf mud deposits, preserved as shales exposed in central New York. (d) Alternating bands of parallel-bedded mud and silt preserved in ancient shelf sediments exposed in western Wales. (a-c: Donald C. Rhoads; d: Geological Survey of Great Britain.)

obscure. Most probably they result from large, infrequent storms that agitate the water to unusual depths and transport near-shore sand particles seaward. Between these events, mud slowly accumulates to give the alternating muddy layers. On the more steeply sloping parts of the shelf, gravity transport of sedimentary particles by turbidity currents can also lead to alternating mud and fine sand sequences, which, however, usually show graded bedding and other distinctive structures. Such **turbidite sequences**, as they are called, are less common in shelf sediments than in sediments accumulating in deeper environments beyond the shelf.

4.9
CARBONATE SHELF ENVIRONMENTS

Land-derived sand and mud are today the dominant sediments on polar and temperate shelves, but they are replaced on many tropical shelves by extensive accumulations of calcium carbonate that have either been precipitated directly from the local ocean water or, more commonly, removed indirectly by the activities of animals and plants. Direct precipitation is favored in tropical regions because the solubility of calcium carbonate in ocean water varies *inversely* with water temperature: the higher the temperature, the less dissolved calcium carbonate it can contain, and vice versa. Only in shallow tropical oceans does the water temperature rise high enough to cause spontaneous precipitation of calcium carbonate. Even then, some reduction in the volume of water by evaporation is probably necessary to increase the calcium concentration further and thus decrease its solubility, although the exact chemistry of the process is still poorly understood. Such conditions are met on many shallow tropical shelves today and result in sedimentary accumulations of directly precipitated calcium carbonate grains (Figures 4.34 and 4.35). Most commonly these grains are rounded, sand-sized particles, called **ooliths**, which show a characteristic concentric pattern of growth (see Figure 4.5).

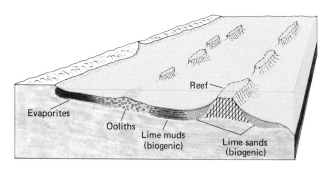

Evaporites
Ooliths
Lime muds (biogenic)
Lime sands (biogenic)
Reef

FIGURE 4.34 Characteristic sediments of carbonate shelves.

(a)

(b)

(c)

(d)

(e)

FIGURE 4.35 Carbonate shelf sediments. (a) Aerial view of a part of the Bahama Bank, a broad shelf off the Florida coast dominated by carbonate deposition. (b-d) Close-up views of nonbiogenic lime mud (b), biogenic lime sand (c), and organic reef (d), all on the Bahama Bank. (e) Ancient lime mud preserved as sedimentary rock exposed in central Alabama. (a-d: Norman D. Newell, The American Museum of Natural History, Library Services Department.)

Under exceptional circumstances, evaporation of ocean water may proceed far enough to precipitate still more soluble dissolved elements (see Figure 4.6). Such conditions are met today only in a few tropical lagoons that receive infrequent inflows of normal ocean water. Between such influxes, intense evaporation may lead to deposition of *marine evaporite* sediments (Figure 4.34). Usually such sediments comprise mostly the minerals halite and gypsum. Less commonly, various unusual sodium, potassium, and magnesium minerals are deposited in such settings.

Directly precipitated calcium carbonate and marine evaporites are not forming today in polar or temperate regions and are only a small fraction of the shelf sediments of tropical regions. Most present-day tropical shelves are covered instead by calcium carbonate particles of *biogenic* origin (Figures 4.34 and 4.35).

When shell-bearing animals and carbonate-secreting plants die, their skeletons do not normally remain intact but are progressively reduced to smaller and smaller particles by such secondary processes as wave abrasion and reworking by predators as the surrounding organic matter decays (Figure 4.36). As a result, most biogenic carbonate sediments consist not of whole shells but of sand- and mud-sized particles derived from whole shells. These **lime sands** and **lime muds** are the dominant shelf carbonate sediments and generally show the same patterns of size sorting and sedimentary structures as do detrital sands and muds. The lime sands tend to be concentrated in near-shore areas of high-energy water motions and show cross bedding and other structures indicative of such motions. The lime muds, on the other hand, tend to accumulate in sheltered or deeper environments where there is less water motion. As on temperate and polar shelves, anomalous relict accumulations of lime sand, formed during recent intervals of lowered sea level, are proba-

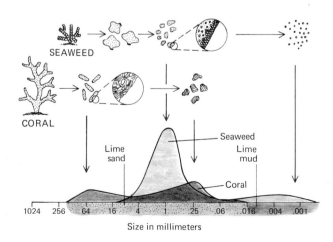

FIGURE 4.36 The breakdown of calcium-carbonate-depositing seaweeds and corals to produce lime sand and line mud. (From Laporte, "Ancient Environments," 1968, after Folk and Robles.)

bly common on deeper tropical shelves today, but this is not yet certain since tropical shelves have been less extensively explored than have those of temperate regions.

In addition to lime mud and lime sand, a third important type of biogenic carbonate accumulation occurs locally on most tropical shelves. These are **organic reefs** made up of closely interlocked skeletons of living and dead marine organisms (Figures 4.34 and 4.35). Many types of organisms contribute to present-day reefs, but the dominant groups are corals, sponges, and certain seaweedlike plants that thrive only in relatively warm tropical waters. Because corals are typically a conspicuous part of modern reefs they are commonly called *coral reefs*, but this term tends to obscure the other equally important reef-building organisms that are always present.

4.10
DEEP-OCEAN ENVIRONMENT

Deep-ocean sediments are mostly either detrital sands and muds or biogenic carbonates, just as are those of the shallower continental shelves. There are, however, significant differences in the depositional processes of these materials in the deep ocean.

Although the volume of land-derived sand and mud ultimately reaching the deep ocean is large, it nevertheless represents only a small fraction—probably about one-tenth—of all such particles delivered by streams to the ocean. The great bulk accumulates instead on the continental shelves.

In addition to land-derived sands and clays, the deep ocean, like the continental shelves, also has large areas dominated by biogenic deposits, which, however, differ fundamentally from the biogenic sediments of the shelves. The principal difference is that deep-sea biogenic sediments are generally formed not from fragments of the relatively large skeletons of bottom-dwelling animals and plants but from the tiny skeletons of the floating animals and plants that are collectively called *plankton*. Such organisms thrive in enormous numbers in the sunlit surface waters of the oceans. As they die and their soft tissues decay, their tiny skeletons sink to the ocean floor and accumulate there.

On those parts of the ocean floor that receive large quantities of land-derived silt and mud, such as the Atlantic basins, the steady rain of planktonic skeletons is diluted and makes up only a small fraction of the bottom materials. In regions where the land-derived influx is small, however, planktonic skeletons may accumulate as the dominant sediment. In the Atlantic, such biogenic accumulations are found mostly on submarine hills and on the slopes of the Midatlantic Ridge (Figures 4.37 and 4.38). Bottom currents periodically

Legend:
- Land-derived sands and mud
- Biogenic carbonates
- Biogenic silica

FIGURE 4.37 Present-day deep-ocean sediments. (Modified from Hill, "The Sea, vol 3, 1963.)

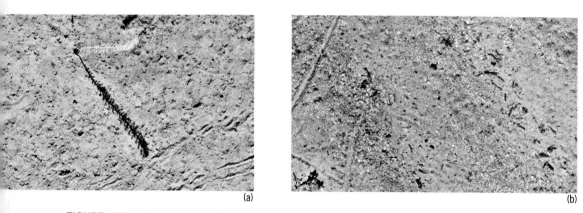

(a)   (b)

FIGURE 4.38 Deep-ocean sediments. (a) Land-derived bottom muds on the floor of the deep Atlantic. Note the abundant animal tracks and burrows. (b) Biogenic calcium carbonate sand on a submarine hill in the deep Atlantic. The smaller particles are skeletons of foraminifers and the larger light-colored particles are pteropod shells. (a,b: Richard M. Pratt, U.S. Geological Survey.)

transport any accumulated clay particles from these higher areas into the surrounding basins, leaving a residue of the larger and less easily transported skeletons. In the Atlantic, the principal contributors to such deposits are two groups of floating animals called *foraminifers* and *pteropods* and one group of tiny plants called *coccolithophores*, all of which build skeletons of calcium carbonate (Figure 4.38).

Carbonate deposits similar to those of the Atlantic also occur in some regions of the Pacific; unlike the Atlantic, however, the deep Pacific also has large areas dominated by planktonic skeletons composed not of calcium carbonate but of *silica*. Two groups of planktonic organisms secrete skeletons of silica, the plantlike *diatoms* and the animallike *radiolarians*. Diatoms are particularly common in surface waters of polar regions, and their shells dominate bottom deposits in the North Pacific and in a broad belt under the ocean that surrounds Antarctica. Radiolarians, in contrast, are most abundant along the equator, and accumulations of their shells floor large regions of the equatorial Pacific (Figure 4.37).

Later, after we discuss the process of plate tectonics at greater length, we shall see how these deep-ocean deposits have been plastered to continental margins throughout earth history.

SUMMARY OUTLINE

SEDIMENTS AND SEDIMENTARY ROCKS

4.1 Detrital sediments: Fine-grained clay minerals and quartz and feldspar particles of various sizes accumulate as muds, sands, or poorly sorted mixtures of the two.

4.2 Chemical sediments: Materials in solution in lakes and the ocean may be precipitated directly as their concentrations are increased by evaporation, or indirectly through removal by animals and plants.

4.3 Classification of sedimentary rocks: Most sedimentary rocks fall into one of four intergrading groups: sandstones, shales, carbonate rocks, and evaporites.

4.4 Sedimentary structures: Detrital and chemical particles moved and deposited by fluids show various kinds of layered bedding, which give clues to the nature of the depositing fluid; other structures originate from the actions of sediment-dwelling organisms.

TERRESTRIAL SEDIMENTARY PATTERNS

4.5 Fluvial environments: These sediments are dominated by alternations of well-sorted sands deposited in the stream channel and overbank muds deposited during floods.

4.6 Desert environments: These sediments show poorly sorted alluvial fan deposits, well-sorted dune sands, and lake evaporites.

4.7 Glacial environments: These sediments are similar to those of desert alluvial fans but often show striated pebbles abraded by moving in ice.

MARINE SEDIMENTARY PATTERNS

4.8 Detrital shelf environments: These sediments normally show an offshore decrease in particle size; modern shelves have anomalous deep sands caused by recent sea level fluctuations.

4.9 Carbonate shelf environments: These sediments replace detrital sands and muds on many tropical shelves; most are composed of fragments of carbonate-secreting animals and seaweeds.

4.10 Deep-ocean environments: These sediments have accumulations of land-derived sands and muds as well as biogenic carbonate and silica derived from planktonic animals and plants.

ADDITIONAL READINGS

*ALLEN, J. R. L.: *Physical Processes of Sedimentation*, American Elsevier Publishing Co., Inc., New York, 1970. An authoritative intermediate text on detrital sediments and their environments of deposition.

BLATT, H. G. MIDDLETON, and R. MURRAY: *Origin of Sedimentary Rocks*, 2nd ed., Prentice-Hall, Inc., Englewood Cliffs, N.J., 1980. A comprehensive and up-to-date intermediate text.

*BREED, W. J., and E. C. ROAT (eds.): *Geology of the Grand Canyon*, Museum of Northern Arizona, Flagstaff, 1974. An excellent intermediate level discussion of sedimentary patterns and the origin of rocks exposed in the Grand Canyon.

DEGENS, E. T.: *Geochemistry of Sediments*, Prentice-Hall, Inc., Englewood Cliffs, N.J., 1965. An intermediate text on chemical sediments.

*LAPORTE, L. F.: *Ancient Environments*, 2nd ed., Prentice-Hall, Inc., Englewood Cliffs, N.J., 1979. A brief, readable introduction to sedimentary environments.

PETTIJOHN, F. J., and P. E. POTTER: *Atlas and Glossary of Primary Sedimentary Structures*, Springer-Verlag New York, Inc., Berlin, 1964. Outstanding photographs of sedimentary structures.

* Available in paperback.

Ancient Shorelines
in the Grand Canyon Region

If we were able to observe the Grand Canyon region as it appeared 750 or 800 million years ago, we would see a very different landscape from what is there now. There would not be a high plateau with a deep canyon carved into it; instead there would be long ranges of mountains bordered by linear valleys trending across the countryside. This terrain slowly underwent the rigors of erosion lasting over 200 million years, until finally the landscape was near sea level and almost flat, except for an occasional promontory here and there. Marine waters then began to encroach across this extensively eroded surface.

When ocean waters move across the land in this fashion, we

FIGURE 4.39 Sedimentary formation of the Grand Canyon.

Rim of Grand Canyon

Limestone

Shale

Cambrian
(550–500
million years
before present.)

Sandstone

Inner
Gorge

Old erosion
surface on which
sandstone was
deposited as the sea
transgressed during
Cambrian time.

Vishnu Schist

refer to it as a *marine transgression*. The geological records of such events are common in many parts of the world. Sediments deposited in the Grand Canyon region during much of Cambrian time (550–500 million years ago) left a rock record of this kind of flooding. Figure 4.39 is a cross section of the Grand Canyon wall as we see it today. Sedimentary rocks of Cambrian age are shown as they rest upon the older deeply eroded rocks found in the inner gorge. First we shall consider this question, "What is there about the rocks that tells us of a 500-million-year-old marine transgression?"

Figure 4.40(a) shows an idealized pattern of the relationship between the kind of sediment deposited in the marine environment and the distance from the shoreline of the depositional setting. Larger fragments of sand come to rest closer to shore, and smaller

FIGURE 4.40 Sediments deposited reflect distance from shore. Note that deeper-water sediments are resting on older shallower-water deposits: Limestone rests on shale at Q, and shale overlies sandstone at R. Thus continued transgression will lead to limestone deposition at R. Marine transgressions are documented. When deposits at a given locality grade upward from shallow to deep water sediments that sequence documents transgressive seas.

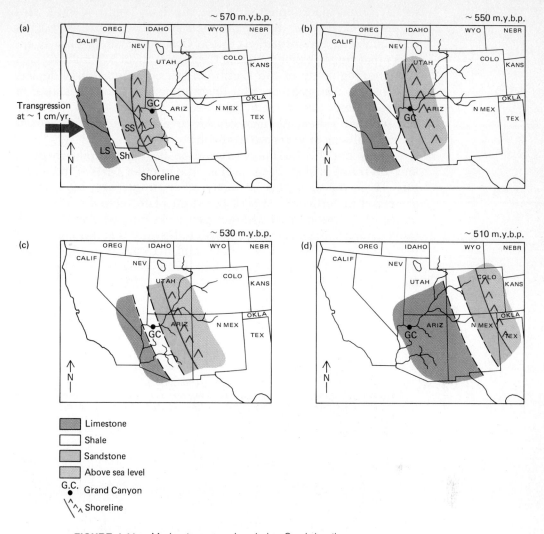

FIGURE 4.41 Marine transgression during Cambrian time.

grains of clay can be transported by water currents to greater distances from shore. The latter settle out of water that is located still greater distances from shore than the sand, and farther out still, organic remains produce limestones as the principal sedimentary layers. The pattern, then, is sandstone close to shore, then shale, and finally limestone farthest from shore. If sea level rises, marine waters transgress across the land, as shown in Figure 4.40(b). The pattern of sedimentation stays the same, but now some of the clay is deposited on the formerly deposited sand (in Figure 4.40b at R), and the carbonate sediment overlies the clay [in Figure 4.40(b) at Q]. If transgression were to continue, we would expect, eventually, to have limestone deposited at the site R in Figure 4.40(b). This sequence, sandstone, then shale, then limestone, is precisely what the Cambrian age formations of the Grand Canyon display. It appears that transgression began in the region about 570 million years ago (the beginning of the Cambrian period). Figure 4.41 depicts this marine transgression in a diagrammatic fashion. The rate of encroachment, about 1 cm/year, seems incredibly slow, but one can see that a great distance can be covered, even at that rate, if tens of millions of years are available.

Why did this marine transgression begin in Cambrian time, and did transgressions occur at this time in other parts of the world too? These questions, like so many others in geology, can now be answered in terms of a model based on plate tectonics. Many sequences of Cambrian age sedimentary rocks from all over the earth show evidence of marine transgressions. It seems that the worldwide sea level rose, so that most continental margins at low elevations became flooded. Figure 4.42 can help us to visualize how this could happen. At the beginning of Cambrian time (570 million years ago), most of the earth's surface above sea level was concentrated into one very large continent. Rift zones developed within this supercon-

FIGURE 4.42   As a rift zone develops the continent stretches out and reduces the area of the ocean basins. Therefore sea level must rise because the volume of water stays the same. Transgression of marine waters occurs.

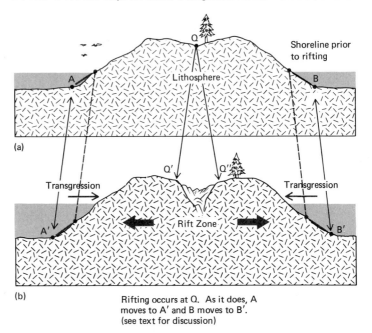

Rifting occurs at Q. As it does, A moves to A′ and B moves to B′. (see text for discussion)

tinent and began to fragment it. Assuming that the earth's volume remained essentially constant, this breakup of continental lithosphere would have created a greater area of the earth above sea level, and therefore a lesser area below sea level (Figure 4.42). Inasmuch as the amount of water in the ocean remained constant, however, the sea level had to rise. And as the sea level rose, marine transgressions occurred along continental margins all over the world. At many places around the world the sedimentary rock record for the Cambrian period is similar to that which is observed at the Grand Canyon. This was triggered by the breaking up of a supercontinent rather than by local coincidences of sedimentation. There are other mechanisms whereby marine transgressions might be initiated, but the one proposed here is prominent among the various models. The Grand Canyon, itself, is a unique geologic feature, but many of the rock formations in it are typical of those found elsewhere in the world.

5

The Geological Time Scale

Our UNDERSTANDING OF events in the earth's past rests almost entirely on studies of crustal rocks exposed at or near the earth's surface. The volatile fluids of past oceans and atmospheres are never preserved to leave a historical record, whereas crustal rocks, particularly those making up the continents, have been slowly accumulating throughout most of the earth's long history. Many of these rocks have survived with little change for millions or even billions of years and may thus provide revealing insights into the earth's past. For example, plutonic igneous and metamorphic regions indicate intervals of mountain-building deformation deep within the crust, whereas volcanic and sedimentary rocks reflect changing landscapes at the earth's surface at the time they were formed. Sedimentary rocks are particularly useful because they may suggest past climates and thus provide *indirect* clues about earlier states of the ocean and atmosphere. To decipher the long sequence of events recorded in the many kinds of crustal rocks, however, we must have some means of determining their relative ages so that a worldwide chronology of events can be established.

There are two complementary, but basically independent, methods for establishing the age relations of ancient rocks. The first is applicable primarily to sedimentary rocks and relates to the sequential nature of sediment deposition and to progressive changes in the animals and plants whose remains are preserved in ancient sediments. The second method applies primarily to igneous and metamorphic rocks and relates to the steady rates of decay of certain radioactive nuclides incorporated into the rocks as they were formed. We shall look briefly at both of these techniques for determining earth chronology before considering the universal time scale of earth history that they have provided.

RELATIVE AGES OF ROCKS AND EARTH CHRONOLOGY

5.1

PHYSICAL RELATIONSHIPS

As long ago as 1669, Steno recognized that the physical process of sediment deposition provided a means of establishing relative chronology that is not available for most rocks that solidify from molten

(a)

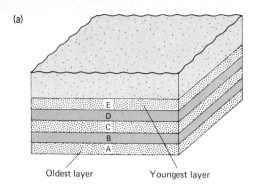

Oldest layer   Youngest layer

(b)

Sedimentary layers

Younger igneous rocks   Fragment of layer E

FIGURE 5.1 *The law of superposition.* (a) In sequences composed entirely of sedimentary rocks, younger beds always overlie older. The sequence shown thus becomes progressively younger from A to E. (b) Igneous rocks, on the other hand, are not necessarily older than overlying rocks. In the sequence shown the igneous unit (G) was emplaced into the sedimentary layers A-F and thus is younger than sediments which overlie it.

magmas. Sediments, we have seen, normally accumulate under the influence of gravity as relatively thin horizontal sheets called *beds* or *strata*. Each such stratum is usually deposited on top of older beds and is, in turn, buried by younger ones. This simple relationship means that when thick sequences of sediment are preserved without deformation, the *underlying beds are always older than those overlying them*. (Note that this relationship is not necessarily true of igneous rocks, which are normally melted from below and may crystallize while overlain by older rocks; see Figure 5.1.) Recall (from the Introduction) that this seemingly obvious principle—that younger sediments always overlie older—is known as the **law of superposition** and provided the first key to deciphering crustal history.

Sequences of ancient sediments thousands of meters thick, representing many different ages and sedimentary environments, are found on every continent. Although about 95 percent of the total *volume* of rocks making up the continental crust is of igneous or metamorphic origin, the remaining 5 percent of sedimentary rock is spread as a veneer that covers much of the *surface area* of the continents (Figure 5.2). As a result, igneous or metamorphic rocks are directly exposed on only about 25 percent of the continental surfaces; the remaining 75 percent is covered by a layer, averaging about 2 km in thickness, of sedimentary rocks. These lie on top of a much greater thickness of igneous and metamorphic rocks. Once the law of superposition was understood, it became possible to infer sequences of ancient sedimentary events merely by observing the progressive upward changes in sediment types preserved in this continental veneer.

Igneous events could also be related to the sedimentary stories told about a region by the application of two additional relative age-dating principles: (1) intrusive rocks are younger than the rock they intrude, and (2) rock fragments are older than the rock that

152   THE GEOLOGICAL TIME SCALE

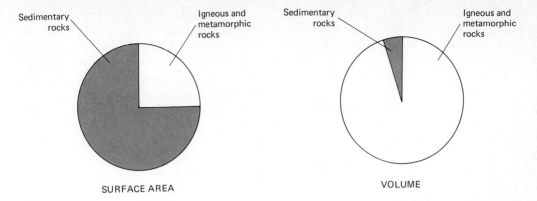

FIGURE 5.2 Surface area versus volume of sedimentary rocks of the continental crust. Although they make up only 5 percent of the volume of crustal rocks, sedimentary rocks cover 75 percent of the continental surfaces.

contains them. Figures 5.1(b) and 5.3 depict these two relationships. Clearly, the igneous rocks *must be* younger than the sediments they intrude. Further, the sedimentary layer E [Figure 5.1(b)] *must have* existed prior to igneous intrusion in order for a fragment of it to be incorporated in the solidified igneous rock.

Using these three relative age-dating tools—superposition, intrusive relationships, and fragment relationships—eighteenth-century geologists began attempts to organize the rock record of the earth's crust. Some of the earliest efforts were conducted in Italy and Germany, where investigators independently arrived at similar conclusions. As a general rule, it was concluded that throughout the earth's crust, plutonic and metamorphic rocks are the oldest and that they are unconformably overlain by highly deformed sedimentary rocks, which in turn are overlain by highly fossiliferous, gently folded sedimentary layers.

FIGURE 5.3 Relative Age-dating tools. (a) Intrusive relationship. (b) Fragment of older rock incorporated in younger rock. (a, b: E. A. Hay.)

(a)

(b)

It was within the framework of these observations that A. G. Werner promoted his once-ruling concept of Neptunism (discussed in the Introduction). Werner decided that granular-textured plutonic rocks everywhere must have been chemically precipitated from a very deep primordial ocean. Following this, the ocean lowered (according to his theory) and eventually yielded mechanically derived sediments (sand, clay, etc.) that were deposited at lower elevation but were nevertheless younger than the crystalline rocks because of superposition (Figure 5.4). Although such a model is consistent with rock relationships that are common, it soon became apparent there are many exceptions. For example, granite or other primary rocks were seen to intrude highly fossiliferous strata, and hard, nonfossiliferous sedimentary layers were found overlying highly folded, yet richly fossiliferous, formations. Werner's attempt to *impose* simplicity and order on the earth simply failed to account for reality. Once geologists began to make close observations of rock types and careful determinations of age sequences using the three techniques we have discussed, Neptunism was sunk. More thorough studies showed the rock histories of different regions to be complex and unique—there was no "universal system" such as Werner had proposed.

A major difficulty in satisfactorily conducting such careful and thorough studies, however, has continued to plague geologists even today. The problem stems from lack of adequate *exposures* of rocks. On most parts of the land surface, the sedimentary rock veneer is itself overlain by a much thinner veneer of soil and vegetation, which largely hides the underlying rock. In such regions, the sedimentary sequence is exposed only where streams cut into bedrock along hillsides or where deep, man-made excavations, such as road cuts, quarries, or mines, extend into the underlying rock. Even where such local exposures of bedrock are abundant, they commonly do not reveal more than a superficial fraction of the underlying sedimentary rock, which has an average thickness of about 2,000 m (meters). Only in mountainous regions of high relief is the complete sedimentary sequence normally exposed for study. As a result of these limitations, it is always necessary to correlate—that is, deter-

FIGURE 5.4 Idealized cross section showing rock relationships as visualized by the late eighteenth-century Neptunists. Younger rocks are (1) less deformed, (2) more fossiliferous, (3) at lower elevation, and (4) less well consolidated.

THE GEOLOGICAL TIME SCALE

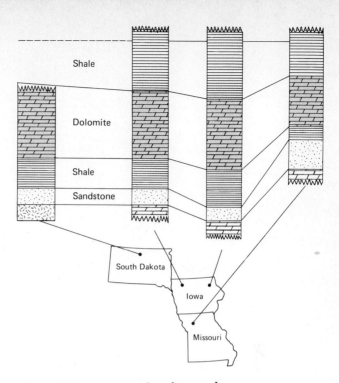

Shale

Dolomite

Shale

Sandstone

South Dakota

Iowa

Missouri

FIGURE 5.5 Physical correlations of sedimentary rocks. Similarities in rock sequence often permit interrelation of the continent's sedimentary veneer over wide areas. The illustration shows a distinctive sequence of sandstone (oldest), shale, dolomite, and shale (youngest) that can be recognized over much of the north-central United States.

mine age equivalencies between the sedimentary rocks observed at widely scattered exposures.

The simplest kinds of sedimentary rock correlations are those based on the physical nature of the rocks themselves. Where exposures are continuous or very closely spaced, as occurs in some desert regions, it may be possible to follow single beds or groups of beds over long distances. More commonly, physical correlations are made by recognizing similar rock types, or sequences of rock types, in discontinuous exposures (Figure 5.5).

The difficulty with physical correlations is that they are useful only for rocks originally deposited over relatively small areas and in the same sedimentary environment or sequence of environments. Physical techniques are useless between continents or over distances of thousands of kilometers on a single continent where sedimentary environments and resulting sediment accumulations must have varied at any time in the past just as they do today. Physical correlations based only on similarities in rock type, in short, can never provide a worldwide chronology of sedimentary events, even though they permit some local events to be worked out in great detail.

Figure 5.6 depicts two geologic settings where relative ages for the exposed rock formations can be determined for each location, but no correlation can be made *between them* because of their separation and because of the likelihood that depositional environments did not persist laterally for such great distances. Sandstone 1 in Region A might be the same as Sandstone 2 or Sandstone 3 in Region

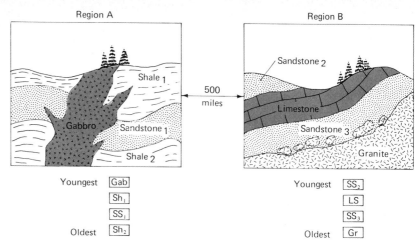

FIGURE 5.6 The exact sequence of relative rock ages can be determined by physical criteria for Region A and Region B, but there is no sure way to interrelate them to each other by physical criteria alone.

B, or it might be much older or much younger than either. In other words, we have no way of knowing the relative age relationships between the rocks in Region A and those in Region B. Thus, what is needed to establish a worldwide chronology is an independent means of determining the relative ages of sedimentary rocks wherever and in whatever environment they were deposited. A close approach to such a chronology is provided by the fossil remains preserved in many sedimentary rocks.

FOSSIL CONTENTS AND THE GEOLOGIC COLUMN

In Chapter 4 we saw that animal and plant remains commonly become buried in sediment accumulations where they may be preserved indefinitely as **fossils**. Such fossil remains have long provided the most useful and widely applicable means of establishing the relative ages of sedimentary rocks. Late in the eighteenth century, about a hundred years after the concept of superposition was first appreciated, an English surveyor, William Smith, noticed that each unit of sedimentary rock that he encountered in excavations for a canal west of London was characterized by a distinctive assemblage of fossil shells. These characteristic fossils allowed each unit to be easily recognized wherever it occurred. Using this knowledge and the law of superposition, Smith over many years worked out the complete sequence of rocks and fossils exposed in England and Wales, and in 1815 he published a geological map illustrating his findings that is a landmark in our understanding of earth chronology (Figure 5.7).

FIGURE 5.7 William Smith's landmark geological map, published in 1815. (a) Title sheet. (b) Rock units of the London region. (c,d) Some characteristic fossil shells of the London clay (c) and chalk (d). (e) A cross section along line X-X'. (Fossils from Smith, "Strata Identified by Organized Fossils," 1816.)

A
DELINEATION
OF THE
STRATA
OF
ENGLAND AND WALES,
WITH PART OF
SCOTLAND;
EXHIBITING
THE COLLIERIES AND MINES.
THE MARSHES AND FEN LANDS *ORIGINALLY OVERFLOWED* BY THE SEA.
AND THE
VARIETIES OF SOIL
ACCORDING TO THE VARIATIONS IN THE SUBSTRATA.
ILLUSTRATED by the MOST DESCRIPTIVE NAMES
BY W. SMITH.

(a)

(b)

(c)

(d)

(e)

London Clay

Brickearth

Chalk

Tertiary System

X — X'

London Clay

Brickearth

Cretaceous System

Chalk

THE GEOLOGICAL TIME SCALE

157

Smith's map clearly demonstrates what later came to be known as the "law of faunal succession" and paved the way for the construction of a worldwide geological time scale, for it was soon discovered that sequences of fossil assemblages very much like those in England occurred in the sedimentary veneer of the European continent and even as far away as North America. This discovery showed that widely separated sedimentary rocks *can be correlated if their fossil remains are essentially the same* as those found in other regions where the fossil sequence has been carefully established. Smith's example, and the law of faunal succession he had so successfully elucidated, served as springboards for the compilation of the relative ages of rock units mapped throughout Europe. By the mid-1800s, a geologic column of essentially modern aspect had been established depicting rock units of the world that had been chronologically ordered (Figure 5.8). Such an ordering process required widespread recognition and description of sedimentary rock units called **systems.** Systems were defined in different localities on the basis of distinctive characteristics such as degree of folding, types of rock, and fossil content. Then by application of the law of faunal succession, different systems throughout Europe were placed in their correct chronology. In Figure 5.7(b), for example, the Chalk unit was used to establish the Cretaceous system (*creta* = chalk), and the Brickearth and London Clay above it were assigned as lower formations of the Tertiary system, seen resting upon the Cretaceous. The modern term *Tertiary* is a holdover from the eighteenth century when it referred to rocks that were believed to be *third* in a depositional sequence of rocks that supposedly formed the earth's original crust. It no longer has the same meaning.

Smith and his followers, who established the sedimentary column, based their work on progressive changes in the kinds of fossil animals and plants but had little understanding of *why* such changes occurred. We now recognize that the underlying cause of faunal

	SYSTEMS	WHERE FIRST DESCRIBED
Youngest	Quaternary	Europe
	Tertiary	Europe
	Cretaceons	England
	Jurassic	Jura Mts. Europe
	Triassic	Germany
	Permian	Russia
	Carboniferous	Great Britian
	Devonian	Great Britian (Devonshire)
	Silurian	Great Britian (Wales)
	Ordovician	Great Britian (Wales)
	Cambrian	Great Britian (Wales)
Oldest	PRECAMBRIAN ERA	Non-fossiliferous, therefore not well subdivided

FIGURE 5.8 The Geologic Column, a composite from many different places around the world.

succession is **organic evolution:** the expansions, contractions, and modifications of the living world that have taken place since life originated early in earth history. Because of this continuous change of living organisms, the fossil record of past life provides a dynamic framework for judging relative time, a framework that is not deducible from examining only the physical properties of the sedimentary particles themselves. So successful has been the "fossil-dating" technique that it is still the principal means of unraveling crustal history in mines and wells that penetrate the sedimentary veneer and in surface rock exposures in relatively unexplored areas of the continents.

In spite of its enormous value, a chronology of earth history based only on fossils also has serious limitations. In the first place, not all sedimentary rocks contain fossils. In general, they are most common in marine sediments, especially those that accumulate on the shallow, submerged margins of continents rather than in deep-ocean basins. Bottom-dwelling organisms, particularly shell-bearing animals, are abundant today, and were for much of the geologic past, almost everywhere on the shallow ocean floor. In contrast, most terrestrial sediments contain very few fossils because even hard skeletal remains rather quickly decay, weather, and disappear when exposed to the atmosphere. Only in relatively rare terrestrial sediments deposited beneath the standing waters of lakes or swamps are animal and plant remains common.

Because fossils are most abundant in marine sedimentary rocks, it follows that it is usually far easier to establish the age relations of such rocks than it is for those deposited in terrestrial environments. If sea level had always stood as low in relation to the continents as it does today, there would be few ancient marine sediments preserved above sea level, and correlations of the continents' sedimentary veneer would be correspondingly difficult. Fortunately, however, shallow seas covered much of the surface of the continents for long intervals during the geologic past (Figure 5.9). For this reason, thin layers of fossil-rich marine sedimentary rock cover a large fraction of the continental surfaces even in regions that today lie far above sea level. The age relations of this sedimentary veneer can thus be far more easily established than it could be if terrestrial sediments made up a larger proportion of it. In those regions where thick sequences of fossil-poor terrestrial sediments *do* occur, it is often difficult or impossible to determine their relative ages.

Still other difficulties arise in applying fossil dating. Fossils, of course, are almost never found in igneous rocks, and only rarely can they be recognized in even slightly metamorphosed sedimentary rocks. More commonly, igneous or metamorphic rocks may be interbedded with, or otherwise related to, fossil-bearing sedimentary rocks in such a way that their relative ages are apparent (Figure

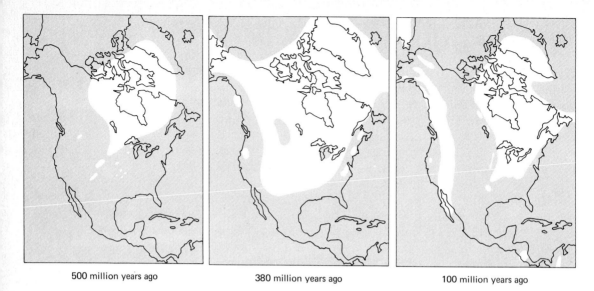

| 500 million years ago | 380 million years ago | 100 million years ago |

FIGURE 5.9 The distribution of land and sea on the North American continent at three levels of the geologic past. Note the occurrence of shallow seas over much of the continental surface. Fossil-bearing marine sediments that accumulated in such seas permit long-range correlation of the continent's sedimentary veneer.

5.10). Usually, however, it is difficult or impossible to relate the bulk of the crust's igneous and metamorphic rocks to the ages established for the sedimentary veneer.

A still greater problem arises from the fact that abundant shell-bearing life arose relatively late in earth history. For this reason, even marine sedimentary rocks representing much of the earth's past cannot be dated by the fossil technique because they contain few fossils.

FIGURE 5.10 Typical relationships of igneous and fossil-bearing sedimentary rocks. (a) The age of the igneous intrusion (B) is "bracketed" by the ages of sedimentary intrusion, and sedimentary unit C, which is clearly younger. (b) The lava flows, having formed at the earth's surface, are clearly younger than underlying sedimentary rocks and older than those which overlie them.

A final, and most important, difficulty with the fossil time scale is that it provides only *relative* ages, not numerical ones. Fossil-bearing rocks can be readily placed in a sequence based on the continuous change of the living world, yet fossils provide no means of determining exactly how long these changes required *in years*. A particular evolutionary sequence might have taken place over thousands, millions, or even hundreds of millions of years, but the fossils themselves provide no means for determining this.

Because of these difficulties with the fossil time scale, there is a clear need for an independent means of determining the age relations of rocks. The most useful would be a technique that would establish numerical ages of rocks, in years, one that would be applicable to the great volume of crustal igneous and metamorphic rocks that cannot be dated by fossils. We shall see in Section 5.4 that a chronologic method filling both of these requirements is made possible by the slow decay of certain radioactive nuclides incorporated into rock minerals when they were formed. Radioactivity has given geologists a powerful tool for converting the **geologic column** into a **geologic time scale**. At first glance, the time scale (Figure 5.11) looks no different from the column. Familiar names such as Cambrian, Cretaceous, and Tertiary are seen in both, but the time scale contains new terms and is calibrated by numerical age estimates that have been made for the rock units composing the column.

One important relationship between the column and the time scale is abundantly clear. It is that our conception of geologic *time*, even before radioactivity, was founded upon observations of *rock* formations. Following the teachings of James Hutton and his views of uniformitarianism (see Introduction), we believe that great thicknesses of sedimentary rock imply long periods of deposition. Further, the appearance of plutonic and metamorphic rocks at the earth's surface similarly requires vast episodes of erosion in order to expose them from beneath the rocks that originally covered them.

All these rocks—sedimentary, igneous, and metamorphic—when ordered into relative age relationships with each other, compose what we call the **geologic column**. From the geologic column we have inferred vast durations of **geologic time**: that is, a great deal of time was necessary to allow geologic processes to form, deform, and erode the rocks composing the geologic column into their present configurations. Figure 5.12 depicts a rock exposure from which we can infer the passage of a great deal of time. Let's say, for example, that the granite is part of the Cretaceous *system* and the marine sedimentary rocks are part of the Tertiary *system*. From these rocks, then, we conceive of the Cretaceous and Tertiary *periods*. The term *period* refers to episodes of *time*, not units of rock.

We believe a great deal of time must have existed in order to allow natural geologic processes to create the granite and the

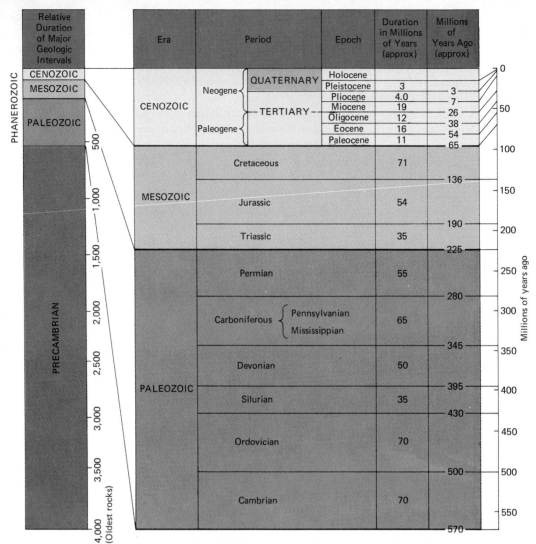

FIGURE 5.11   The time scale of earth history.

sedimentary rocks. How else but by slow natural processes could they have formed?

Today we speak of the Paleozoic era as having begun about 570 million years ago, the Cretaceous period as having ended approximately 65 million years ago, and the Pleistocene epoch as having commenced 2 to 3 million years ago. The terms **era, period,** and **epoch** refer to different subdivisions of this geologic time scale. To speak of the Cretaceous period is roughly analogous to speaking of the Middle Ages or the Victorian period—or perhaps "February." As *time* units, none of these possesses any tangible physical entity; one cannot touch Monday, March, the Victorian period, or the Cretaceous period. On the other hand, we might sustain a severe injury

FIGURE 5.12 Part of the Geologic Column and the description of the geologic processes required to create it. Vast durations of time are required to allow the processes of erosion and deposition to create the observed relationships.

if struck by some of the *rock* to which the name "Cretaceous system" was originally assigned in England (Figure 5.13). The point is this: The geologic time scale was originally abstracted from a geologic column of primarily sedimentary rocks that had been synthesized through the application of *relative* age-dating techniques. It was many years later before geologists were able to assign to the subdivisions of the geologic time scale reasonably accurate ages in "years b.p." (years before the present).

The largest subdivisions of the geologic time scale are known as **eras;** four eras are recognized, each bounded by times of *relatively* profound, sudden, and worldwide changes in the living organisms preserved as fossils. These are: the Precambrian era (the long interval of time before organisms secreted abundant hardparts), Paleozoic ("ancient life") era, Mesozoic ("middle life") era, and Cenozoic ("recent life") era. The four eras are further subdivided into **periods,** each bounded by episodes of somewhat less profound change in

FIGURE 5.13 Relationship between the geologic column and the time scale.

the living world. Eleven periods are now recognized: the Paleozoic era includes six of them—Cambrian (oldest), Ordovician, Silurian, Devonian, Carboniferous, and Permian (youngest); the Mesozoic era has three periods—Triassic (oldest), Jurassic, and Cretaceous (youngest); and the Cenozoic era includes only two—Paleogene and Neogene.* The eleven geologic periods are in turn further subdivided into still smaller units of time, called **epochs**. Most of the many names of these smaller divisions of geologic time need not concern us. The most important are the seven epochs of the Cenozoic era, the next-to-youngest of which, the Pleistocene epoch, includes the recent intervals of ice-sheet expansion and contraction.

The oldest sedimentary rocks bearing abundant fossils are those of the Cambrian system, which were deposited at the beginning of the Paleozoic era. Wherever they occur around the world, fossil-bearing Cambrian rocks contain the same distinctive association of shell-bearing marine animals dominated by the long-extinct trilobites (Figure 5.14), which were distant relatives of modern crabs and shrimps. All these earliest Cambrian sediments overlie older rocks that *lack* abundant fossils.

Commonly, early Cambrian sediments rest upon a "basement complex" of older igneous and metamorphic rocks, which, we have seen, make up the bulk of the continental crust. In many regions, however, the earliest Cambrian fossils occur above thick sequences of sedimentary rocks that are identical to the overlying Cambrian rocks *except* that they contain no fossils. This *abrupt†* appearance of trilobites and other relatively advanced kinds of animal life in the sedimentary record is perhaps the most significant milestone in the earth's long history, for it serves to divide the earth's past into two great divisions. Before this event lies "Precambrian time," whose rocks contain few fossils, because organisms living then had not yet developed hard parts that favor fossil preservation, and therefore the rocks provide no worldwide time scale based on changing life. With the early Cambrian expansion of animal life comes

---

* Many geologists divide the Cenozoic era into the Tertiary and Quaternary periods, as shown in Figure 5.11.

† *Abrupt*, that is, in a geological sense—occurring perhaps within 10 to 20 million years.

FIGURE 5.14 Cambrian trilobites. (Vladimir J. Oku-litch.)

"Phanerozoic ('exposed life') time"—and the worldwide applicability of the sedimentary time scale that we have been considering.

Because Precambrian igneous, metamorphic, and sedimentary rocks make up a large percentage of all the rocks of the continental crust, it has long been assumed that they represent a very long span of earth history. Before the widespread application of radiometric dating, however, no worldwide chronology was available for this great volume of Precambrian rocks. As with younger, fossil-bearing rocks before the discovery of the "law of faunal succession," local sequences of Precambrian rocks and the events they record had been worked out by purely physical means, but there was still no reliable way to interrelate these events over long distances. This situation has been profoundly changed by radiometric dating. Techniques for radiometric dating will be discussed later in this chapter.

5.3
SEDIMENTARY ROCKS AND PAST ENVIRONMENTS

So far we have emphasized only how the physical relationships and fossil contents of the continents' sedimentary veneer permit a determination of the relative ages of ancient sediments. As yet, however, we have said almost nothing about the *kinds of events* in the earth's past that may be inferred from the sedimentary rocks once their ages are understood.

As might be predicted from our discussion of present-day sediments in Chapter 4, sedimentary rocks provide much information about ancient environments on the earth's surface at the time and place of their deposition. Thus they may answer such questions as: Was the area submerged by the sea, or did terrestrial sediments accumulate above sea level? If below sea level, was the region receiving only carbonate sediments, as do many tropical shelves today, or were sands and muds dominant as on present-day polar and temperate shelves? If the sediments were deposited above sea level, do they reflect fluvial, desert, or glacial environments?

In Chapter 4, we saw that the composition and structure of the sediments themselves usually provide criteria for answering such environmental questions. When these answers are pieced together for sedimentary rocks of many different ages distributed over much of the present-day surface of the continents, they provide an invaluable record of past changes in the geography of the earth's surface.

The principal problem in reconstructing earth history from sedimentary rocks relates to areas where no sediment accumulates. Much of the surface area of the continents today is not covered by sites of sediment deposition but is instead being actively eroded; such areas can obviously leave no future sedimentary record. Similar conditions existed through much of the earth's past, and thus the continents' veneer of sediments never reveals the *complete* sequence of surface events but only those times and places where sediment *accumulation* was taking place.

As a further complication, even areas that receive sediment at one time may, because of mountain-building deformations, lowered sea level, or other causes, be subject to subsequent erosion that destroys their record of earlier events. For these reasons, sedimentary rocks seldom reflect a *continuous* sequence of local sediment accumulation through long intervals of earth history; instead, the sedimentary veneer at any one place always shows discontinuities representing long time intervals when no sediment was accumulating in that area. We have already mentioned such discontinuities, called **unconformities,** in the Introduction (see Figure I.9). Even though unconformities reflect intervals of no local sediment accumulation, however, it is often possible to make inferences about the events they represent from the nature of the contact between the rocks above and below the surface of the unconformity.

Three significantly different kinds of unconformities exist, but in each case the surface separates rocks of distinctly different age, and the younger of the two formations lies upon, and essentially parallel to, a buried surface of erosion. **Angular unconformities** separate layered rocks where those beneath the contact have been *de-*

FIGURE 5.15   (p. 167) Typical unconformities. (a) The steep tilt and irregular topography of the rocks beneath the surface of unconformity suggest that an interval of mountain-building deformation and erosion occurred between the times of deposition of the sedimentary units separated by the unconformity. The rocks are exposed in southeastern California. (b) The parallel relationship of the beds below and above the surface of unconformity suggests relatively minor erosion of the underlying unit during the time interval represented by the unconformity. The rocks are exposed in northern Arizona. (c) Sedimentary rocks deposited on eroded plutonic rocks, representing a long time gap. (a,b: John S. Shelton; c: E. A. Hay.)

(a)   Angular unconformity

Unconformity

(b)   Disconformity

Unconformity

(c)   Nonconformity

formed and eroded so as to lie at distinctly different angles from the younger strata [Figure 5.15(a)]. **Disconformities** are the most subtle of all unconformities because the strata above and below the surface of contact are essentially parallel to each other [Figure 5.15(b)]; sometimes only by careful fossil age determinations can the existence of some disconformities be discovered. **Nonconformities** result from deposition of sediments upon eroded surfaces of nonstratified rocks such as granites or metamorphics [Figure 5.15(c)]. Almost without exception, nonconformities represent *large gaps* in the rock record due to the large amount of erosion required to expose plutonic and metamorphic rocks at the surface prior to the deposition of younger strata upon them.

In spite of the problem of an incomplete sedimentary rock record, the continents' sedimentary veneer, when viewed on a worldwide scale, preserves a remarkably complete record of events that have taken place through much of the earth's history. Undoubtedly, the reason the record is so good is that through much of the earth's past, the continents have stood much lower in relation to sea level than they do today. During long intervals, shallow seas repeatedly covered the continents, thus minimizing erosion and allowing the accumulation of the thin but widespread layers of marine sediment that make up much of the continents' cover of sedimentary rock.

NUCLEAR CLOCKS AND EARTH CHRONOLOGY

The time scale of earth history based on fossil remains has been established for well over a hundred years; for most of that time, fossils provided the *only* worldwide scheme for working out earth chronology. Within about the last 35 years, however, relative age-dating using fossils has been supplemented by a powerful new chronologic tool based on the decay of certain radioactive atomic nuclei. We are able now to assign *numerical* ages (in years) to many rocks.

5.4
RADIOACTIVE DECAY

In discussing our model for the structure of matter in Chapter 2, we noted that the small nucleus at the center of every atom is composed of two principal kinds of particles: noncharged **neutrons** and positively charged **protons**, the latter being the same in number as the negative electrons that orbit around the nucleus. All atoms of a particular element have the same number of protons in the nucleus, but they may have different numbers of uncharged neutrons, giving rise to different **nuclides** of the element.

Nuclides are distinguished by two important numbers. The first is the **atomic number,** which is simply the number of protons in the nucleus; the atomic number is constant for all nuclides of a particular element. The second is the **mass number,** which is the total of both protons and neutrons in the nucleus and differs for different nuclides of the same element. All calcium atoms, for example, have 20 nuclear protons whose positive charges are balanced by 20 orbital electrons; thus the atomic number for calcium atoms is always 20. Naturally occurring calcium, however, is a mixture of six different calcium nuclides that have either 20, 22, 23, 24, 26, or 28 neutrons in the nucleus. These neutrons, added to the constant number of 20 nuclear protons, give these six nuclides the mass numbers of 40, 42, 43, 44, 46, and 48, respectively. For brevity, nuclides are normally referred to by the name of the element and their mass numbers—for example, "calcium-40" or "carbon-14."

Many different nuclides of almost every element can be prepared artificially in nuclear reactors or particle accelerators by adding protons and neutrons to, or subtracting them from, atomic nuclei. Most such artificial nuclides, however, are very unstable or "radioactive," which means that they decay rapidly to more stable nuclides of other elements. During decay, the original radioactive nuclide is called the *parent* nuclide and the nuclide or nuclides produced by the decay are called *daughter* nuclides. Each different radioactive nuclide decays into daughter nuclides at a constant rate, a rate that is unaffected by such physical conditions as temperature or pressure. Most artificial nuclides decay very rapidly (usually in a few hours or days) to more stable nuclides, but some may persist for many years. The average lifetime of a radioactive parent nuclide is indicated by the time required for half the atoms in any given mass of the nuclide to decay, and is the nuclide's **half-life** (Figure 5.16).

In contrast to the many radioactive nuclides produced in reactors and accelerators, most natural nuclides are stable—that is, they have no tendency to decay to other nuclides. Most natural elements are mixtures of several (usually from two to eight) such stable nuclides of that element. If all naturally occurring nuclides were stable, however, they would be of no value for earth chronology. Fortunately, there are several *natural radioactive nuclides* that make possible the use of radioactive decay as a tool of earth chronology.

All naturally occurring radioactive nuclides come from one of two sources. The first group have such extremely long half-lives that they have persisted since the earth first formed (Figure 5.17). About twenty such nuclides have been detected, but only four are sufficiently widespread and abundant to be generally useful as chronologic tools: potassium-40, which decays to argon-40 and calcium-40; rubidium-87, which decays to strontium-87; uranium-235, which decays, through a series of intermediate radioactive nuclides, to lead-

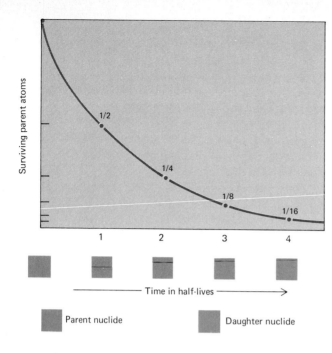

FIGURE 5.16 Half-life of a radioactive nuclide. The half-life is the time required for half of any initial mass to decay to a daughter nuclide. With each half-life interval, the remaining mass is reduced by 50 percent. The initial mass never decays completely because some small proportion of the initial atoms persists indefinitely.

Radioactive Parent Nuclide	Type of Decay	Stable Daughter Nuclide	Half-life (years)	Minimum ages that can be determined
Potassium-40 ($^{40}_{19}$K)	Electron capture	Argon-40 ($^{40}_{18}$Ar)	1.3 billion	100,000 years
Rubidium-87 ($^{87}_{37}$Rb)	Beta	Strontium-87 ($^{87}_{38}$Sr)	47 billion	50 million years
Uranium-235 ($^{235}_{92}$U)	7 alpha and 4 beta	Lead-207 ($^{207}_{82}$Pb)	0.7 billion	10 million years
Uranium-238 ($^{238}_{92}$U)	8 alpha and 6 beta	Lead-206 ($^{206}_{82}$Pb)	4.5 billion	10 million years

FIGURE 5.17 The principal primary nuclides used as geologic clocks. All are capable of dating the earth's oldest rocks.

207; and, finally, uranium-238, which decays, also through an intermediate series of nuclides, to lead-206 (Figure 5.17).

In addition to these long-lived radioactive nuclides left over from the earth's formation, there is a second group of much shorter-lived radioactive nuclides that are continually being produced in the earth's upper atmosphere by cosmic rays. These "rays" are really extremely high-energy nuclear particles moving in space from unknown sources. When such particles enter the earth's atmosphere, they collide with atmospheric gas particles and produce nuclear reactions similar to those of man-made particle accelerators. Some of these reactions form short-lived radioactive nuclides. At least eight such **cosmic ray-induced nuclides** have been identified, but only

FIGURE 5.18   The carbon-14 cycle. Radioactive carbon-14 is produced from atmospheric nitrogen by cosmic rays (inset). It then enters into CO_2 molecules and becomes incorporated into carbon-bearing sediments and organic remains. The amount of remaining carbon-14 is used to date such materials.

one, carbon-14, has proved to be a widely useful chronologic tool.

Carbon-14 is produced by cosmic rays acting on atoms of nitrogen, the most abundant atmospheric gas (Figure 5.18). Atmospheric nitrogen is composed of only stable nuclides, principally nitrogen-14. Through a complex series of nuclear reactions, high-energy cosmic rays may subtract a proton and add a neutron to some of these nitrogen atoms to produce radioactive carbon-14, which then decays back to stable nitrogen-14 with a half-life of about 5,600 years.

Once produced, the carbon-14 atoms quickly combine with atmospheric oxygen to become carbon dioxide. Most atmospheric carbon dioxide is made up of stable carbon-12 or carbon-13 nuclides; the relatively small quantity of cosmic ray-induced "carbon-14 dioxide" quickly mixes in a fixed proportion with this more abundant and stable atmosphere carbon dioxide and, in this manner, enters into the earth's general carbon cycle (Figure 5.18). There it may be dissolved in the oceans, precipitated as carbonate minerals, or used in the structures of animals and plants. The small amounts of radioactive carbon-14 that ultimately enter animals, plants, and minerals in this fashion provide an extremely useful tool for dating the very latest interval of earth history.

5.5
RADIOMETRIC AGES

All natural nuclides of the same element, whether radioactive or not, have the same general chemical behavior and thus tend to occur mixed together wherever the element is found. When the mixture contains a radioactive nuclide, however, small quantities of a different element—the daughter element produced by decay of the radioactive nuclide—are also present in the mixture. In theory, all that is necessary to use radioactive nuclides as geologic clocks is to measure the amounts of both the radioactive parent nuclide (normally either potassium-40, rubidium-87, uranium-235, uranium-238, or carbon-14) and the stable daughter nuclide (normally either argon-40, strontium-87, lead-207, lead-206, or nitrogen-14, correspondingly) that are present today in the rock or mineral to be dated (Figure 5.19). Since the decay rates of the radioactive nuclides are known with considerable precision from laboratory measurements, a simple calculation (the ratio of parent to daughter nuclides

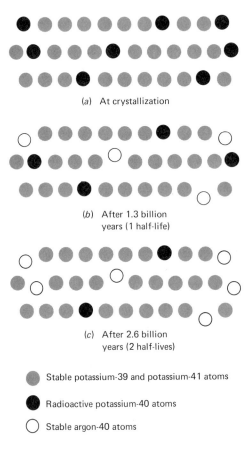

(a) At crystallization

(b) After 1.3 billion
years (1 half-life)

(c) After 2.6 billion
years (2 half-lives)

FIGURE 5.19   The progressive decay of potassium-40 atoms incorporated into a mica mineral at the time of crystallization. The ratio of remaining potassium-40 atoms to atoms of the daughter nuclide argon-40 is used to determine the age of the mineral.

Stable potassium-39 and potassium-41 atoms

Radioactive potassium-40 atoms

Stable argon-40 atoms

THE GEOLOGICAL TIME SCALE

multiplied by the decay rate) gives the *length of time* since the radioactive parent nuclide was first isolated in the mineral and thus provides a **radiometric age** for the mineral. Precise techniques have been developed for measuring very small quantities of parent and daughter nuclides, but there still remain several complications in obtaining ages by this means.

In order for radiometric ages to be accurate, the radioactive parent nuclide and the stable daughter nuclide must have been a *closed system* since their formation; that is, there must have been no later additions or subtractions of either parent or daughter. Unfortunately, these conditions are seldom met. Loss of some of the daughter nuclide is the most usual problem for, being a different element with different chemical properties, the daughter nuclide is not in equilibrium with its surroundings once formed [Figure 5.20(a)]. Daughter nuclide escape is particularly common when the nuclide is a gas, such as argon-40, or when the mineral to be dated has been secondarily heated by earth movement or deep burial. Although ingenious techniques have been developed to estimate the amounts of daughter elements lost from various minerals, this remains one of the principal difficulties in radiometric dating.

Because of daughter element loss, the most accurate radiometric ages are always considered to be those where calculations on two or more parent-daughter pairs give the same result. In such cases it is unlikely that the different daughter elements, each having different chemical properties, would be lost at the same rate and thus provide the same erroneous ages. Fortunately, many rocks and minerals contain more than one of the principal radioactive nuclides,

FIGURE 5.20 Two of the principal complicating factors in radiometric age determinations (see text).

Argon-40 trapped in crystal at crystallization

(a) Loss of daughter element from crystal

(b) Contamination by original presence of daughter element

Stable potassium-39 and potassium-41 atoms

Radioactive potassium-40 atoms

Stable argon-40 atoms

so that cross-checking is frequently possible. Uranium-bearing minerals are particularly useful in this regard since they all contain both uranium-235 and uranium-238, each of which provides an independent test of the age.

A second major difficulty in radiometric dating is that the parent nuclide must have been free of contamination by the daughter nuclide when it was originally incorporated into the mineral to be dated. That is, *all* the daughter nuclide subsequently measured must result from radioactive decay rather than original contamination [Figure 5.20(b)]. Seldom is this condition fulfilled, but here again ingenious methods have been developed for estimating the amount of daughter element originally present, so that this difficulty can frequently be overcome.

Various techniques for getting around the daughter element loss and contamination problems have been developed for the long-lived primary nuclides, but these problems are insoluble for carbon-14, the principal short-lived nuclide that is useful in radiometric dating. Carbon-14, we have seen, decays to nitrogen-14, which is the principal constituent of the atmosphere. The daughter element is thus present in large contaminating quantities both when the carbon-14 is produced in the atmosphere and, commonly, when it decays as well. For this reason, carbon-14 dating is not based on measurements of both parent and daughter nuclides; instead, it requires the *assumption* that carbon-14 has been produced at a constant rate in the atmosphere and is quickly mixed, in constant proportions, with nonradioactive carbon to enter the earth's overall carbon cycle. If these assumptions are correct, all carbon at the time it is incorporated into carbonate minerals and living organisms has a constant proportion of carbon-14, which steadily decreases by decay after the materials are formed. It is therefore necessary only to measure the present ratio of carbon-14 to nonradioactive carbon in such materials to determine their ages by this method (Figure 5.18).

Because carbon-14 dating can be extended back in time only about 50,000 years, it is not applied to most geological problems. Determination of the frequency of major earthquakes, however, is one area of geologic research wherein carbon-14 age-dating has made significant contributions. Earthquakes cannot directly be dated by carbon-14, but sedimentary layers that are either older than or younger than earthquake-produced ground ruptures are datable if they contain charcoal, wood, or other organic fragments.

So far we have said very little about the specific kinds of rocks, minerals, or other materials that contain the five principal radioactive nuclides in measurable amounts and can therefore be dated by radiometric techniques. Both the potassium-40 and rubidium-87 methods have been applied most successfully to micas found in a variety of igneous and metamorphic rocks. In addition, some other igneous and metamorphic minerals—for example, certain types of feldspar and amphibole—are commonly dated by these techniques. Normally, the individual mineral grains are separated from the rest of the rock to minimize contamination, but it is sometimes possible to obtain accurate dates for very fine-grained igneous and metamorphic rocks simply by analyzing crushed samples of the whole rock rather than individual mineral grains.

The uranium dating technique was the first to be established, but for many years it could be applied only to certain rare minerals that contain relatively large quantities of the element. More recently, the development of precise analytical techniques has permitted accurate measurements of very small traces of uranium that occur in the silicate mineral zircon. Zircon occurs as a minor accessory mineral in many igneous rocks, and thus it permits a wide application of the uranium dating technique.

Radiometric dating by means of potassium, rubidium, and uranium nuclides is applicable mostly to minerals found in igneous and metamorphic rocks. In contrast, the carbon-14 technique is principally useful for sedimentary materials; carbonate sediments and fossil shells, bones, and wood fragments are the materials most commonly dated by this technique.

5.6
NUMERICAL RADIOMETRIC DATING

The application of radiometric dating techniques has, over the past three decades, made three principal contributions to our understanding of earth chronology. First, these techniques have led to a calibration, in years, of the relative geologic time scale. In addition, they have revolutionized our understanding of the enormous volume of Precambrian rocks that cannot be dated by fossils. Finally, they have greatly clarified the events of the past 50,000 years, a span of time too short to include significant changes in living organisms and thus also beyond the application of fossil dating techniques. We shall briefly consider each of these contributions before turning to the more complex question of the overall age of the earth.

Perhaps the most significant achievement of radiometric dating has been to provide numerical dates for the relative geologic time scale. Since the early nineteenth century, attempts have been made to calibrate the sedimentary time scale. Most of these involved estimates of the rates at which sediments are currently accumulating and extrapolation of these rates into the past to account for the total thicknesses of sedimentary rocks of different ages. Such estimates all suggested that many millions of years were required to account for the crust's sedimentary veneer, but only with the advent of radiometric dating could the precise number of years be determined.

Radiometric dating techniques are usually applicable only to the minerals of igneous or metamorphic rocks, and for this reason radiometric dating of the sedimentary time scale requires rather unusual associations of sedimentary and igneous rocks (see Figure 5.10). Such associations are far from common, but fortunately enough are known to give a reasonable calibration. See Box 5.1.

BOX 5.1

Calibration of the Geologic Time Scale

Cross section of relationships that might be observed somewhere in the western United States. See text for discussion.

Let us specifically consider the method used to achieve numerical calibration of the geologic time scale. The figure above suggests that the Cretaceous period ended approximately 65 million years ago, yet the rocks used to establish the close of Cretaceous time are sedimentary limestones from Dover, England, and thus cannot be directly dated by radioactivity. Radiometric dating in combination with an analysis of certain geologic relationships could, however, yield such a numerical age for the Cretaceous period. With reference to the above figure (which presents a situation that *might* exist), the following conditions *could* lead to a solution to this problem:

1. The "law of faunal succession" makes possible a correlation between the limestone formation shown in the western United States and the youngest of the rocks from Dover, England, where the Cretaceous system was defined. This can be achieved if similar assemblages of fossils are found in both the British and the American limestones.

2. Suppose Uranium-bearing minerals (usually zircon) from the granite yield a numerical age of 70 million years b.p. (before present).

3. We know the limestone (hence the late Cretaceous) to be younger than 70 million years by applying the "law of superposition," and also by noting that there are fragments of the older granite contained within the younger limestone.

4. The igneous dike can be dated by the potassium-argon radioactive-decay method. Suppose an age of 60 million years b.p. is determined for it.

5. We know the limestone (and late Cretaceous) to be *older* than the igneous dike by observing fragments of limestone in the dike and also by recognizing that any intrusive rock must be younger than the rock into which it is intruding.

6. Given observations such as described above, we can conclude that the age for the youngest part of the Cretaceous period is less than 70 million years old and greater than 60 million years old—65 million years b.p. is a reasonable *estimate*, therefore, for the end of the Cretaceous period.

What has been described is a very special set of geologic circumstances. Such ideal relationships are rare. What if, for example, the granite had been 370 million years old? Or suppose the limestone had not contained fossils suitable for correlation? Nevertheless, this is the basic approach that geologists have used in calibrating the geologic time scale. Note again that these conceptions of *time* are derived from *rocks*. Sometimes datable lava flows and volcanic ash are layered among sediments in a manner that simplifies the process described above, but ultimately the problem of making bridges between dates determined for igneous rocks and "ordered" *sedimentary* rocks remains as a major task for the geologist.

The calibration shown in Figure 5.11 shows that the early Cambrian expansion of animal life took place about 570 million years ago. The oldest *Precambrian* rocks so far dated are about 4,000 million (4.0 billion) years old, and thus Phanerozoic (exposed life) time represents only the most recent 15 percent of the time since the formation of the oldest known crustal rocks. Within this 570 million years of Phanerozoic time, the Plaeozoic era accounts for about the first 345 million years, the Mesozoic era the next 160 million years, and the Cenozoic era only the last 65 million years. The average length of the 11 Phanerozoic periods is about 55 million years, but radiometric dating has shown that the changes in the living world that mark the periods were not regularly spaced. Instead, the periods range in age from a minimum of 35 million years (Silurian period) to a maximum of 71 million years (Cretaceous period). Radiometric dating has also shown that the great ice sheet expansions and contractions of Pleistocene time—events that have had such a profound effect on the earth's present climates, landscapes, and sediments—have been concentrated in about the last

2 or 3 million years, less than 1 percent of the total of Phanerozoic time.

In addition to furnishing a numerical calibration for the Phanerozoic time scale, radiometric dating has provided the *only* chronologic tool applicable to the great mass of Precambrian rocks that represent over 3,400 million (3.4 billion) years of earth history. As a result, a general worldwide chronology and sequence of events are beginning to be established for this long and significant interval. Finally, the carbon-14 dating technique has permitted a refined understanding of events over the most recent 50,000-year span of Pleistocene time.

5.7
THE AGE OF THE EARTH

The oldest crustal rocks so far dated, granites from southwestern Greenland, have radiometric ages of about 4 billion years. In other regions, metamorphosed sedimentary rocks surround similar ancient granites that were injected into, and thus are younger than, the deformed sediments that surround them. It is therefore clear that crustal erosion, sediment deposition, and the formation of sedimentary rocks were all taking place very early in earth history. Apparently these processes have completely recycled, and thus obliterated, any original rocks formed as the crust first consolidated. Direct dating of crustal rocks can therefore only indicate that the earth is older than 4.0 billion years; to answer the question, "How much older?" we must turn to less direct evidence of two sorts.

The first piece of evidence comes from radiometric dating of meteorites and rocks recovered from the surface of the moon. All the solid material of the solar system, including the earth, moon, and the small particles that fall on the earth as meteorites, is believed to have had a common origin in the materials that formed the sun. Neither the rocks of the moon nor, presumably, the meteorites have been subjected to the intense, continuous erosion and weathering imposed by an atmosphere on rocks of the earth's crust. For this reason, some of them might be expected to give ages indicating the time that they—and by extrapolation the earth as well—first consolidated from solar matter (sun material). Most significantly, almost all meteorites have been found to have radiometric ages between 4.5 and 5.0 billion years, suggesting that the earth has about the same overall age. In addition, the oldest rocks so far recovered from the surface of the moon have ages of about 4.5 billion years, suggesting that the earth is at least that old.

The second kind of indirect evidence for the overall age of the earth is based on the present-day abundance of the various nuclides of lead that occur in minerals of the earth's crust. Natural lead is a mixture of four stable nuclides: lead-204, -206, -207, and -208. Three of these (206, 207, and 208) are produced by the radioactive decay of uranium and other less common radioactive elements. The fourth, lead-204, is not produced by radioactive decay: *all* of it present on the earth today originated when the earth was formed, whereas only a *part* of present-day lead-206, -207 and -208 originated at that time—the rest has been slowly added through the course of earth history by radioactive decay of other elements (Figure 5.21). Now if there was some means of determining the *original* relative abundance of the four nuclides (at the time the earth was formed), the earth's age could be estimated by first measuring their *present* relative abundance and then calculating the time required for the additional lead-206, -207 and -208 to have been added by radioactive decay (the decay rates producing each are constant and are precisely known from laboratory measurements). Although there is no direct way of estimating the original lead abundances, certain meteorites that contain no uranium or other radioactive elements

FIGURE 5.21 Determination of the age of the earth from its initial and present-day abundances of lead nuclides. The initial abundance is estimated from meteorites and the present abundance from the average of many rock measurements. The difference represents addition from the decay of radioactive uranium and thorium through earth history.

that decay into lead are thought to provide a reasonable approximation of the earth's original lead. Using this information, about 4.5 billion years of radioactive decay would be necessary to produce lead having the average nuclide abundances found on the earth today. This estimate further confirms the suggestion that the earth originated at least 4.5 billion years ago.

SUMMARY OUTLINE

RELATIVE AGES OF ROCKS AND EARTH CHRONOLOGY

5.1 Physical relationships: The law of superposition and other relative age-dating principles provide a means of establishing local sequences of events in rocks.

5.2 Fossil contents and the geologic column: Progressive evolutionary changes in ancient life provide a worldwide chronology based on fossil-bearing sedimentary rocks.

5.3 Sedimentary rocks and past environments: Sedimentary rocks reveal much about ancient geography at their time of deposition; areas of nondeposition and erosion leave unconformities in the sedimentary record.

NUCLEAR CLOCKS AND EARTH CHRONOLOGY

5.4 Radioactive decay: Radioactive parent nuclides gradually decay into stable daughter nuclides of other elements.

5.5 Radiometric ages: The decay rate of radioactive nuclides is constant and can be determined by laboratory measurements; by measuring amounts of parent and daughter nuclides and applying the decay rate, the time of origin of many igneous and metamorphic minerals can be determined.

5.6 Numerical radiometric dating: Radioactive nuclides provide numerical ages for the 600 million years of Phanerozoic history, and also permit establishing a chronology for the preceding 3.4 billion years of Precambrian rocks, which lack abundant fossils.

5.7 The age of the earth: The oldest known crustal rock formed 4.0 billion years ago and indicates a still earlier, unrecorded phase of earth history; various lines of evidence suggest that the original consolidation of the earth took place at least 4.5 billion years ago.

ADDITIONAL READINGS

*BERRY, W. B. N.: *Growth of a Prehistoric Time Scale*, W. H. Freeman and Company, Publishers, San Francisco, 1968. A brief, readable history of the development of the sedimentary time scale in the eighteenth and early nineteenth centuries.

* Available in paperback.

*EICHER, D. L.: *Geologic Time*, 2nd ed., Prentice-Hall, Inc., Englewood Cliffs, N.J., 1976. An introduction to all aspects of earth chronology.

*FAUL, H.: *Ages of Rocks, Planets, and Stars*, McGraw-Hill Book Company, New York, 1966. A good introduction to radiometric dating.

*HARBAUGH, J. W.: *Stratigraphy and Geologic Time*, William C. Brown Company, Dubuque, Iowa, 1968. A brief introduction to earth chronology.

*MATTHEWS, R. K.: *Dynamic Stratigraphy*, 2nd ed., Prentice-Hall, Inc., Englewood Cliffs, N.J., 1982. An up-to-date advanced text on sedimentary chronology.

*YORK, D., and R. M. FARQUHAR: *The Earth's Age and Geochronology*, Pergamon Press, Inc., Elmsford, N.Y., 1972. A brief intermediate-level survey emphasizing radiometric techniques.

* Available in paperback.

Ancient Mountains
in the Grand Canyon Region

The modern-day Grand Canyon bisects the Colorado Plateau. The region is relatively high (8,000 feet above sea level at the north rim of the canyon), but late Cenozoic uplifting that enabled the Colorado River to erode this impressive canyon was not the kind of deformation that led to intense folding and faulting of rocks, such as occurred in the Appalachians or the Alps. Instead, the uplift was essentially vertical, and it was distributed nearly uniformly over a broad region. Thus, the development of mountainlike topography did not result until long after the uplift, caused then by streams that carved deep canyons into the plateau. This was how the Grand Canyon as we know it today was formed.

Long ago, however, this same region experienced two separate episodes of mountain building due to folding and faulting. We will consider evidence for these two events, and then show how geologists used radioactive age-dating techniques to ascertain when this mountain building occurred.

Major episodes of mountain building in the geologic past are usually recognized by geologists because of *unconformities* observable in the rocks. There are several unconformities in the wall rocks of the Grand Canyon, and two of them provide evidence of large-scale folding and faulting. Consider the geologic cross section of rock formations of this area shown in Figure 5.22. Underlying the Bass Dolomite is a buried surface of erosion that developed following mountain building, folding, faulting, plutonism, and metamorphisim. These geologic processes left the Vishnu Schist and the Granitic plutons high above what was then sea level. Unknown thousands of feet of rocks that once lay above the schist and granite were stripped away by erosion, thus creating the relatively flat surface upon which the Bass Dolomite strata were subsequently deposited. The layers of the Bass Dolomite were horizontal then, but later they were deformed to the inclination they show in the cross section. Another major unconformity can be recognized beneath the Tapeats Sandstone. Here the eroded upturned edges of the Dox, Shinumo, Hakatai, and Bass formations are unconformably overlain by layers of Tapeats Sandstone. From evidence found near the Grand Canyon, we know that over 12,000 feet of these rocks were eroded away

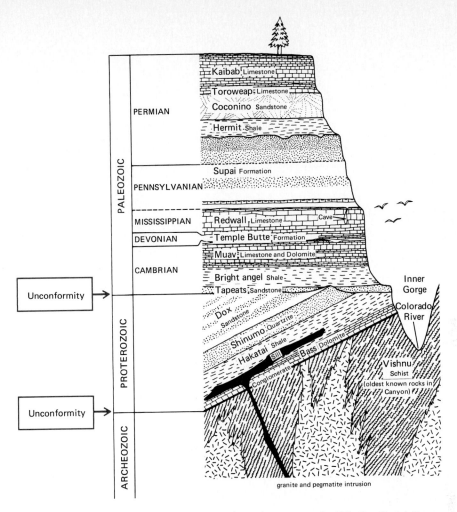

FIGURE 5.22 Cross section showing rock formations exposed within the Grand Canyon, Arizona.

in some places before the Tapeats Sandstone was deposited on the floor of a shallow sea as it encroached upon that surface of erosion (see Fig. 4.41). The formation of these two unconformities is diagrammatically represented in Figure 5.23 (a through g). Part (a) represents deposition of the sediments and lavas that would later be metamorphosed and become the Vishnu Schist. Part (b) shows the intense deformation of the layers into mountains. Emplacement of granite plutons and metamorphism of sediments and lavas occurred in the core of these mountains. Part (c) shows the region after a very long period of erosion. The oldest of the two unconformities comes into existence in (d) with the deposition of the Bass Dolomite and the younger formations upon the Bass. Part (e) depicts the deformation

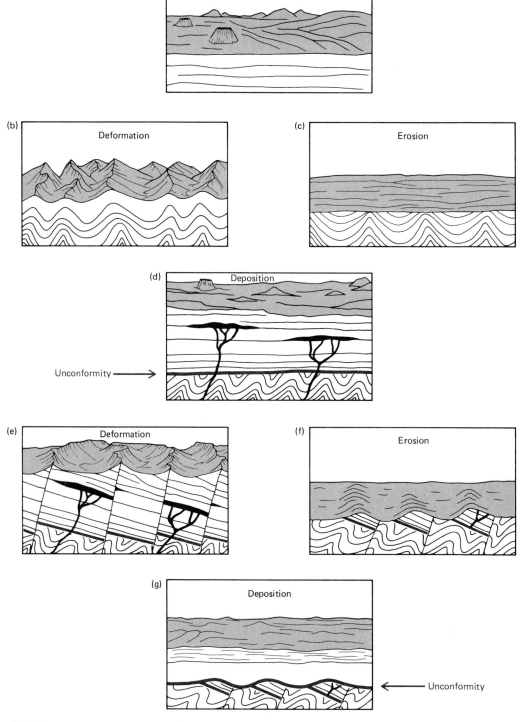

FIGURE 5.23 Sequence of geologic events during Precambrian and Paleozoic time in the Grand Canyon region (see text for discussion).

that next occurred: Folding was not as intense as before, but large, gently tilted blocks of rock were formed due to faulting on a grand scale. Thicknesses of over 12,000 feet of these tilted rocks were eroded away in some places, leaving behind only islandlike exposures of the Bass, Hakatai, Shinumo, and Dox formations (f). Finally, shallow marine waters again moved over this deeply eroded region, and the Tapeats Sandstones buried the second erosion surface, thus giving rise to the angular unconformity shown in (g).

All this took place more than 500 million years ago. How can we tell more precisely just when these important mountain-building activities occurred? The answers are to be found only by using radioactive elements contained in the igneous rocks of the region. The oldest rocks are located in the inner gorge of the Grand Canyon. Figure 5.22 shows the Vishnu Schist and related granitic rocks. These materials have been dated using two different radioactive pairs: Uranium (U) decaying to lead (Pb), and potassium (K) decaying to argon (Ar). The ages indicated by the two methods are not the same, yet the difference does not seem to result from experimental error! The U-Pb age is 1,700 million years and the K-Ar age is 1,400 million years—300 million years different from each other! Can both the ages have meaning, or does the discrepancy between them invalidate their use? We think they both have an important message to tell. The U-Pb age of 1,700 million years is our best value for the time at which the granitic rock crystallized from a molten state. At that time, the lattice structure of a uranium-bearing mineral, zircon, began to trap all the radiogenic lead, thus starting the radioactive clock. Radiogenic argon from the decay of potassium was also trapped in different crystals at that time, too, and should have yielded the same age as that from U-Pb, but we believe that the clock for K-Ar was "reset" after about 300 million years had passed. What event could cause argon trapped in a crystalline lattice to be lost, thus resetting the K-Ar clock, yet not affect the U-Pb clock? Another pulse of strong deformation, causing the rocks to be heated and squeezed, would have just this effect. Argon, being a *gas*, can be lost from crystalline lattices far more easily than can lead, strontium (Sr), or other *solid* elements. Heating and squeezing, therefore, would not have the same influence on the U-Pb clock as it would on the K-Ar one. So it appears that the last major pulse of uplift affecting the region prior to the development of the oldest unconformity was about 1,400 million years ago.

How long then did erosion dominate this region prior to the deposition of the Bass Dolomite? In other words, how much time, *missing time*, is represented by the unconformity beneath the Bass Dolomite? The answer would be easy if we knew the age of the Bass, but we don't, and we can't, because it is too old to contain fossils, and being a marine sedimentary deposit, it isn't amenable to radioactive age-dating techniques. Our best estimate of its age comes from dating the igneous sill material shown in Figure 5.22. The sill rock is somewhat younger than the Bass Dolomite because the sill intrudes the sediment. The radioactive age for the sill (using the Rb-Sr decay scheme) is 1,200 million years. It seems likely, therefore, that a duration of about 200 million years is represented by the unconformity. Subtract the age of rocks *above* the unconformity (1,200 m.y.) from the age of deformation indicated by the K-Ar age of the rocks *below* the unconformity (1,400 m.y.), and you have the interval when erosion was the dominant geologic process: 200 million years.

The approach discussed above can also be applied to the younger unconformity shown on Figure 5.22. Lava flows near the top of the Dox Sandstone are 1,100 million years old, based on Rb-Sr age-dating. The same lavas yield ages of 800–900 million years using the K-Ar method. Here again we believe the older figure represents the age of the rocks, and the younger value indicates the time of deformation. Fossils contained in the Tapeats Sandstone above the unconformity establish it as middle Cambrian in age—therefore about 550 million years old. The difference between deformation (about 800 m.y.) and deposition of the Tapeats (about 550 m.y.) indicates another very long episode of erosion was responsible for this unconformity: about 250 million years.

These two very old unconformities in the Grand Canyon provide outstanding examples of mountain-building episodes in the southwestern United States. Were it not for radioactive age-dating techniques, however, we would be totally ignorant about when they occurred.

6

Crustal Rock Deformation

IMAGINE FOR A MOMENT THAT the oceans could somehow be drained to leave the entire surface of the earth exposed as dry land. An explorer traveling in this strange world would discover that the earth's surface consists of two fundamentally different landscapes. The most obvious would be broad, flat plains covering millions of square miles, interrupted only by long, narrow chains of high mountains. These plains would contrast sharply with the second major feature, plateau areas—also relatively flat with linear mountain ranges—that would tower several miles above the surrounding plains and would be separated from them by the highest and most continuous scarps (steep slopes) on earth. The lower plains would, of course, be the floors of today's oceans, and the higher plateaus the surfaces of today's continents. This division into low *ocean basins* and much higher *continents*, which is the most obvious feature of the earth's crust, is caused by fundamental differences in the composition and structure of continental versus oceanic rocks.

ROCKS OF THE CRUST

6.1
CONTINENTS AND OCEAN BASINS

In general, we have observed and studied continental rocks much more than those making up the ocean floor. Continental rocks are more accessible at the earth's surface and in mines and bore holes. Rocks from the *surface* of the ocean floor, however, have been recovered by dredging along submarine cliffs and canyons in many parts of the oceans, and additional information about oceanic rocks is provided by islands that are far from the nearest continental land masses. Data on oceanic rock composition, combined with information from hundreds of thousands of surface rock exposures and tens of thousands of mines and wells on the continents, have shown that *continents are largely composed of silicic igneous rocks, particularly granite*, whereas *ocean basins are largely underlain by more dense, mafic igneous rocks, particularly basalt*. These direct observations of rock composition are further confirmed by seismic wave velocities, which show values in the range expected for granitic rocks through-

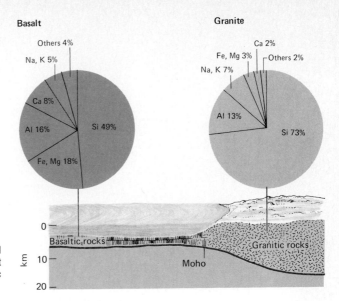

FIGURE 6.1 Generalized chemical compositions of the basaltic rocks that underlie the ocean floor and the granitic rocks that underlie the continents.

out the continental crust, but are generally higher in the oceanic crust, thus suggesting a predominance there of more rigid and more dense, basaltic materials.

In summary, the differences between continents and ocean basins are primarily related to the concentration, in the continents, of the relatively light elements that are abundant in the minerals of granite—particularly silicon, sodium, and potassium; the rocks under the ocean floors, in contrast, have a higher concentration of heavier iron-magnesium—and calcium-rich minerals and are therefore closer in composition to the inferred rocks of the underlying mantle than are continental rocks (Figure 6.1).

6.2
CONTINENTAL ROCKS

Although most of the surface rock of the continents is covered by a thin layer of soil, it is usually easy to determine the nature of the underlying "bedrock," either by digging through the soil or, more commonly, by observing the rock where it is exposed in stream banks and cliffs or in man-made quarries, excavations, and road cuts. In addition, data from surface rock exposures may be supplemented by information on the "subsurface" rock distribution in areas that have been mined or explored for petroleum. In studying the rocks of a particular continental region, geologists normally seek out all this evidence and use it to prepare a **geologic map** showing the distribution of different rocks as they would look if all the soil were removed from the surface (Figure 6.2). The degree of detail shown

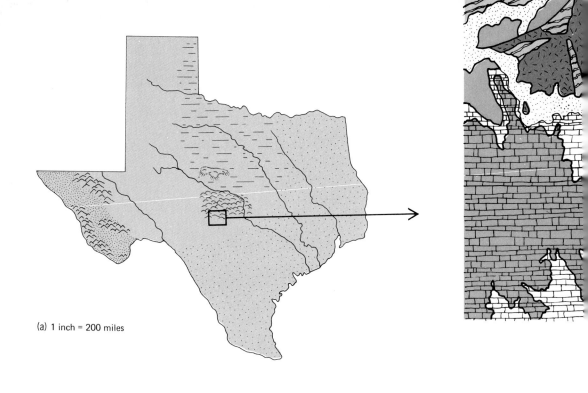

(a) 1 inch = 200 miles

(d) 1 inch = 1/13 mile (400 ft)

FIGURE 6.2 Typical geologic maps at different scales. (a) Index map of Texas. (b-d) Geologic maps at progressively larger scales. Map d, which is exceptionally detailed, was prepared to locate small "soapstone" deposits (dark color; soapstone is a metamorphic rock made up of fine-grained mica-like mineral used in the paint, ceramic, paper, and rubber industries).

(b) 1 inch = 8 miles

(c) 1 inch = 1/2 mile

b

c and d

granite	Town Mountain Granite

Basement Igneous

and

Metamorphic Rocks

schist, gneiss	Packsaddle Schist
	Big Branch Gneiss
	amphibole masses
	soapstone masses

Sedimentary Veneer

Fredericksburg Group	Comanche Peak Limestone
Trinity Group	Glen Rose Limestone
	Hensell Sandstone
Ellenberger and Wilberns Formation	
Hickory Sandstone	Hickory Sandstone

OXFORD
CLICK
BLOWOUT
EDERICKSBURG

in geologic maps varies with the purpose of the map and the amount of field study that has gone into its preparation. At one extreme, areas with valuable mineral deposits may be mapped in such detail that 1 inch on the map equals only a few hundred feet on the ground [Figure 6.2(d)]. At the other extreme, large areas are commonly mapped by rapid reconnaissance methods, usually with the help of aerial photographs, at scales in which 1 inch on the map equals 8 miles or more on the ground [Figure 6.2(b)]. Most geologic mapping falls between these extremes [Figure 6.2(c)]. Most of the United States, for example, has been geologically mapped at scales of 1 in. = 1 mi, and many local regions at scales as great as 1 in. = ¼ mi. In preparing a geologic map, each distinctive unit of rock, called a **formation**, is given its own two-part name. The first part of the name is some geographic locality where the rock is well exposed; the second part describes the general rock type. Thus Manhattan Schist, St. Louis Limestone, and Columbia River Basalt are typical formation names used in the preparation of local geologic maps. Other examples, from a single region, are shown in Figure 6.2.

Geologic mapping not only shows the distribution of different formations, but also the rock's three-dimensional appearance, particularly as revealed by sedimentary layers (the technique for showing this three-dimensionality is described in Box 6.2, later in this chapter). An extremely significant conclusion is forced upon us by our geologic maps—or, for that matter, by an observant stroll through the countryside: *most rocks have been appreciably changed from the positions they occupied at their time of origin*. For example, sedimentary rocks that were once flat-lying are found to be intensely folded and broken, and plutonic and metamorphic rocks are observed at the earth's surface, a site quite different from environments of their genesis. The present state of all these rocks provides abundant evidence that crustal rocks are continually being moved and altered by dynamic forces originating beneath the crust. Flat-lying sedimentary rocks can be seen to have been crumpled into huge mountain ranges by enormous lateral pressures, and even larger blocks of crustal rocks have moved hundreds of miles along lengthy ruptures. These and other kinds of evidence indicate that most of the topographic features of the earth's surface—features such as mountain ranges, basins, and plateaus on the continents, and island chains, deep trenches, and submerged mountains on the ocean floor—have their origin in complex crustal movements caused by the interaction of lithospheric plates. For the remainder of this chapter, we shall consider the nature of these fundamental movements, particularly as they apply to the more easily observed rocks of the continents. In Chapter 8, we shall seek a more nearly complete understanding of the mechanism for this deformation when the topic of plate tectonics is more thoroughly considered.

Until the 1960s, most evidence for crustal movements came from the study of continental rocks, which are of course far more accessible than are those of the ocean floor. Geologic mapping showed that intense movements had not taken place randomly over the surface of the continents, but instead tended to be concentrated in long, narrow belts that usually parallel continental margins. Continental **mountain ranges,** formed adjacent to and above subduction zones by the compression and distortion of previously flat-lying and nondeformed rocks or by the uplift of plutonic masses, provide the principal evidence for movements of the continental crust.

MODES OF ROCK DEFORMATION

When rocks of the crust are subjected to mountain-building forces, they can respond in two ways: either they bend or they break. These two responses define the two major structural features seen in deformed crustal rocks: **folds,** the result of rock deformation of a primarily plastic nature (Figures 6.3 and 6.4); and two kinds of *fractures*, called **joints** and **faults.** Joints are fractures along which no apprecia-

(a)

FIGURE 6.3 Folds. (a) Small-scale, in limestones of northern Scotland; the camera case a top left provides scale. (b) Intermediate-scale, in limestones of northern England. (a,b: Institute of Geological Sciences: British Crown copyright reserved.)

(b)

FIGURE 6.4   Large scale folds. (R. H. Chapman, U.S. Geological Survey.)

ble movement has occurred (Figure 6.5), whereas faults show displacements, or offset, of one side of the break with respect to the other (Figures 6.6 and 6.7). Jointing is so commonplace as to have perhaps gone unnoticed by many, but these fractures, which typically display some geometrically regular pattern, are noteworthy examples of small-scale rock deformation. Folds and faults are much more significant features and occur in limitless variations of size

FIGURE 6.5   Geometrically regular jointing. (Institute of Geological Sciences: British Crown copyright reserved.)

CRUSTAL ROCK DEFORMATION

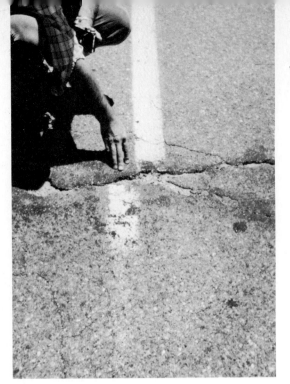

FIGURE 6.6   An offset center line: California Highway 46, San Andreas Fault (1966). (E. A. Hay.)

FIGURE 6.7   Faults. (a) Small dip-slip fault in shales of northern England. (b) Reconstruction of (a) as it appeared prior to erosion. (a: Institute of Geological Sciences: British Crown copyright reserved.)

(a)

(b)

and shape. Entire mountain ranges may be formed by a single huge fold or fault, whereas at the other extreme, pieces of rock small enough to be held in one's hand may be marked by tiny folds and faults that can be seen only under a microscope.

Careful descriptions and geologic maps of the folds and faults seen in continental mountain ranges have been made since the nineteenth century, and these have provided a wealth of information about the geometry and distribution of various kinds of deformed rocks. We shall first introduce the terminology used to describe folds and faults and then deal with the problem of graphically depicting such three-dimensional features on flat, two-dimensional pieces of paper in the form of geologic maps and structure sections.

6.3
FAULTS

When crustal rocks are dislocated, there are three varieties of movement possible: **dip-slip**, where the movement is primarily in an up-and-down sense [Figure 6.7(a) and (b)]; **strike-slip**, commonly called **transcurrent**, having essentially horizontal movement (Figure 6.6); and **oblique-slip**, with elements of both directions of movement (Figure 6.8).

The complex models that geologists have developed to account for these different types of movement are beyond the scope of this book; nevertheless, we can point out some general relationships existing between directions of stress within the crust and the variety of faulting that results. See Box 6.1. Dip-slip movements manifest either *compressional* forces, which give rise to *shortening* of the crust in reverse (*thrust*)-slip faulting, or tensional forces, causing crustal *lengthening*, for normal-slip faulting (Figure 6.9). Transcurrent faults, on the other hand, appear to have resulted from crustal movements of a more nearly shearing nature. These faults are described as either right-lateral slip or left-lateral slip, depending on

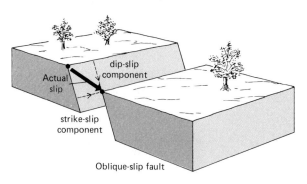

FIGURE 6.8   Oblique-slip faulting.

CRUSTAL ROCK DEFORMATION

(a)   (b)

FIGURE 6.9   Distinction between normal-slip and reverse-slip faults. (a) Reverse-slip. Note overlapping due to crustal shortening. (b) Normal-slip. Note extension due to crustal lengthening. (a,b: E. A. Hay.)

the direction each side of the fault has moved with respect to the other. Figure 6.10 explains the system used to apply the terms *right-lateral* and *left-lateral*.

Figure 6.10(a) shows the results of movement that occurred a few miles north of San Francisco on the famous San Andreas Fault during the great 1906 earthquake. Figure 6.6 also depicts right-lateral slip on the San Andreas Fault that occurred in 1966. In addition to these recent offsets, we have excellent evidence based on the displacements of different-aged rock formations that this major fault has moved hundreds of kilometers in a right-lateral-slip manner during the last 30 million years or more (Figure 6.11). Although we recognize right-lateral slip on the San Andreas Fault, we also refer to it as a **transform fault**. This is because it connects two different centers of sea-floor spreading: one off the coast of northern California and one in the Gulf of California (Figure 6.12). Thus it is a transform fault that ruptures in a right-lateral sense. We shall discuss transform faults in greater detail in Chapter 8.

Because we usually observe the faults in the three-dimensional earth on a surface that is, for all practical purposes, two-dimensional—such as in a road cut or on flat terrain—it is possible to be misled or uncertain about the actual sense of *movement* that has taken place on a fault. We must make a distinction between the fault *slip*, which reflects its *actual* movement, and the fault *offset*, which reflects only *apparent* movement resulting from erosional effects (Figure 6.13). Some such distinctions are not possible, but for those that are, terminology should be applied in a manner to differentiate between slip and offset. In Figure 6.13, for example, we would describe the fault as a normal-slip fault showing left-lateral offset at A and right-lateral offset at B.

(a)

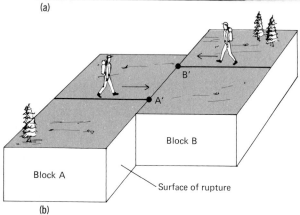

B'

Block B

A'

Block A

Surface of rupture

(b)

FIGURE 6.10 Right-slip and left-slip faults. (a) Right-slip, offset road near Olema, California (1906). (b) Block diagram showing left-lateral movement by faulting. A' and B' were at the same point prior to faulting. A person walking toward A' in Block A would have to turn left at the fault to reach B'; therefore the offset is left-lateral. (A person walking toward B' in block B would also have to turn left to reach A'.) (a: G. K. Gilbert.)

Distinctive group of volcanic rocks, believed to have once been connected.

Approximately 300 km

FIGURE 6.11 Example of a right-lateral slip that has accumulated on the San Andreas fault during the last 25 million years.

Gorda
Rise

N

United
States

San Andreas Fault

Pacific
Ocean

Mexico

East
Pacific Rise

FIGURE 6.12 The San Andreas Fault connects two spreading centers; thus it is a transform fault.

(a) Following normal-slip faulting:

Actual movement

B

A

Grooves on fault plane indicate true sense of movement

(b) Erosion wears away the higher rocks on the up-faulted block.

B

A

FIGURE 6.13 Distinction between apparent and actual movement. In the figure the arrows at A and B indicate apparent movement: at A ir is left-lateral and at B it is right-lateral. They describe offset, not slip. The actual slip is normal.

199

BOX 6.1

Style of Faulting is a Function of the Direction in which the Greatest Stress is Applied

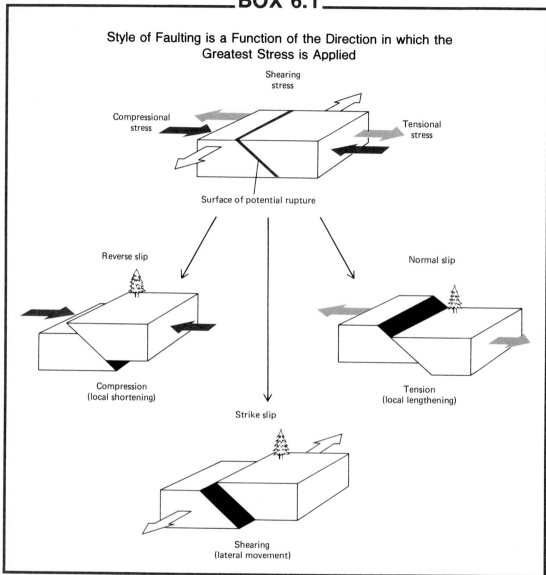

6.4
FOLDS

The classification of folded rocks basically employs two categories: archlike folds are called **anticlines** (*anti* = opposed, *cline* = inclination), where the *limbs* (opposite sides) of the fold are inclined downward and away from each other; and troughlike folds are called **synclines** (*syn* = together, *cline* = inclination), having their limbs

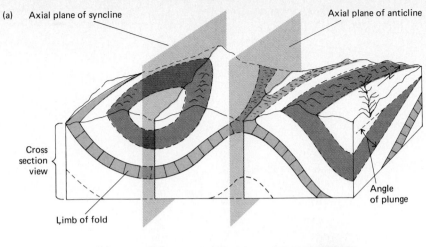

(a) Axial plane of syncline   Axial plane of anticline

Cross
section
view

Angle
of plunge

Limb of fold

(b)

Axis,
or hinge,
of syncline

Axis, or hinge,
of anticline

N

MAP VIEW

(c) Limbs: the sides of a fold

Axial plane: imaginary surface dividing the opposite limbs.

Axis: imaginary line *on the surface* that divides the opposite limbs.

Plunge: the condition where the axis is inclined downward, rather than remaining horizontal.

FIGURE 6.14   Fold terminology. (a) Block diagram. (b) Map view. (c) Definitions of fold terminology.

dipping toward each other. Figure 6.14 shows useful terminology for describing the elements of folds. It is no surprise that folded rocks have curved archlike and troughlike appearances when viewed in cross section as shown on the front surface of Figure 6.14(a), but an explanation for the fact that most folds display similar curved patterns when viewed on the earth's surface is not so obvious [Figure 6.14(b)]. If the axes (hinges) of all folds were parallel to the earth's surface of erosion, such map patterns would not be common; as a general rule, however, not only are the limbs folded, but also the axis of these limbs undergoes tilting or folding (Figure

(a) Originally flat-lying sedimentary layer

Horizontal
reference plane

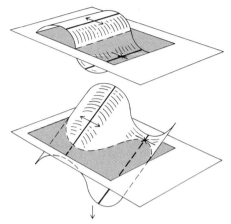

(b) Folded, with fold axes remaining horizontal

(c) Axes are tilted downward (plunging)
toward the viewer

FIGURE 6.15   Origin of plunging folds. In (c) note that a horizontal plane (such as a typical eroded surface) cuts the deformed layer to expose a curved outcrop pattern.

FIGURE 6.16   Plunging folds. (a) Plunging anticline in Wyoming. (b) Plunging syncline in California. (a: John S. Shelton; b: E. A. Hay.)

(a)

(b)

Oldest exposed rocks

Youngest exposed rocks

IV

V Youngest

IV

III

II

I Oldest

FIGURE 6.17 Age relationships of folded sedimentary rocks. Imagine walking across the surface of this terrain. At the anticlinal axis you would be on the oldest exposed rocks, and at the synclinal axis you would be on the youngest. The arrows on the cross section show the direction toward which the tops of the beds are facing: away from from the axial plane of the anticline and toward the axial plane of the syncline.

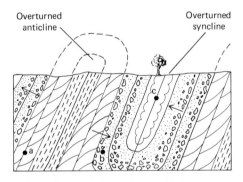

Overturned anticline

Overturned syncline

FIGURE 6.18 Isoclinal folds. Arrows indicate the facing of tops of sedimentary layers, as indicated by (a) cross-bedding, (b) graded bedding, and (c) ripple marks. Review section 3.4 regarding sedimentary structures.)

6.15). The result is an eroded pattern of rock exposures that bend around in a "hairpinlike" manner. Figure 6.16 (a and b) shows that the map pattern of a **plunging fold** is the same for both anticlines and synclines. The distinction is that in anticlines, the limbs dip away from each other; and in synclines, they dip toward each other.

Because of the law of superposition, two important generalizations can be made regarding the relationships between sedimentary strata and the folds in which they are found: (1) Rocks become progressively *older* toward the axes of *anticlines* and *younger* toward synclinal axes; and (2) the *tops* of beds face *away from anticlinal* and *toward synclinal* axial planes (Figure 6.17). In regions of intense deformation, folds are frequently overturned, sometimes becoming **isoclinal** (*iso* = equal, *clinal* = inclination), where both limbs are dipping at the same angle in the same direction (Figure 6.18). Methods for distinguishing between the top (youngest) and bottom (oldest)

(a)

Monocline
(mono = one;
cline = inclination)

(b)

Homocline
(*homo* = same;
cline = inclination)

(c)

Recumbent Folds (axial
planes are flat–lying)

(d)

Drag Folds
(small folds on the limb
of a larger fold)

FIGURE 6.19 Varieties of folding.

side of a sedimentary layer become exceedingly important as tools for analyzing such folds. Recall from Chapter 4 that there are a variety of *sedimentary structures* useful in this regard: cross bedding, graded bedding, ripple marks, and mud cracks, to mention the most obvious.

Isoclinal folds are not the only variation of the basic pattern of anticlines and synclines. Figure 6.19 shows patterns and terminology for other styles of folding.

Folds and faults are commonly very large features—large enough so as not to be readily apparent to a person standing at a single location. This makes it necessary to make observations of many different places in order to recognize fully the manner in which a particular area of the earth has been deformed (see Figure 6.2). This activity involves the making of a **geologic map.**

Geologic maps are products of strenuous physical and mental labor. Although aerial photography often facilitates coverage of inaccessible areas, most geologic mapping is done by a geologist walking over the earth's surface in order to trace contacts that delineate formational boundaries and to plot other symbols, called **attitudes,** used to indicate the three-dimensional orientations of rock units. An attitude consists of two elements, a direction of **strike** and an amount and direction of **dip** (Figure 6.20). A geologist must carefully observe and measure rock strata in the field in order to plot these symbols on a map. Figure 6.21 depicts a variety of attitudes and their field and map appearances. Many large-scale folds are made apparent only by the accumulation and plotting of many such attitudes on a map. In addition to being concerned with folding geometry, the field geologist must impose some order on what at first commonly seems to be a bewildering array of different kinds of rock. The immediate goal of all this is to make a geologic map; the ultimate goal is usually to understand earth history, or to achieve an economic objective.

Obviously it is easier to appreciate the three-dimensional relationships in Figure 6.21 by consulting the block diagrams with their cross-sectional views on the front faces than by studying the map views. It is for this reason that side views called **geologic structure**

FIGURE 6.20 Determination of attitude.

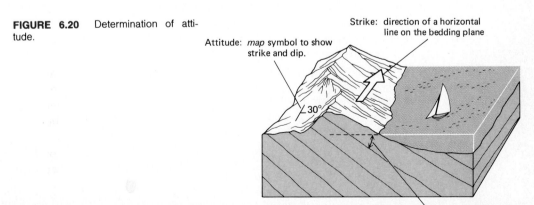

Attitude: *map* symbol to show strike and dip.

Strike: direction of a horizontal line on the bedding plane

30°

Dip: angle of downward inclination of bedding plane from horizontal.

FIGURE 6.21 Map appearance of an eroded stratum. Note that in the bottom map-drawings the direction of dip can be determined from the appearance of the stratum as it crosses the valley.

sections are almost always prepared from geologic maps. Examples of how such geologic structure sections are prepared are shown in Figures 6.22 and 6.23. First, the reader should look at the map view in Figure 6.22 and review the terminology found on it.

Now let us redraw this map, this time showing only the contour lines [Figure 6.23(a)]: This illustrates the technique of constructing a **topographic profile** along the line of section X–X′ in the space immediately below the map [Figure 6.23(b)]. A topographic profile, like the profile of a person's face, shows a side view, with its highs and lows, of how the earth's surface appears along a given line. By way of analogy, the X–X′ map and topographic profile views respectively correspond to the A–A′ front and profile views of the man's face shown in Figure 6.23(c).

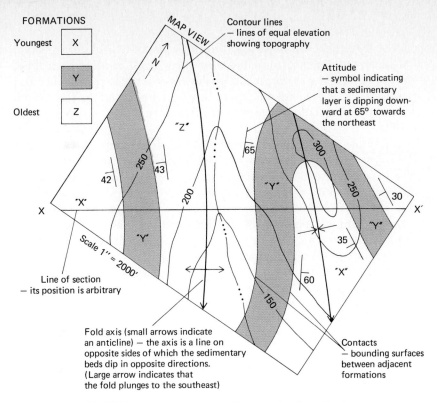

FORMATIONS

Youngest X

Y

Oldest Z

MAP VIEW

Contour lines
— lines of equal elevation
showing topography

Attitude
— symbol indicating
that a sedimentary
layer is dipping down-
ward at 65° towards
the northeast

"Z"

250

43

42

200

65

300

250

30

"Y"

"Y"

35

"Y"

"X"

X   X'

Scale 1" = 2000'

60

150

Line of section
— its position is arbitrary

Fold axis (small arrows indicate
an anticline) — the axis is a line on
opposite sides of which the sedimentary
beds dip in opposite directions.
(Large arrow indicates that
the fold plunges to the southeast)

Contacts
— bounding surfaces
between adjacent
formations

FIGURE 6.22   Geologic map. (See text for discussion.)

MAP VIEW

(a)

250   Pine   200
       Tree

300 250

X   X'

1   2 3   4   5 6 7 8

Scale 1" =
2,000'

150

X   X'

ELEVATIONS

300   1'   2'   3'   4'   5' 6' 7' 8'
200
100

The distance between these lines is arbitrarily chosen.
Note that the vertical scale is exaggerated with respect to
the horizontal scale.

(c)

A   A'

A   A'

FIGURE 6.23   Contour map and topographic profile derived from Figure 6.22.
(See text.) A topographic profile is compared to the profile of a face.

Every time the line X–X' crosses a contour line on the map, we have precise information about the elevation above sea level for that point as shown on the profile. It is for this reason that the points 1, 2, 3, etc., on the map can be transferred to the points 1', 2', 3', etc., below as a means of constructing the topographic profile.

Finally we return to our original geologic map (Box 6.2), add the topographic profile below it, and proceed with the construction of a geologic structure section to show the appearance at depth of the rock formations along the line X–X' as they would appear below the surface (topographic profile) of the earth. This time we shall transfer contacts between formations, rather than contour elevations, from the map view to the topographic profile, again recognizing that any point on the map X–X' line has a precisely corresponding position on the X–X' topographic profile. Recall that if these sedimentary formations were originally deposited in essentially horizontal, blanketlike layers, with "Z" on the bottom and "X" on the top, the contacts between them have become exposed at the earth's surface because erosion has cut into this pile of layered rocks after the folding occurred. If there had been no folding nor erosion, we would see only the top layer formation "X."

6.6
EXPERIMENTAL ROCK DEFORMATION

It is readily apparent that rocks of the earth's crust have responded to deforming forces in a variety of ways, some breaking and others folding in a more plastic manner. Descriptive mapping studies have raised questions about rock deformation that can best be approached by theoretical or experimental studies.

Most of the rocks exposed at the earth's surface are very brittle. If forces are applied to them—for example, by striking with a hammer or squeezing with a vise—they yield only by breaking. Because familiar rocks respond in this way, it is easy to visualize how rocks can deform by breaking along faults, but more difficult to understand how they can deform by *bending* to form folds. Obviously, folded rocks now exposed at the earth's surface must have originated under other conditions, conditions that made the rocks less brittle and more *ductile*—that is, able to flow and deform without fracture. Theoretical and laboratory studies have shown that ductility is not constant for a particular kind of rock but varies with changing environmental conditions. Three environmental factors are particularly important in affecting rock ductility: pressure, temperature, and the rate at which deforming forces act on the rock.

The effect of variations in pressure and temperature upon rock

BOX 6.2

Construction of a Geologic Structure Section

The stages of the construction of a geologic structure section can best be done by proceeding in a step-by-step fashion. Note that each of these steps is indicated in the figure; study it carefully.

Step 1 Using a straight-edge, carefully project the points where contacts cross the line of section on the map to the corresponding points on the topographic profile.

Step 2 These projected contacts represent the bounding surfaces between the rock formations they separate. Label (or color) each formation's location on the profile so as not to lose track of the location of each.

Step 3 Project the attitudes (⊤ symbols) on the map into the line of section and then down to the topographic profile. Use these symbols to determine the direction and amount of dip for each of the formations to be used in the structure section. Remember that these dips are only valid right at the surface of the profile and should not be extended indefinitely into the subsurface.

Step 4 Using the surface dips as guidelines, and contacts as starting points, extend the formational contacts into the subsurface. Endeavor to connect like-surfaces in the subsurface, as in a syncline, and dash their projections above the surface, as in a partially eroded anticline.

Step 5 Always maintain the thickness of a formation throughout the geologic structure section.

Making a geologic structure section from a geologic map. Note sequence of steps (1 through 5) shown in the figure.

deformation can be investigated by subjecting rock specimens—usually cut into the shape of cylinders about 3 to 15 centimeters (1 to 6 inches) long—to deforming forces at varying temperatures while they are held in special high-pressure presses (Figure 6.24). These

FIGURE 6.24 Experimental rock deformation. (a) Schematic drawing of a rock deformation press. (b) Cylinders of limestone shortened 15 percent at increasing confining pressures (left to right) in a deformation press. At low pressures the specimens break as in faulting; at higher pressures they deform without breaking as in folding. (Photos courtesy F. A. Donath; from "American Scientist," vol. 58, 1970.)

Increasing pressure

presses simulate the increased pressures and temperatures to which rocks are subjected as they are buried deeper and deeper in the earth. Such presses can achieve pressures in excess of those occurring anywhere in the crust and can be operated at temperatures high enough to melt most rocks. Studies using these presses show that most rocks tend to become more ductile as pressures and temperatures increase. Thus the brittle behavior we associate with rocks at the earth's surface may be replaced by ductile deformation and by folding when the same rocks are subjected to deforming forces while deeply buried. By observing the patterns of deformation seen in rocks now exposed at the surface, it is sometimes possible to infer, from laboratory experiments on similar materials, the approximate depths, temperatures, and pressures at which the rocks were deformed.

The effects of temperature and pressure on rock ductility are relatively easy to study in laboratory experiments and are now reasonably well understood. In contrast, the third major factor controlling rock ductility—the rate at which the deforming forces act—is an area of great uncertainty because very small forces, when applied over very long times, can lead to ductile deformation in otherwise brittle materials. A familiar example is a wax candle, which may over a long period bend under its own weight but which can also be easily broken by a sharp blow. Similarly, gravestones made of brittle natural rocks such as marble have been observed to bend under their own weight over many years. These observations suggest that time is an extraordinarily important factor in rock ductility; over long periods even brittle rock masses exposed at or near the earth's surface might deform by ductile flow under the action of relatively small forces, such as the force of gravity. For larger forces of shorter duration, the same rocks would break like brittle solids. Thus either folding or faulting might occur depending on the rate at which the deforming forces acted. Unfortunately, the effect of time on rock deformation has been little studied because laboratory experiments cannot duplicate the effects of small forces acting on rocks for thousands or millions of years.

SUMMARY OUTLINE

ROCKS OF THE CRUST

6.1 Continents and ocean basins: Crustal rocks show a basic division into high-standing continents and low-lying ocean basins.

6.2 Continental rocks: Continents are composed mostly of granite and granitic gneiss covered by a thin veneer of sedimentary rocks; most of these rocks now occupy positions quite different from their sites of origin.

MODES OF ROCK DEFORMATION

6.3 Faults: Crustal rocks may be dislocated to produce strike-slip, dip-slip, or oblique-slip movements.

6.4 Folds: Anticlines are archlike folds, and synclines the troughlike folds.

6.5 Geologic maps and structure sections: These depict the distribution, relative age, and geometry of different rock units (formations).

6.6 Experimental rock deformation: Folding occurs only when rocks are made ductile by burial at high temperatures and pressures.

ADDITIONAL READINGS

BILLINGS, M. P.: *Structural Geology*, 3rd ed. Prentice-Hall, Inc., Englewood Cliffs, N.J., 1972. A standard intermediate text on crustal folds, faults, and mountain building.

*CAILLEAUX, A.: *Anatomy of the Earth*, McGraw-Hill Book Company, New York, 1968. A popular introduction to the solid earth, emphasizing crustal rocks and structures.

*CLARK S. P., JR.: *Structure of the Earth*, Prentice-Hall, Inc., Englewood Cliffs, N.J., 1971. Chapter 2 provides a good summary of crustal structures.

COOK, F. A., L. D. BROWN, and J. E. OLIVER: "The Southern Appalachians and the Growth of Continents," *Scientific American*, October 1980.

* Available in paperback.

Different Styles of Deformation
Affecting the Eastern United States

(THE APPALACHIANS: THEN AND NOW)

There are no high-standing mountain ranges in the eastern part of the United States—at least not now. In the geologic past, however, there certainly were, and furthermore, they appeared more than once and displayed different styles of deformation. In this brief section we will discuss the origin of two *major* pulses of mountain building that affected this region. We can describe them in terms of accordianlike movements between large lithospheric plates. The plates involved were ancestors of what today we call the North American Plate and the European Plate.

Figure 6.25 reconstructs a simplified model for an accordianlike sequence of opening-closing-opening that took place between regions now located on opposite sides of the Atlantic Ocean during the past 570 million years. This process began in early Paleozoic time and is continuing still today. Figure 6.25(a) shows the initial early Paleozoic breakup. Lithosphere was being created then, much in the same fashion as is currently going on in the mid-Atlantic. Cambrian and Ordovician age sedimentary rocks were deposited along the training edges of the two separating continents [Figure 6.25(b)].

The first of the two major deformations affecting the eastern United States was triggered when the proto-Atlantic began to close. This happened in late Ordovician time [Figure 6.25(c)]. Because of compressive stresses associated with the subduction zone that was formed beneath the ancestral Appalachians during this closing, strong folding, reverse faulting, and magmatism continued episodically throughout the Paleozoic. Finally, the proto-Atlantic became completely closed near the end of the era [Figures 6.25(d) and 6.26(a)]. By this time, high-standing mountains had been formed.

A few tens of millions of years later when rifting between North America and Europe again resumed (during late Triassic time), *tensional stresses* were applied to the then deeply eroded Appalachians. These new stresses caused normal faulting to occur. Continental sediments (red sandstones, conglomerates, and shales) as well as basaltic volcanics and intrusive dikes and sills were em-

FIGURE 6.25 See text for discussion. (After Robert S. Dietz, "Geosynclines, Mountains and Continent-building," March, Copyright © 1972 by Scientific American, Inc. All rights reserved.)

FIGURE 6.26   Formation of the Newark Deposits. (See text.)

FIGURE 6.27   Distribution of Newark deposits of late Triassic age.

placed within the fault-generated troughs formed during this episode of block-faulting [Figures 6.25(e) and 6.26(b) and (c)]. New
mountains were formed, but they were not the result of folding,
as were those formed in the late Paleozoic. As erosion has continued
until the present day, we find only isolated remnants of the Triassic
sediments and volcanics (the Newark deposits). Figure 6.27 shows
the current distribution of these rocks along the east coast of the
United States. High-standing mountains are no longer there, but
careful geologic mapping makes it clear that on at least two occasions
in the past, the topographic setting was very different. Additionally,
our recently achieved understanding of plate tectonics enables us
to reconstruct the global movements that gave rise to these ancestral
mountains in the Appalachian region.

7

Seismology and Other Geophysics

THE ONLY ROCKS AND MINERALS that earth scientists can study *directly* are those exposed on the earth's surface and those that can be sampled in mines and bore holes. The deepest mines extend downward only about 3 kilometers (2 miles), and the deepest bore hole drilled to date (an oil well in Texas) reached a depth of about 8 km (5 mi). Since the earth's radius is almost 6,400 km (4,000 mi), clearly only its most superficial skin can be directly sampled (Figure 7.1). For this reason, our understanding of the earth's interior depends on various indirect clues, most of which are provided by four physical properties: its *wave transmission, heat transmission, magnetism* and, *gravity*. Each of these can be measured at the surface and then used to infer characteristics of the materials below. By combining evidence from these properties, geophysicists have developed a model for the structure and composition of the earth's vast interior; the nature of this model and the supporting evidence for it will be the subject of this chapter.

EARTHQUAKES AND THE EARTH'S INTERIOR

The most important clues to the earth's interior are provided by the manner in which various shock waves are transmitted through the body of the earth. Such shock waves have two sources: some result from man-made explosions of dynamite or nuclear devices; the largest, however, are caused by natural phenomena such as volcanic eruptions or faulting in the lithosphere. Large earthquakes, when they occur in densely populated regions, are among the most devastating natural phenomena on earth. Later we shall introduce techniques for measuring the sizes of earthquakes and also discuss the variety of hazards they pose for man.

In general, shock waves from explosions are most useful for determining relatively local properties of the earth's crust, whereas earthquakes may reveal both small- and large-scale patterns of the earth's internal structure. Indeed, the study of earthquake wave transmission has provided more information about the earth's interior than have clues from the properties of gravity, magnetism, and heat transmission combined.

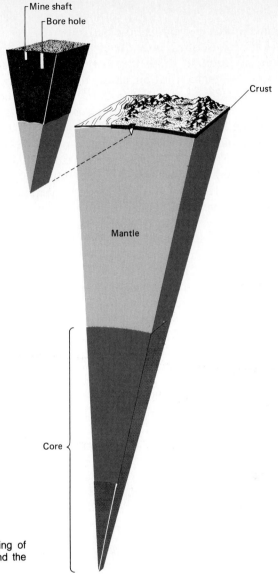

FIGURE 7.1 Scale drawing of a deep mine, bore hole, and the earth's interior.

Mine shaft
Bore hole
Crust
Mantle
Core

EARTHQUAKE WAVES

The rock movements responsible for earthquakes are not randomly distributed throughout the solid earth but occur only in the lithosphere, which even in subduction zones extends downward no more than 700 km (400 mi), a little over 10 percent of the distance to the center of the earth (Figure 7.1). Only a few earthquakes occur at depths as great as 700 km; most take place in the outermost 70 km representing only about 1 percent of the radius of the earth. In addition to these depth restrictions, earthquakes show a geographic concentration along three great belts. Most large earthquakes, and virtually all of those occurring at depths below 300 km (180 mi), take place in a zone around the edges of the Pacific Ocean where subduction is occurring; a second zone of smaller earthquakes occurs along chains of submerged mountains that extend through the ocean basins; a third zone borders the Mediterranean and southern Asia (Figure 7.2).

Earthquakes arising in these regions cause various kinds of shock waves to move upon and through the earth three-dimensionally in much the same way that surface waves and ripples are caused by dropping a pebble into quiet water. These waves, known collectively as **seismic waves**, are of three principal kinds: **body waves**, which travel from the source or focus of the earthquake through the main mass of the earth to emerge at the surface; **surface waves**, generated at the earth's surface above the focus of a large earthquake when body waves strike, which travel only in the outermost layers of the earth; and **free oscillations**, vibrations of the earth as a whole, caused by only the largest earthquakes, which can be likened to

FIGURE 7.2 Locations of epicenters for all earthquakes recorded from 1961 through 1969. (From National Earthquake Information Center, U.S. Department of Commerce.)

SEISMOLOGY AND OTHER GEOPHYSICS

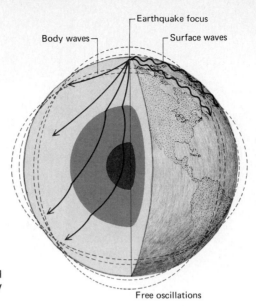

Body waves —
Earthquake focus
Surface waves

Free oscillations

FIGURE 7.3 The three principal types of seismic waves: body waves, and free oscillations.

the vibrations of a bell when struck by a hammer (Figure 7.3). Most of our knowledge of the earth's interior has come from study of body waves, but in recent years, analyses of surface waves have provided additional information, particularly about the outermost layers of the earth. Free oscillations were first recorded by special instruments after the disastrous Chilean earthquake of 1960, although their existence had been predicted earlier. Like surface waves, they are useful in interpreting the structure of the earth's outermost layers, but they also provide some independent clues to the deep interior. All three wave types are measured by sensitive instruments called seismographs, which, when anchored to solid rock, record even the slightest earth shocks (Figure 7.4). Universities and government research institutes have established around the world about 150 major *seismic observatories* containing such instruments, and these are the principal source of information on earthquake wave transmission.

Earthquake body waves, on which most of our knowledge of the earth's deep interior rests, can be subdivided into two types known as primary (P) and secondary (S) waves. In P waves, the individual particles of the material through which the wave travels are elastically vibrated *back and forth* in the direction of wave movement; in S waves, the particles are sheared *sideways*, at right angles to the direction of wave motion (Figure 7.5). Because of these different motions, the two waves move at different speeds: In the same material, S waves travel only about half as fast as P waves. The names reflect this fact, for "primary" P waves arrive at distant

(a)

(b)

FIGURE 7.4   Seismographs. (a) Schematic diagram. Earthquake waves cause movements of the underlying rock and attached support; the weight tends to remain stationary while the pen records the motion. (b) A seismograph registering a large, distant earthquake. (United Kingdom Atomic Energy Authority.)

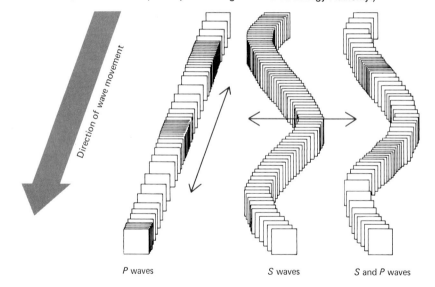

FIGURE 7.5   Schematic representations of the motions of P and S waves as they pass through the body of the earth.

seismic observatories before "secondary" S waves from the same earthquake. In addition to these inherent velocity differences, the speed at which *both* waves move depends on the physical properties, particularly the density and rigidity, of the materials they are passing through. Both types move faster as the density decreases and the rigidity increases. Because of this influence on velocity, P and S waves are bent or *refracted* at the boundaries of layers with differing densities or rigidities, just as light waves are bent in passing from less dense air into more dense glass (Figure 7.6).

One easy way to visualize the bending of waves (seismic, light, water, etc.) is to employ a model proposed in the seventeenth century by the Dutch physicist Christian Huygens. Figure 7.6(a) depicts a seismic wave front striking a rock boundary on opposite sides of which the waves will move at different velocities. Refraction (bending) occurs because the end of the wave front that first reaches the boundary experiences "drag," or slowing, while the other end is still moving at the original velocity. This is much like having your left front automobile tire catch in a deep puddle: It is dragged, and your car swerves to the left [Figure 7.6(b)]. Like light waves, seismic waves may also be *reflected* from reflecting boundaries without penetration. Because of both reflections and refractions, the earthquake body waves reaching a distant seismic observatory consist not only of simple P and S waves that have traveled by the most direct route but also of dozens of additional waves that have reached the station by more circuitous reflected and refracted paths.

How might we record and analyze these many seismic waves? If we want to make a permanent record of a visual experience,

(a)

(b)

FIGURE 7.6 Wave refraction. (a) Wavefront A-B progresses as indicated by arroys. A travels only to A' during the time B goes to B', because the B end of the wavefront is traveling faster. By the time of A"–B", complete refraction of this wavefront has occurred. (b) Sketch showing a similar response as an automobile strikes a mud puddle with one front tire before the other.

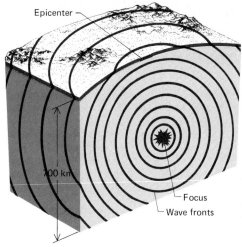

FIGURE 7.7 Relative locations of focus and epicenter (point on earth's surface directly above focus) of an earthquake. Earthquake foci do not occur below 700 km because rigid lithosphere becomes plastic beneath that depth.

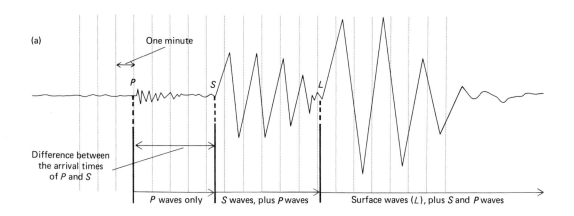

(a)

One minute

P

S

L

Difference between the arrival times of *P* and *S*

P waves only   *S* waves, plus *P* waves   Surface waves (*L*), plus *S* and *P* waves

(b)

L

S

P

Time (minutes)

difference between arrival times of P and S for two different earthquakes.

0

Distance (kilometers or miles)

FIGURE 7.8 (a) Diagrammatic seismogram showing the first arrivals of *P,S,* and *L* waves. (b) Travel time curves: these curves are compilations of many years experience relating the time taken by *P, S,* and *L* waves to travel known epicentral distances. It can be seen that the farther the seismic waves travel, the greater will be the time gap between the arrival of *P* and *S* waves. Thus, the epicentral distance is proportional to this time difference and can be determined from it.

we use a special instrument—a camera—to do so. Once the photographic record has been made, it can be studied carefully to discover and interpret its contents. Similarly it is necessary to acquire recordings, called **seismograms**, of earthquakes in order better to "see" the earth's interior. Seismograms are also our principal means of locating the **epicenter** (the point on the earth's surface directly above the **focus**) and *focus depth* (Figure 7.7) for an individual earthquake. Figure 7.8(a) depicts a seismogram of a distant earthquake. It can be used in the manner shown in Figure 7.8(b) to determine how far away from the seismographic station the earthquake occurred.

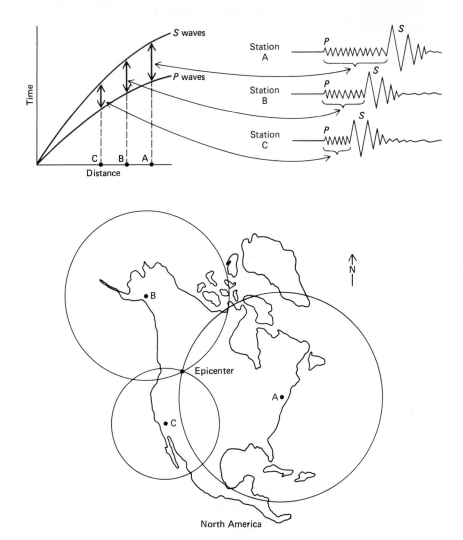

FIGURE 7.9   Location of an epicenter. The epicentral distances from the three seismographic stations (A, B, and C: the epicenter.)

Once the distances from three or more widely spaced seismo-graphic stations to an earthquake epicenter become known, a good approximation of the geographic location of that epicenter can be determined in the manner shown in Figure 7.9.

7.2
ELASTIC REBOUND THEORY

We have described the properties of seismic waves and how records of these waves have been analyzed to yield travel-time curves. In the following section we shall show how such data can be interpreted to generate a *model* for the earth's interior. Before doing that, how-ever, one important question remains: What is the principal *cause* of earthquakes? At the beginning of this chapter we suggested that faulting is the principal answer to that question. In other words, the energy of most earthquakes is believed to come from tectonic interactions. Early in this century, following a careful analysis of ground survey data for the region around San Francisco from before and after the great 1906 earthquake there, H. F. Reid* proposed the elastic rebound theory as the mechanism for generating that earthquake. Since then, most geologists have come to accept this model as essentially valid for most earthquakes, although certain variations and exceptions are still under study. Figure 7.10 shows a sequence of crustal configurations from an unstrained state, through the accumulation of elastic strain, to the rupturing of the rock, allowing it to rebound to an unstrained state. Here, then, we have elastic rebound as the cause of faulting, and the faulting as the cause of the earthquake. You can visualize an analogy to this process by slowly stretching a rubber band until it breaks. The only rapid movement occurs when the two elastically strained pieces rebound back to equilibrium. You are made aware that energy has been released by the accompanying sound and the sting of the pieces as they snap against your fingers.

Our model of plate tectonics suggests that plate boundaries are the principal places where rocks interact with each other and thus become strained. The strained rocks eventually rupture and rebound, thus generating earthquakes. Figure 7.2 plots worldwide epicenters over a five-year span of time, and indeed their locations define the margins of lithospheric plates very well. As mentioned briefly in Chapter 1, spreading ridges, subduction zones, and trans-form faults are the three kinds of plate margins, and earthquakes are generated at all of them. In the next section we will discuss

---

* A professor of Geology from Johns Hopkins University visiting at the University of California at Berkeley.

SEISMOLOGY AND OTHER GEOPHYSICS

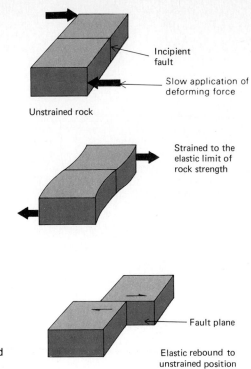

Incipient
fault

Slow application of
deforming force

Unstrained rock

Strained to the
elastic limit of
rock strength

Fault plane

FIGURE 7.10 Elastic rebound
theory of faulting.

Elastic rebound to
unstrained position

earthquake strength, but for now, it should be mentioned that the very largest shocks occur only where two plates are converging. We call these places **subduction zones,** and they are not only where the greatest earthquakes occur but also are the sites of the only seismic events that are located deeper than about 70 km.

When the geometry of these deep earthquakes was first discussed by Hugo Benioff, a seismologist, at the California Institute of Technology, in 1954, the plate tectonic model had not yet come into existence; hence notions of subduction zones and lithosphere were nonexistent. It was recognized that earthquake foci sometimes occurred as deep as 700 km, and that when many foci that were known from observations over a period of years were plotted on a cross section of an active earthquake region, an inclined zone of earthquakes was defined (Figure 7.11). A satisfactory explanation for these **Benioff Zones,** as they became called, was lacking. Today we recognize that Benioff Zones are the regions where rock is rigid enough to store elastic strain. Such rigidity is found only in lithosphere, and since lithosphere is only 60 km–100 km thick, earthquakes deeper than 100 km occur only when lithosphere has been subducted. Benioff Zones, in other words, are subduction zones in the modern terminology of plate tectonics.

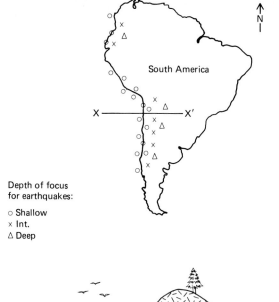

South America

Depth of focus
for earthquakes:

○ Shallow
× Int.
△ Deep

Benioff Zone

FIGURE 7.11   Map and cross section showing a Benioff zone. This is a region of inclined earthquake foci, occurring within subducting lithosphere.

7.3
MEASURING EARTHQUAKE STRENGTH

There are two approaches to measuring the strength of an earthquake. One involves instrumentally recorded seismograms, and the other depends on assessments of how much damage was done. Inasmuch as the amount of ground motion generated near the focus of an earthquake, and hence its potential for damage, dies out with distance traveled, two scales of measurement have been developed: one, called *magnitude*, describes maximum ground movement *at the focus*; the other, *intensity*, describes the amount of damage done at *any* geographical location. **Magnitude** is a measure of how much motion would be recorded by a "standard" seismograph at a fixed distance from an earthquake focus. Any seismogram can be interpreted to determine magnitude if the focal distance of the earthquake is known and if the recording instrument has been calibrated with respect to the standard instrument. Thus, although a seismograph in San Francisco would record less ground motion for an Alaskan earthquake than would appear on a seismogram recorded in Seattle, seismologists in both cities, using accepted procedure, would assign essentially the same magnitude value to the earthquake. The relationship of less ground motion as a function of greater distance explains how seismographic stations all around the world can determine the same value for an earthquake's magnitude, even if the seismic vibrations are too faint to be felt by humans. Magnitude, then, is an absolute measure of the energy liberated by an earthquake, and its determination depends solely on the analysis of seismograms.

The first magnitude scale to be applied successfully was developed by U.S. seismologist Charles Richter* in 1935. His pioneering work dealt with local earthquakes in the seismically active region of southern California. Richter's magnitude, designated M_L (for local earthquakes), was so successful that a colleague named Beno Gutenburg applied the approach to larger, more distant earthquakes. By doing this he created another magnitude scale, M_s, based on the size of *surface waves* recorded on a seismogram. These larger waves can be recorded all over the world when a large earthquake occurs, so the M_s scale greatly extended the range of Richter's original magnitude scale. The magnitude assigned to any given earthquake is a numerical value determined from the amount of ground motion produced by that seismic event. The great 1906 San Francisco earthquake, for example, was 8.3, whereas the Hebgen Lake temblor near Yellowstone Park in 1959 was 7.1 [see Chapter 12, Figure 12.17(a) and (e)]. The largest earthquakes ever recorded had values of 8.6 on this scale, whereas the smallest that can be felt by humans are in the vicinity of 2.5.

The numerical values of the magnitude scale are logarithms of the amount of ground motion. The significance of this is that the relationships between magnitude, ground motion, and energy generated at the focus are not simple geometrical proportions. Without pursuing the mathematics, we can summarize the relationships as follows:

* A professor of seismology at the California Institute of Technology.

Each magnitude numeral represents 10 times the amount of ground motion and approximately 31.5 times the amount of energy as the next lower numeral.

Thus an earthquake of magnitude 8 releases about 1,000 times as much energy (31.5 × 31.5) as a magnitude-6 event.

Recently seismologists recognized that some earthquakes liberated far more energy than others, yet their magnitudes (based on surface waves) were essentially the same. We know now that when a fault surface ruptures for a length greater than about 60 km, the size of the surface wave does not increase even though more and more energy is released as the fault rupture becomes longer and longer. Since magnitude is based on the maximum size of surface waves recorded, earthquakes caused by extensive fault rupture, and therefore a great release of energy, appear not to differ from earthquakes having a more modest amount of energy release. To deal with this problem a new concept, called the **seismic moment** (M_0), has been introduced. M_0 is the product of three characteristics of the earthquake-producing fault: its surface area, its average displacement, and the rigidity of the rocks affected. After basic corrections are made, M_0 can be determined directly from certain waves recorded on seismograms of great earthquakes. Today many seismologists prefer to characterize the size of an earthquake by *seismic moment* (M_0) rather than *magnitude* (M_s) because of its more nearly accurate measure of the energy released. This move to define a new magnitude scale is an example of the evolving nature of science. As our understanding increases, our needs for new tools emerge. Popular accounts, however, such as those reported by the news media, will no doubt continue to use a magnitude scale patterned after the early work of Charles Richter since we have become familiar with this approach.

Prior to the development of an instrumental technique for assessing an earthquake's strength, the only widely used approach involved field evaluations of its effects: Was it felt by most people? Were they frightened? Did buildings collapse? Did water splash over river banks? These kinds of questions were asked in order to ascertain an earthquake's **intensity**. Today American geologists use the Modified Mercalli Intensity Scale (Figure 7.12), adapted to North American conditions from a scale originally designed for use in Italy. Following an earthquake, investigators frequently compile data on its effects in order to prepare **isoseismal maps** (Figure 7.13), which are a graphic means of delineating regions of varying intensities. Under ordinary circumstances, the epicenter of an earthquake is approximately coincident with the central region of highest intensity. Indeed, prior to instrumental techniques for locating epicenters (see Section 7.1 and Figure 7.9), using this rule of thumb was the only method for locating epicenters.

FIGURE 7.12 Modified Mercalli Scale of earthquake intensity. (After Hodgson, 1964.)

The Modified Mercalli Scale

I Not felt except by a very few under especially favorable circumstances.

II Felt only by a few persons at rest, especially on upper floors of buildings. Delicately suspended objects may swing.

III Felt quite noticeably indoors, especially on upper floors of buildings, but many people do not recognize it as an earthquake. Standing motor cars may rock slightly. Vibration like passing truck. Duration estimated.

IV During the day felt indoors by many, outdoors by few. At night some awakened. Dishes, windows, doors disturbed; walls make creaking sound. Sensation like heavy truck striking building. Standing motor cars rocked noticeably.

V Felt by nearly everyone; many awakened. Some dishes, windows, etc., broken; a few instances of cracked plaster; unstable objects overturned. Disturbances of trees, poles, and other tall objects sometimes noticed. Pendulum clocks may stop.

VI Felt by all; many frightened and run outdoors. Some heavy furniture moved; a few instances of fallen plaster or damaged chimneys. Damage slight.

VII Everybody runs outdoors. Damage negligible in buildings of good design and construction; slight to moderate in well-built ordinary structures; considerable in poorly built or badly designed structures; some chimneys broken. Noticed by persons driving motor cars.

VIII Damage slight in specially designed structures; considerable in ordinary substantial buildings, with partial collapse; great in poorly built structures. Panel walls thrown out of frame structures. Fall of chimneys, factory stacks, columns, monuments, walls. Heavy furniture overturned. Sand and mud ejected in small amounts. Changes in well water. Disturbs persons driving motor cars.

IX Damage considerable in specially designed structures; well-designed frame structures thrown out of plumb; great in substantial buildings, with partial collapse. Buildings shifted off foundations. Ground cracked conspicuously. Underground pipes broken.

X Some well-built, wooden structures destroyed; most masonry and frame structures destroyed with foundations; ground badly cracked. Rails bent. Landslides considerable from river banks and steep slopes. Shifted sand and mud. Water splashed over banks.

XI Few, if any, (masonry) structures remain standing. Bridges destroyed. Broad fissures in ground. Underground pipelines completely out of service. Earth slumps and land slips in soft ground. Rails bent greatly.

XII Damage total. Waves seen on ground surfaces. Lines of sight and level distorted. Objects thrown upward into the air.

FIGURE 7.13 Isoseismal map of earthquake, San Francisco, 1957, Richter magnitude 5.3. (From California Division of Mines and Geology Special Report 57.)

7.4
THE EARTH'S INTERIOR

Observations on the arrival time of seismic waves coming from thousands of different earthquakes recorded at many observatories have also provided data for the calculation of **velocity-depth curves,** which show the change in speed of both *P* and *S* waves as they go deeper into the earth. These curves, shown in Figure 7.14, are the primary tools used for interpreting the earth's interior. See Box 7.1.

The velocity-depth curves of Figure 7.14 show three depths at which earthquake wave velocities abruptly change: one at the

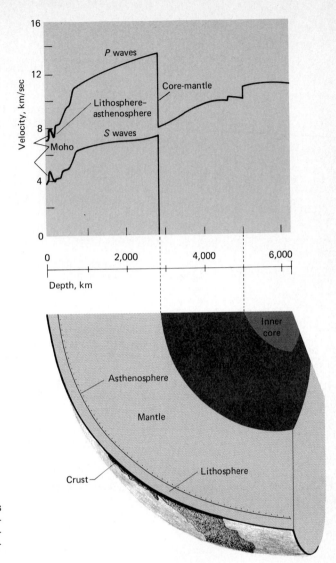

FIGURE 7.14 Velocity-depth curves for *P* and *S* waves (above) and the inferred internal structure of the earth (below). (Data from Anderson, et al., "Science," vol. 171, 1971.)

relatively shallow depth of about 16 km (10 mi) (marked "Moho"); another at about 100 km (marked "lithosphere-asthenosphere"); and another much deeper, at about 2,900 km (1,800 mi) (marked "core-mantle"), or about halfway to the earth's center. Such abrupt velocity changes are called **seismic discontinuities**. They clearly show that the materials of the earth's interior are not uniform in density and rigidity. Instead, the major discontinuities define concentric layers with differing properties: a thin outer **crust**, a central **core**, and a thick **mantle** lying between the crust and core. The mantle makes up about 80 percent of the earth's total volume, the core about 19 percent, and the crust only about 1 percent. A region called

BOX 7.1

Formulas Describing Relationships between Seismic Wave Velocities and Physical Properties of Rocks

Two relatively simple formulas describing the relationship between seismic wave velocities for *P* waves and *S* waves and the physical properties of rocks through which they travel within the earth have been determined as follows:

$$V_p = \sqrt{\frac{k + 4/3\mu}{\rho}} \qquad V_s = \sqrt{\frac{\mu}{\rho}}$$

k = incompressibility (water is less compressible than air)
μ = rigidity (steel is more rigid than butter)
ρ = density (basalt is more dense than granite)

It is not necessary to go very far into the mathematics of the equations above to see that increases in rock density (ρ) should have the effect of reducing seismic velocities (note that ρ is in the denominator for both V_p and V_s). Yet we know from general experience that more dense rocks transmit both *P* waves and *S* waves faster than less dense rocks—seismic velocities are greater in basalt than in granite. This apparent contradiction is explained by the fact that the influence of rigidity in *increasing* velocities is greater than that of density in *decreasing* them. In other words, a rock that is more dense is also more rigid, and the effect of the rigidity is greater, so seismic waves travel faster in more dense rocks *in spite of* the greater density rather than because of it.

---

the **lithosphere**, in which the crust is embedded, is now recognized as having particular importance in Plate Tectonics. We will discuss this importance more fully in Chapter 8.

The outer discontinuity, that separating the crust and mantle, was discovered in 1909 by the Serbian geophysicist Andrija Mohorovičić. It has since come to be known as the **Mohorovičić discontinuity**, commonly abbreviated "Moho." The Moho seismic discontinuity provides the principal evidence that the rocks and minerals exposed on the earth's surface are but a thin veneer or "crust" overlying a much larger volume of materials with differing properties—the mantle and core.

The most abrupt major discontinuity, first recognized in 1924, is commonly referred to as the **core-mantle discontinuity**. Note in Figure 7.14 that not only does the velocity of *P* waves decrease dramatically at this discontinuity, but *S* waves *stop completely* at that depth—that is, they do not penetrate the core. This fact is of prime importance because *S* waves, you will recall, result from a *sidewise shearing* movement within the transmitting medium. Unlike the *pushing* motions of *P* waves, which can be transmitted through both solids and liquids, *S* waves can be transmitted only in solids, where the particles have enough adhesion to be pulled by one another. Liquids, of course, lack such adhesion and therefore do not transmit *S* waves. The lack of *S* wave transmission through the core provides strong evidence that at least the *core is liquid*, whereas the transmission of both *P* and *S* waves through the crust and mantle indicates that both the *crust and mantle are composed of solid materials*. To speak of "the solid earth" is therefore something of an oversimplification, since only the outer four-fifths of the earth's volume demonstrably is made up of solid materials.

In addition to the major seismic discontinuities defined by sharp breaks in the velocity-depth curves, minor discontinuities occur at several depths where the curves show less abrupt changes (Figure 7.14). These minor discontinuities provide additional clues to the structure of the core and mantle.

7.5
INTERNAL DENSITIES, PRESSURES, AND TEMPERATURES

We have noted that the velocity of *P* and *S* waves is dependent on both the density and the rigidity of the materials through which they pass. Neither of these properties can be directly measured for materials deep within the earth, and thus it is not completely certain whether the velocity changes seen in the velocity-depth curves result from changes in one or the other property, or both. Calculations based on the earth's gravity show, however, that the *average density* of the *entire* earth is about 5.5 grams per cubic centimeter (g/cm³). This figure puts a restriction on the densities of the material in the mantle and core (since the crust makes up only about 1 percent of the earth's volume, it can be effectively ignored), for together they must have this average density. Because of this restriction and certain others caused by the manner in which the earth wobbles on its axis of rotation, it is possible to construct a reasonable model of the density distribution within the earth that is consistent with the velocity-depth curves. Such a model is shown in Figure 7.15(a). Note that the densities of the mantle materials increase from the crustal value of 2.8 to about 5 at the base of the mantle. Then there is a sharp density increase to about 10 at the boundary of the core, and thereafter an increase from 10 to about 12 at the center of the earth. The average of these values, based on the different volumes of mantle and core material, is 5.5.

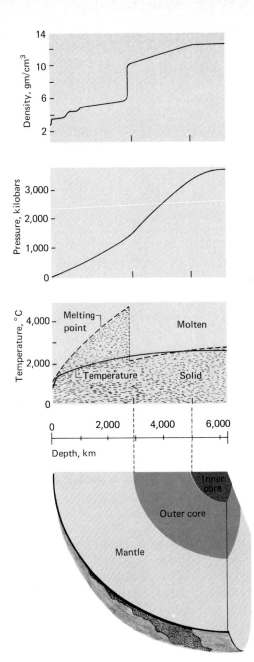

FIGURE 7.15 Inferred densities (a), pressures (b), and temperatures (c) of the earth's interior. (Data from Stacey, ''Physics of the Earth,'' 1969; Verhoogen, ''American Scientist,'' vol. 48, 1960.)

From the density curves, it is then possible to calculate the probable increase in pressure downward, which varies with both the amount and density of the overlying material. Such calculations show a steady pressure increase, from atmospheric pressure at the surface, to pressures about 1,000 times as great at the base of the crust and over 3 *million* times as great at the earth's center [Figure 7.15(b)]. These internal density and pressure curves are derived from the earthquake wave velocity-depth curves (Figure 7.14), but it should be stressed that these determinations also require educated guesses about the composition and elastic properties of the earth's interior materials and are therefore less certain than are the velocity-depth curves themselves, which are based on direct records of earthquake wave velocities.

Earthquake wave data provide little information about still another fundamental property of the earth's interior: its range of temperatures. The most obvious and important temperature inference that can be made from the velocity-depth curves is that the materials of the mantle, as solids, must be cooler than their melting point; whereas the materials of the core, as liquids, must be heated beyond their melting point.

Additional clues to the earth's internal temperatures are provided by still another physical property that can be measured at the surface: the manner in which heat is transmitted from the earth's warm interior to its cooler surface. Observations in mines and bore holes show that temperatures everywhere increase rapidly downward through the outer few miles of the earth's crust. The rate of this increase varies from place to place, giving rise to differing *temperature gradients*; these range from about 9°C for each kilometer of depth (25°F/mi) to about 52°C/km (150°F/mi), with an average value of about 28°C/km (80°F/mi). Thus at the bottom of some of the deepest bore holes (about 8 km), temperatures are often far above the surface boiling point of water. Below the very shallow zone of direct measurement in mines and bore holes, the earth's internal temperature gradient is poorly understood. The rapid rate of temperature increase seen in the outer crust probably does not persist farther downward, however, for if it did, the materials making up much of the mantle would almost certainly be melted. [Figure 7.15(c) shows one estimated temperature-depth curve that fits this requirement.] The reason temperature increase is so great in the crust is that radioactive nuclides are concentrated there. Uranium, potassium, and rubidium are more abundant in low-density rocks than in high-density ones.

THE CORE AND EARTH MAGNETISM

Studies of earthquake waves show that the earth's interior has a basic threefold division into a thin solid crust, a massive solid mantle, and a central liquid core. As we have seen, earthquake wave data also permit the calculation of the probable densities and pressures within these fundamental units. There are, however, many other things that we would like to know about the earth's interior. For example, the composition and structure of the minerals that compose the mantle and core can only be inferred, for unlike the minerals of the outer crust, these deeper materials cannot be directly sampled. Furthermore, the mantle and core are certainly not uniform and static masses but dynamic units that show variations in their composition and structure. Although much remains to be learned about these variations, geophysicists have combined various indirect clues to arrive at reasonable hypotheses about some of them. For the remainder of the chapter we shall review these clues and hypotheses, beginning with the earth's central core and progressing outward to the mantle and, finally, to the deeper, hidden parts of the earth's crust.

7.6
COMPOSITION OF THE CORE

Seismic evidence indicates that the core is largely composed of a liquid whose probable density ranges from about $10 g/cm^3$ at the outer core margin to about $12 \ g/cm^3$ at the earth's center. Most geophysicists now believe that this liquid is *molten iron*, with small amounts of other molten elements, particularly nickel and either sulfur or silicon, mixed in. Three principal lines of evidence suggest this. Two such factors are discussed in this section; the third will be covered in the next section.

First of all, we know that molten iron has a density of about $7.5 \ g/cm^3$ at the earth's surface, but calculations show that at the extreme pressures encountered in the core, the iron atoms would be forced into a close-packed arrangement with a density slightly higher than that suggested for the core by seismic evidence. The slight discrepancy is believed to be due to small quantities of a lighter element, probably sulfur or silicon, in the liquid iron.

Additional evidence for an iron core is provided by the composition of **meteorites,** fragments of matter from interplanetary space that fall to the earth's surface. The materials in meteorites are believed to be similar to those that long ago consolidated to make the earth and other planets of our solar system (this will be discussed in more detail in Chapter 13). The composition of meteorites should, therefore, be similar to the bulk composition of the earth; that is, the most common elements in meteorites should also be the most common in the earth's core and mantle (recall that the highly variable rocks and minerals of the crust make up only 1 percent of the earth's volume and can be disregarded in considerations of the earth's bulk composition). Meteorites are of two principal kinds:

iron meteorites, composed predominantly of iron, but containing between 5 and 20 percent nickel, and stony meteorites, composed of silicate minerals. The iron meteorites suggest that the earth's core may have a similar composition; in contrast, the stony meteorites may be similar in composition to the earth's mantle.

7.7
EARTH MAGNETISM

The third reason for suggesting that the core is composed of molten iron is based on an important source of indirect evidence about the earth's interior that we have not yet introduced—that provided by surface measurements of the earth's magnetic field. The most familiar demonstration of the earth's magnetism is the common compass, the needle of which is merely a small bar magnet mounted on a swivel so that it may align itself with the earth's magnetic field. Compass observations have long shown that the earth behaves much as if it were a gigantic bar magnet with poles near the axis of rotation (Figure 7.16). Because the earth's magnetic poles are near the rotational poles, the compass needle always aligns itself

FIGURE 7.16 A generalized view of the earth's magnetic field. The magnetism is believed to be caused by motions within the liquid iron core.

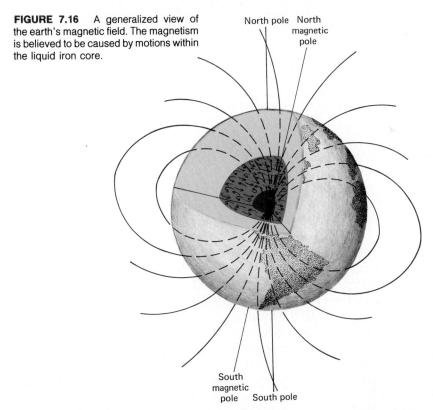

North pole North magnetic pole

South magnetic pole South pole

(a) Fixed eyepiece

Scale

Mirror

Balanced magnet

(b)

FIGURE 7.17 Magnetometers. (a) Schematic diagram. A balanced magnet moves either up or down with slight changes in the earth's magnetic field; the position of the magnet is read by means of the eyepiece, mirror and scale. More complex electronic magnetometers are commonly used for surveying large areas. (b) A simple magnetometer in use. (Texas Instruments.)

in approximately a north-south direction, unless interfered with by strong local magnetic anomalies.

The exact strength and direction of the earth's magnetic field at different points on the surface are measured by sensitive instruments called **magnetometers,** which can be used on land, at sea, or even in moving airplanes for rapid surveys of large areas (Figure 7.17). Such measurements show that the earth's overall magnetic field consists of two components that can be analyzed separately to yield different kinds of information. The largest component, the **main magnetic field,** originates deep within the earth and is a principal source of information about the interior. The second, much smaller component originates from the distribution of magnetic minerals, primarily magnetite (Fe_3O_4), in the earth's outer crust; this is of great value in understanding crustal composition and structure.

The origin of the main magnetic field is far more difficult to understand than is the simple magnetism caused by magnetic minerals in the outer crust. The main internal field cannot have such a source, for when magnetic minerals are heated, they quickly reach a temperature, known as the **Curie temperature,** at which they lose their magnetism yet still remain solid. Curie temperatures are usually far lower than the melting temperatures of minerals, and are also far lower than the temperatures to be expected in the solid mantle. For these reasons, any solid magnetic minerals present below the cool outer crust have almost certainly lost their magnetism and cannot be a source of the main magnetic field. There remains, however, one other potential source of internal magnetism—that associated with electrical currents (Figure 7.18).

All electrical currents have associated magnetic fields. An electric current flowing through a wire will affect a compass needle placed near the wire. If there were some means by which electrical currents were generated deep within the earth, the main magnetic field could be understood as a direct natural consequence. The silicate minerals that make up the crust and, probably, most of the mantle are poor electrical conductors and thus are unlikely sources of electric currents and electromagnetism. Iron, on the other hand, is an excellent conductor, and thus motions in a core of fluid iron (see Figure 7.19) might well create both electrical currents and the main magnetic field. This possibility adds additional strength to the suggestion that the core is, indeed, composed of molten iron.

One final bit of information about the structure of the core is provided not by magnetic data but by earthquake wave transmission. The *P* wave velocity-depth curve of Figure 7.14 shows a relatively sharp velocity change within the core at a depth of about 5,000 km (3,200 mi). This discontinuity indicates a change in physical properties in the innermost part of the core; the small spherical inner core defined by this discontinuity is generally considered to be under such intense pressures that the iron atoms are closely compressed and respond as a solid, rather than as a liquid as does

FIGURE 7.18 The magnetic field produced by a loop of wire carrying an electric current is similar to that produced by a bar magnet.

Wire carrying
electric current

(a) 1922

(b) 1942

FIGURE 7.19 Westward drift of the residual field from 1922 to 1942. Strong positive values of the residual field are shown in color; strong negative values in gray. Note the slight westward shift of patterns during the 20-year interval. (From Vestine et al., Description of the Main Magnetic Field, 1947.)

the bulk of the core. Such a solid inner core would best account for the observed velocities and patterns of wave transmission, but the evidence is still far from conclusive.

THE MANTLE

The mantle makes up about 80 percent of the volume of the solid earth, but because the average density of mantle material is about half that of the underlying core, the mantle accounts for about 67 percent of the earth's total mass. Besides occupying most of the earth's interior volume and contributing two-thirds of its total mass, the mantle is of extraordinary importance because its properties have largely determined the nature of the crust that overlies it. Direct studies of crustal rocks thus provide some clues to the hidden mantle, but as with the core, most of our understanding of mantle composition and structure is based on indirect evidence.

Unlike the liquid iron of the core, the solid mantle is believed to be composed predominantly of silicate minerals, just as are the more familiar rocks of the crust. This composition is indicated by three lines of evidence. The principal evidence of mantle composition is provided by meteorites that, as mentioned earlier, are of two principal types: iron meteorites, whose composition is probably similar to that of the core; and stony meteorites, composed of silicate minerals. Because there are compelling reasons for believing that meteorites are similar to the materials that originally consolidated to make the earth, stony meteorites may well reflect the general composition of the huge volume of material in the mantle. Stony meteorites do not in fact show the variety of compositions seen in crustal rocks; instead, they are composed largely of the silicate minerals *olivine* and *pyroxene* and are similar in composition to the relatively rare ultramafic rocks found in the crust. This suggests that the bulk of the earth's mantle may have an ultramafic composition.

The second kind of evidence of mantle composition is provided by laboratory experiments on the wave transmission characteristics of various silicate minerals at high temperatures and pressures. Such studies show that most crustal rocks transmit seismic waves too slowly to account for the velocities observed in the mantle [Figure 7.20(a)]. There are, however, various mixtures of dense silicate min-

FIGURE 7.20 Mantle composition. (a) Seismic wave velocity (color) and inferred density (gray) of the mantle, at a depth of about 200 km, compared to those for the two principal crustal rocks—granite and basalt. (Data from Clark, Geological Society of America Memoir 97, 1966.) (b) Seismic wave velocity (color) and inferred density (gray) of the mantle, at a depth of about 200 km, are identical to those of laboratory mixtures of olivine, pyroxene, and garnet. Such mixtures in the proportions shown, are called pyrolite. (Data from Anderson et al., "Science," vol. 171, 1971.)

(a)

(b)

(c)

FIGURE 7.21 "Diamond pipes," cone-shaped masses of ultramafic rock that are believed to represent materials of the upper mantle forced upward into the crust and exposed today at the earth's surface. (a) Schematic cross section. (b) Ultramafic rock being mined near the surface in South Africa. (c) A deep diamond pipe, the abandoned Kimberly diamond mine in South Africa. The ultramafic rocks below the thick, overlying soil were dug out, crushed and screened to remove the diamonds. (b: De Beer Consolidated Mine; c: Bob Landry.)

244   SEISMOLOGY AND OTHER GEOPHYSICS

erals that have mantlelike wave transmission properties, and among these are mixtures dominated by olivine and pyroxene. The properties of one such mixture, called *pyrolite*, are shown in Figure 7.20(b). This experimental work therefore supports the inference, based on examining the composition of meteorites, that olivine and pyroxene make up much of the mantle, at least in its outermost parts.

The final form of evidence of mantle composition comes from rare occurrences at the earth's surface of olivine- and pyroxene-rich ultramafic rocks that are believed to have crystallized in the upper mantle (Figure 7.21). These rocks contain small amounts of certain minerals (diamond, for example) that can form only under extremely high pressures—pressures greater than those normally encountered in the crust. Such minerals suggest that the ultramafic rocks originated in the upper mantle and were then somehow transported into the overlying crust, where they are exposed today on or near the earth's surface.

7.9

MANTLE STRUCTURE

Recent seismic studies indicate that the mantle is not uniform throughout but instead shows both horizontal and vertical changes in seismic properties. Figure 7.22 shows a modern survey of *P* wave

FIGURE 7.22   Seismic wave velocities and inferred structure and composition of the outer 1,000 km of the mantle. (P wave data from Knopoff, "Science," vol. 163, 1969.)

velocities through the upper 800 km (500 mi) of the mantle, the region lying closest to the earth's surface, which can be studied with high precision by seismic techniques. Note that in addition to the Moho marking the upper boundary of the mantle, there are three additional zones of very rapid increase in wave velocity bounded by regions of much less abrupt increase: these zones lie at depths of about 100, 400, and 650 km (approximately 60, 250, and 400 mi). There is also a single zone of sharp *decrease* in wave velocity lying not far below the crust, between depths of about 60 and 100 km (40 and 60 mi). This marks the base of the lithosphere. The asthenosphere beneath is the weak, more plastic, low-velocity zone.

Some increase in density with depth is to be expected in the mantle because of the increasing pressures caused by the overlying materials, but calculations show this simple pressure increase to be both too small and too gradual to account for the sharp zones of velocity change. Instead, it is relatively certain that the lower two zones, at least, mark regions in which there is an *abrupt* change in the crystal structure of the silicate minerals that make up the mantle. At the temperatures and pressures occurring near the earth's surface, olivine and pyroxene are relatively stable minerals. Theoretical calculations and laboratory experiments show, however, that at higher temperatures and pressures, olivine converts abruptly to a more dense and closely packed crystal structure (Figure 7.23). At still higher temperatures and pressures, the silicon is forced from both olivine and pyroxene to yield a kind of quartz, while the remaining magnesium and iron convert to oxide minerals with very compact crystal structures and high densities (Figure 7.22). These transitions occur at about the pressure-temperature conditions expected in the mantle at depths of 400 and 650 km, respectively, a finding that strongly suggests that the two lower zones of velocity increase are regions of abrupt structural changes in the minerals of the man-

(a)

(b)

FIGURE 7.23 Diagrammatic structural change in olivine at high pressures. (a) Crystal structure of normal olivine as found in the crust and upper mantle. (b) More dense olivine with compacted crystal structure, inferred to be present in the transition zone of the mantle.

SEISMOLOGY AND OTHER GEOPHYSICS

tle. The region surrounding these changes is called the **transition zone** of the mantle; it separates the relatively thin and variable *upper mantle* from a much larger and probably more uniform mass of material composing the underlying *lower mantle* (Figure 7.22).

The velocity increase in the upper mantle at 100-km depth is more complex because no transitions in the crystal structure of olivine and pyroxene should occur at such shallow depths. In addition, this zone of increase is closely associated with the overlying asthenosphere, the single region of sharp velocity *decrease* in the mantle. Several lines of evidence suggest that this low-velocity zone is a region in which a *decrease in rigidity*, rather than a sharp increase in density, accounts for the low wave velocities; that is, it marks a zone wherein the minerals of the upper mantle are unusually warm, plastic, and mobile in contrast to the rocks above and below, which have the same composition but are cooler and more rigid (see Figure 7.22). Indeed, in some regions, the low-velocity zone fails to transmit *S* waves, indicating that it is heated beyond the melting point to form local pockets of liquid magma. The velocity increase below the low-velocity zone apparently marks the zone in which the effect of increased pressure dominates the effect of increased temperature and the mantle materials resume their normal rigidity. Because the low-velocity zone lies only slightly below the crust, it is probably the source for much of the molten magma that reaches the earth's surface to form volcanic rocks. In addition, the zone is intimately interrelated with movements of the lithosphere.

The velocity-depth relations shown in Figure 7.22 are based on detailed seismic data for the upper mantle lying beneath western North America. Generally similar patterns have been found in other regions, but these differ enough in detail to suggest that the low-velocity zone, and the deeper zones of change in crystal structure, are not simple, earth-encircling spheres but show lateral variations that, in part at least, reflect similar variations observed in the thin overlying crust.

THE DEEP CRUST AND EARTH GRAVITY

Only half of the crust's average 16-km (10-mi) thickness is accessible to direct sampling by the deepest bore holes. The depths of the crust, like the mantle and core, are therefore known mostly from indirect physical measurements. As with the core and mantle, the principal evidence of deep crustal structure is provided by seismic wave velocities. Strong supporting evidence comes from an additional clue to the earth's interior that we have not yet introduced—that provided by gravity measurements.

7.10
GRAVITY

Gravity is a property of all bodies of matter by which they are attracted to other bodies by a force that increases as the mass (total amount of matter) of the bodies increases and as the distance between their centers grows smaller. This is the familiar force that causes unsupported objects to fall to the earth's surface; on a larger scale, the gravitational attraction of the sun, whose total mass is very great, holds the planets in their orbits.

If the earth were a perfectly spherical body with a symmetrical internal structure, then the gravitational force acting at all points on its surface would be exactly the same. Neither of these conditions is true: the earth's subsurface materials are not distributed with perfect symmetry, nor is the earth a perfect sphere, for its rotation causes it to bulge out slightly at the equator and become slightly flattened at the poles. Because of these variations in internal symmetry and external shape, measurements of the earth's gravitational force vary from place to place over its surface (Figure 7.24). These gravity measurements, made by sensitive instruments called **gravimeters** (Figure 7.25), can be considered to include three separate gravity components: a very large component resulting from the principal mass of the earth; and two smaller components, one result-

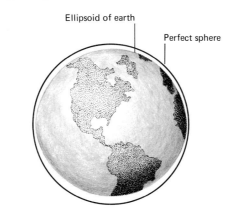

Ellipsoid of earth

Perfect sphere

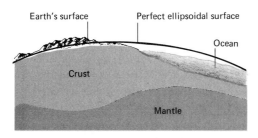

Earth's surface

Perfect ellipsoidal surface

Ocean

Crust

Mantle

FIGURE 7.24 Departures from uniform gravity caused by variation in the earth's external shape and internal symmetry. The earth is neither a perfect sphere nor are its surface and internal layers uniform in thickness and composition; these variations lead to differing values of the earth's gravitational force when measured at different points on the surface.

FIGURE 7.25 Gravimeters. (a) Schematic diagram. Gravity variations cause the suspended weight to move up or down. The screw is then adjusted to raise or lower the weight to a constant height (mirror horizontal, lamp centered in eyepiece); the gravitational force is read from the height of the screw. (b) A gravimeter in use. (Texas Instruments.)

ing from local variations in the earth's shape and the other from local differences in the thicknesses and densities of the underlying rocks. It is the two smaller components that make gravity measurements useful for interpreting the earth's interior, for they can be analyzed separately by first subtracting the large component contributed by the main mass of the earth and then making certain simplifying assumptions about either the local rock distribution or the general shape of the earth, depending on which factor the geophysicist wishes to measure. Tens of thousands of such gravity measurements have been made on land and, more recently, from gravimeters on surface vessels at sea, and these have provided a wealth of information about the earth's shape and the varying densities of rocks in the deep crust and upper mantle.

7.11
ISOSTASY

There is still another kind of information provided by gravity data. If reasonable values are assigned to each of the gravity components, it should be possible to *predict* the force of gravity at any point on the earth's surface. Such predictions have been made for many years, and their careful correlation with actual gravity measurements shows that the two fit *only* over continental areas of low relief. In mountainous regions, the force of gravity is normally *lower* than would be predicted, whereas over the deep ocean basins, it is normally *higher*. These **gravity anomalies**, as they are called, are caused by variations in the rocks of the crust: Apparently crustal rocks are relatively less massive under mountain ranges and more massive under ocean basins. This systematic variation of gravity with surface topography was discovered over a hundred years ago and has since been confirmed by thousands of gravity measurements.

The discovery that mountain ranges are underlain by relatively less massive rocks quickly led to the suggestion that mountains stand high because they are "floating" on the underlying rocks in much the same way that a block of copper or iron will float in heavier liquid mercury. The introduction of this concept of "floating," of the gravitational balance between light crustal rocks and denser mantle rocks—a concept termed **isostasy** (*iso* = equal, *stasy* = standing)—had far-reaching implications for the study of the deep structure of the crust. In particular, it was hypothesized that such floating could come about in two different ways. If all the rocks of the crust had approximately the same density, then mountains would require a large buried *root* of similar material to support them on the "fluid" subcrustal material. To provide buoyancy, this root would have to be much larger than the rocks exposed at the surface, just as the submerged part of a log or iceberg is larger than the part exposed above the surface [Figure 7.26(a)]. But if there were density varia-

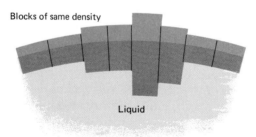

Blocks of same density

Liquid

(a)   Airy

FIGURE 7.26 The Airy and Pratt isostatic hypotheses. In the Airy scheme (a) mountains and lowlands are composed of the same materials and mountains float higher because they have large roots; in the Pratt scheme (b) they float higher because they are composed of lighter materials.

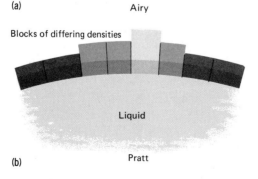

Blocks of differing densities

Liquid

(b)   Pratt

SEISMOLOGY AND OTHER GEOPHYSICS

tions in the rocks of the crust, then mountains might "float" higher because they are composed of lighter materials than surrounding lowlands [Figure 7.26(b)]. This second scheme was first proposed in 1854 by J. H. Pratt, an English geographer, and has come to be known as the *Pratt hypothesis*; the constant-density scheme was proposed the following year by another Englishman, the astronomer G. B. Airy, after whom it is called the *Airy hypothesis*. These isostatic hypotheses were the first clues to the deep structure of the earth's crust because, under either hypothesis, simple calculations showed that the rocks exposed in continental mountain ranges must extend far beneath the earth's surface and "float" in rocks of higher density.

7.12
SEISMIC EVIDENCE
OF DEEP CRUSTAL STRUCTURE

It was not until 1909, when Mohorovičić discovered the seismic discontinuity at the base of the crust, that there was any additional evidence of deep crustal structure. Subsequent observations showed that the depth of the Moho discontinuity averages about 35 km (22 mi) under the continents but, in striking contrast, *is much shallower under the ocean floors*, where it has an average depth of only 8 km (5 mi). These observations were extremely important for they showed that, on a continental scale, the base of the crust "mirrors" the topography of the earth's surface; that is, the crust is thickest under the high-standing continents and thinnest under the low-lying ocean basins (Figure 7.27)—as predicted by the Airy scheme of isostasy.

This is not the whole story, however, for seismic evidence *also* indicated that the continents are composed of less dense rocks than are those of the ocean floors, a finding that supported the Pratt isostatic hypothesis. By making certain reasonable assumptions about the relationship between the density and rigidity of crustal rocks, it is possible to infer crustal densities directly from seismic velocities;

FIGURE 7.27 Moho depth and crustal thicknesses under continents and ocean basins.

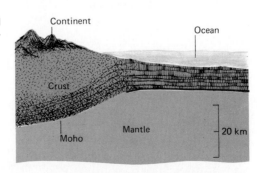

that is, higher velocities occur within denser rock. We should remember, however, that the velocity increase is actually due to the fact that rocks become more rigid as their density increases. It is the increase in rigidity that speeds up seismic waves. Early in the history of seismic studies it was noted that velocities in the continental crust are generally slower than in the oceanic crust, and these observations showed that continents are composed of less dense rocks than are the ocean floors. Seismic evidence thus indicates that *both* the Airy and Pratt schemes of isostasy play a role in the deep structure of the crust.

Early seismic studies also suggested that the crust itself is composed of "layers" of rock, each having a relatively constant wave velocity (and, by inference, a constant density), and each separated by a minor discontinuity in wave velocity. Continents were considered to have two principal layers: an upper, low-density layer and a lower layer of higher density. Oceans, on the other hand, showed evidence of only one principal layer whose density was about equal to the lower layer of the crust. These observations were interpreted to mean that the "oceanic crustal layer" is worldwide, extending under the lighter, upper continental layer as well as under the oceans.

Intensive modern seismic studies using precisely timed artificial explosions have shown that deep crustal structure, like that of the upper mantle, is more complex than this simple layered model would suggest. Some continental regions show one or several small discontinuities within the crust, whereas in others the wave velocities increase uniformly with depth rather than changing abruptly. In all regions, however, there is a tendency for the velocities to increase downward, suggesting that although continental rocks may not necessarily be underlain by oceanic materials, they do become progressively denser and more rigid with depth.

Plate tectonics emphasizes that the lithosphere-asthenosphere boundary has greater geologic significance than any of the boundaries indicated by velocity variations within the crust. We know that crustal relations are complex, but no longer are they as important to our understanding of earth dynamics as we once thought.

SUMMARY OUTLINE

EARTHQUAKES AND THE EARTH'S INTERIOR

7.1 Earthquake waves: Some seismic (earthquake-shock) waves travel through the earth and provide the principal evidence of its internal structure; among the several types, body waves (primary and secondary) that pass deep within the earth are the most instructive.

7.2 Elastic rebound theory: When the slow accumulation of strain in rocks reaches a limit, faulting is caused when the rocks elastically rebound to an unstrained condition.

7.3 Measuring earthquake strength: Various magnitude scales are used to determine the amount of ground shaking and the amount of energy released by an earthquake. Charles Richter pioneered this approach in 1935.

7.4 The earth's interior: Seismic velocity-depth curves have provided a basis for subdividing the earth into a crust, mantle, and core.

7.5 Internal densities, pressures, and temperatures: The probable pressures and densities of the earth's internal materials can be inferred from seismic velocity-depth curves; internal temperatures, on the other hand, are more poorly understood.

THE CORE AND EARTH MAGNETISM

7.6 Composition of the core: Seismic data indicate that the core is mostly liquid; this liquid is probably molten iron with small amounts of nickel and either sulfur or silicon.

7.7 Earth magnetism: The earth's magnetic field is believed to originate from electrical currents caused by motions within the liquid iron core.

THE MANTLE

7.8 Mantle composition: The mantle occupies 80 percent of the earth's volume; it is probably composed of magnesium- and iron-rich silicate minerals, which are principally olivine and pyroxene in its outer regions.

7.9 Mantle structure: Seismic discontinuities in the mantle indicate a warm, plastic zone just below the crust and two deeper, more rigid zones where olivine and pyroxene are believed to convert abruptly to denser mineral structures.

THE DEEP CRUST AND EARTH GRAVITY

7.10 Gravity: The force of gravity varies at the earth's surface due to variations both in the earth's shape and in the characteristics of the underlying rock.

7.11 Isostasy: Gravity measurements suggest that high-standing mountains and continents of the crust "float" on denser underlying rock.

7.12 Seismic evidence of deep crustal structure: The Moho seismic discontinuity, which separates the crust from the mantle, lies far deeper under continents than under ocean basins; the continental crust is therefore much thicker than the crust underlying the oceans.

ADDITIONAL READINGS

*BOLT, B. A.: *Earthquakes: A Primer*, W. H. Freeman & Company, Publishers, San Francisco, 1978. An excellent introductory and intermediate discussion dealing with both descriptive and theoretical topics.

* Available in paperback.

BOTT, M. H. P.: *The Interior of the Earth*, St. Martin's Press, Inc., New York, 1971. An excellent intermediate text.

*CLARK, S. P., JR.: *Structure of the Earth*, Prentice-Hall, Inc., Englewood Cliffs, N.J., 1971. A brief, authoritative introduction, emphasizing the earth's interior.

GASKELL, T. F.: *Physics of the Earth*, Funk & Wagnalls, New York, 1970. A well-illustrated elementary introduction to the earth's interior.

*HODGSON, J. H.: *Earthquakes and Earth Structure*, Prentice-Hall, Inc., Englewood Cliffs, N.J., 1964. A brief, popular introduction stressing the relation of earthquakes to man.

PHILLIPS, O. M.: *The Heart of the Earth*, Freeman, Cooper and Co., San Francisco, 1968. A readable introduction to all aspects of the earth's interior.

PRESS, F.: "Earthquake Prediction," *Scientific American*, May 1975.

STACEY, F. D.: *Physics of the Earth*, John Wiley & Sons, Inc., New York, 1969. An intermediate-level survey of the earth's interior.

8

Mountains and Plate Tectonics

P LATE TECTONICS WAS INTRODUCED
in Chapter 1 with the promise that this powerful new model for
explaining mountain building, earthquakes, and volcanism would
be developed more fully in a later chapter. We will begin by reviewing the geology of continents. Attention will then turn to the ocean
floor, and finally we will summarize the plate tectonics model as
it currently exists.

CONTINENTAL MOUNTAINS

8.1
MOUNTAINS AND GEOSYNCLINES

On the largest scale, continental mountain ranges may be divided
into two broad categories: those that originate largely from faulting,
known as **fault-block mountains,** and those dominated by folding,
which are called simply **fold mountains*** (Figure 8.1). Most of the
large mountain ranges seen on earth today, such as the Himalayas,
Alps, and large segments of the Rockies, are fold mountains. The
Sierra Nevada, on the other hand (Figure 8.2), is a fine example
of an exceptionally large fault-block range. Most mountains of this
origin are somewhat less conspicuous than fold mountains and are
frequently associated with them in a secondary manner, having
formed after a prior episode of strong folding. The Great Basin
region of the western United States comprises many distinct basins
and ranges, called **grabens** and **horsts,** respectively, of classic fault-
block origin (Figure 8.4).

Detailed studies of many folded mountain ranges have shown
most of them to have similar patterns of rock deformation. Viewed
in cross section, the outer flanks typically consist of thick sequences
of sedimentary rocks that become progressively less folded and deformed away from the central axis of the range. Toward the axial
regions, these deformed but otherwise unaltered sedimentary rocks

---

* Still a third kind of mountain range originates not from deformation of preexisting solid rocks
but from volcanic lavas. Such *volcanic mountains* (see Figure 8.3) are common on the ocean
floor and around the margin of the Pacific Ocean but are less important within the continents
than either fold or fault-block mountains. (See the discussion of volcanic landforms in Section
3.3.)

(a)

FIGURE 8.1 Fold mountains. (a) Southern
Idaho. (b) Schematic block diagram of fold
mountains. (a: John S. Shelton.)

(b)

give way first to metamorphosed sedimentary rocks and finally to
large elongate masses of granite that form the central core of the
range.

In many regions the typical fold mountain rock sequence, grad-
ing from relatively nondeformed sediments near the flanks of the
range to granite at the core, can be shown to have formed by the
progressive alteration of an unusually thick accumulation of sediments deposited near the margins of the continents. When the thin
veneer of sedimentary rocks that covers much of the surface of

(a)

FIGURE 8.2   Fault-block mountains. (a) Mt. Whitney region from over Owens Lake. (b) Block diagram of Sierran tilted fault-block. (a: U.S. Geological Survey.)

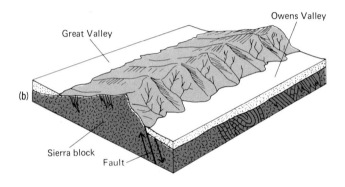

Great Valley

Owens Valley

(b)

Sierra block

Fault

FIGURE 8.3   The Cascade Range, showing volcanic mountains. (U.S. Department of Agriculture.)

(a)

Panamint Range   Death Valley   Black Mountains

Graben

Horst

(a)

(b)

(c)

GREAT
BASIN

FIGURE 8.4   Fault-blocks forming basins and ranges. (a) Simplified diagram of the structure characterizing the Death Valley region, showing fault-block mountains and basins. (b) Photo of basins and ranges. (c) Geologic map of the Great Basin. Note the N-S trend of basins and ranges. They are the result of normal faulting that created horsts and grabens. (b: John S. Shelton.)

the continents is traced laterally into the flanks of the mountain range, the total thickness of the original sediment can be seen to increase dramatically at just about the point at which the mountain-building deformation begins. Furthermore, this rapid thickening continues toward the axis of the mountain range, where the metamorphosed sediments give way to granite. This general pattern was first described in 1859 by James Hall, a U.S. geologist studying relationships between the Appalachians and the adjacent interior lowlands. Further investigations and theorizing gave rise to the concept of the geosyncline a few years later. Geosynclines were believed to have been formed where large volumes of relatively shallow-water sediments accumulated in subsiding elongate basins. According to the geosynclinal model, this thick accumulation of strata would eventually undergo intense compressional shortening, causing large-scale folding and reverse faulting, often combined with metamorphism and plutonism in the deep core of the newly formed mountain range due to the extreme pressures and temperatures that were reached (Figure 8.5). Although this model was generally accepted, it did not account for several important facets of the geosyncline's evolution: (1) What was the mechanism of basin subsidence?—It

FIGURE 8.5 Model for the evolution of a geosyncline. (a) Geosynclinal phase: subsidence and sedimentation. (b) Mountain-building phase: crustal shortening, folding and faulting, metamorphism, and plutonism.

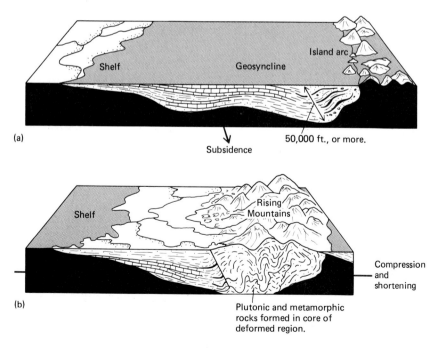

(a)

Shelf Geosyncline Island arc

Subsidence 50,000 ft., or more.

(b)

Shelf Rising Mountains

Compression and shortening

Plutonic and metamorphic rocks formed in core of deformed region.

FIGURE 8.6 The eroded roots of an ancient mountain range, exposed in the central Canadian shield area. (Canada, Department of Energy, Mines, and Resources.)

could be shown that sediment weight alone was not sufficient. (2) Why does subsidence, which is a vertical movement, give way to horizontal compressional forces? (3) What forces within the earth are capable of causing tens, and even hundreds, of miles of crustal shortening? All of these questions were troublesome, but the evidence for geosynclines was so compelling that their existence in the past was not denied.

The conspicuous folded mountain ranges seen on the continents today have all formed relatively recently in earth history. Most older fold mountain ranges no longer stand high above sea level but have been worn down to zones of little or no relief through millions of years of erosion. Such ancient mountain ranges are best exposed in regions known as **shield areas,** where they can still be recognized, even though they now lack mountainous relief, by their characteristic pattern of elongate granite masses flanked by progressively less deformed sedimentary rocks (Figures 8.6 and 8.7).

Over eons of geologic time the dimensions of the earth's continents are believed to have increased in the following manner: Sedimentary debris resulting from the erosion of old mountain ranges typically accumulated near the continental margins, where it ultimately became deformed to create new mountain ranges. The granitic cores of these newly formed mountains were welded to the silicic nucleus of the "parent" continent. Through this process the rocks of the continental crust were continually recycled, as granitic mountain cores were eroded to form sediments which then

FIGURE 8.7 The principal shield areas, which are the regions where the igneous and metamorphic basement rocks of the continents are exposed at the earth's surface. Elsewhere on the continents the basement rocks are covered by a veneer of predominantly sedimentary rock. The arrow indicates the small area of basement exposure that is enlarged in Figure 6.2. (Modified from Kummel, "History of the Earth," 1970, after various sources.)

melted deep within the crust to form new granites, which in turn became the cores of new mountain ranges. In developing this model, the steps involving the erosion of old mountains and the subsequent accumulation of sediments near the continental margins were more clearly understood than were the forces that deform and uplift the geosynclinal sediments to produce new mountains. These complex forces are, however, beginning to be recognized as but a side effect of still more fundamental motions of the earth's crust.

The classical model of the geosyncline has been modified by insights gained through plate tectonics. We shall develop our new understanding in the following sections.

8.2
CONTINENTAL DRIFT

One of the first suggestions that continental mountains might result from large-scale crustal motions was made in 1912 by Alfred Wegener, a German geophysicist. Wegener was impressed by the jigsaw puzzlelike fit between the shapes of some of the continental margins. The most obvious fits are those between western Africa and eastern North and South America, but with suitable juggling, rough fits can be made for other continental margins as well (Figure 8.8). A considerable amount of other evidence was advanced by Wegener supporting his view that our present continents have been horizontally displaced thousands of miles from the positions they occupied in the Mesozoic era. Figure 8.9 summarizes only some of Wegener's evidence based on various fields of study: geologic similarities of fold belts, related fossil organisms that were incapable of swimming across deep ocean basins, and paleoclimatic ("ancient climate") data that strongly suggest large-scale continental reorientations since late Paleozoic time.

All these associations led Wegener to suggest that the continents were originally joined in a single large landmass—which he called **Pangea** (*pan* = all, *gea* = earth)—that was subsequently broken apart, beginning in Mesozoic time, to create the separate continents that we see today. If entire continents were moving relative to one another, mountain-producing deformations along their margins might be explained as some sort of relatively minor frictional or drag effect at the edges of the moving mass. Wegener's model to explain *how* the continents moved about and his unsuccessful efforts to provide a plausible force capable of causing these movements proved to be the undoing for **continental drift**, as his idea came to be called. Wegener envisioned masses of continental silicic rock "plowing" through oceanic mafic rock (Figure 8.10). This model was quickly rejected as unacceptable in light of the fact that mafic rock is *more* rigid than silicic rock: butter could hardly plow through steel! Geophysicists were among the most skeptical of continental drift because they (like Wegener) knew of no energy source capable of providing the immense mechanical work required to move continental masses. Primarily for these reasons, plus the natural conservatism of the scientific community, the notion of continental drift was largely dismissed.

FIGURE 8.8 A reconstruction of the probable relationships of the continents before "continental drift." ("The Breakup of Pangaea" by Robert S. Dietz and John C. Holden. Copyright © 1970 by Scientific American, Inc. All rights reserved.)

PANGAEA

80°
N Latitude

40°
N Latitude

Equator

40°
S Latitude

GEOLOGIC: ⬛⬛⬛⬛⬛ ☐☐☐☐☐ ⬤⬤⬤⬤⬤ } Trends of Pre-Cenozoic fold belts

PALEONTOLOGIC: Limits of the distribution of Mesosaurus; a shallow water Mesozoic reptile

PALEOCLIMATIC: Regions of late Paleozoic glaciation

⬤ S   Spitzbergen: fossil ferns from late Paleozoic rocks

FIGURE 8.9   Evidence for continental drift as proposed by Alfred Wegener.

   In the Introduction (Section I.2), we discussed the concept of prematurity in science. Wegener's early work regarding continental drift seems clearly to be an example of a premature hypothesis. Even in the face of strong evidence that continents had once been connected and subsequently drifted apart, the idea was rejected for lack of a satisfactory mechanism; the science of Wegener's time provided no clues as to *how* it could happen—so it was concluded that it had *not* happened.

FIGURE 8.10 Wegener's continental drift: silicic rock "plowing" through mafic rock; quickly recognized as unacceptable, since mafic rock is more rigid than silicic rock.

In the early 1950s, new evidence derived from study of the earth's magnetic field began to suggest that large-scale continental motions had indeed taken place. When igneous rocks first crystallize, any magnetic, iron-bearing mineral that they contain becomes magnetized in the direction of the earth's magnetic field. Any subsequent change in the orientation of the mineral with respect to the earth's magnetic field also affects the mineral's magnetism. By using precise analytic techniques first developed in the 1950s, however, it is often possible to isolate the original magnetic component, which thus provides a record of the direction of the earth's magnetic field at the time the rock crystallized. By combining data from many such "fossil magnets" taken from rocks of different ages found on each continent, it is possible to get strong clues about the changing positions of the continents relative to the magnetic pole (which is assumed to have always remained relatively near the earth's rotational pole, as it is today—see Figure 8.11). Such paleomagnetic studies of continental rocks provided additional evidence that the continents had moved relative to one another and led to a revival

FIGURE 8.11 Paleomagnetic reconstruction of Africa's position, relative to the south pole, from 350 million years ago to the present. (After compilation by Clark, "Structure of the Earth," 1971, from various sources.)

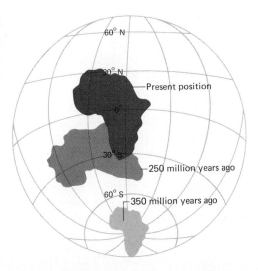

of interest in the idea of continental drift. General acceptance of the idea did not come, however, until the mid-1960s when it was discovered that still more fundamental crustal movements take place beneath the ocean floor.

THE OCEAN FLOOR

Among the most significant scientific advances of recent years was the discovery, first suggested as a hypothesis in the 1950s and then firmly supported in 1966, that the oceanic crust is in continuous movement like a giant conveyor belt. This discovery of what has come to be called **ocean-floor spreading** was a result of two principal kinds of research: one of these concerned the topography of the ocean floor, the other, magnetism of the ocean floor. This section first will discuss these two research areas and their findings and then will move on to consider how ocean-floor spreading has provided a unifying principle that also helps to explain continental deformation.

8.3
TOPOGRAPHY OF THE OCEAN FLOOR

Because of the ease with which we can observe mountains, hills, and valleys on the continents, most of us are not accustomed to thinking of the extraordinary problems involved in learning whether similar topography exists on the ocean floor. Before 1920 the only method of determining ocean depths and, conversely, sea-floor topography was laboriously to lower a heavy weight, attached to thousands of feet of steel wire, over the side of a ship. Even though many such "soundings" were made, they were so scattered over the vast expanse of the oceans that they provided little evidence for ocean-bottom irregularities. The ocean floors were generally believed to be flat, featureless plains broken here and there by mountains that rose above the surface as islands.

In the 1920s, the first *echo sounders* were developed for more rapid determination of ocean depths and bottom topography (Figure 8.12). These instruments measure depths by noting the time required for sound waves to reach the bottom and be reflected back to a shipboard recording device. The first systematic surveys of ocean-bottom topography using these instruments were undertaken in parts of the Pacific Ocean in the early 1940s. The principal result

(a)

(b)

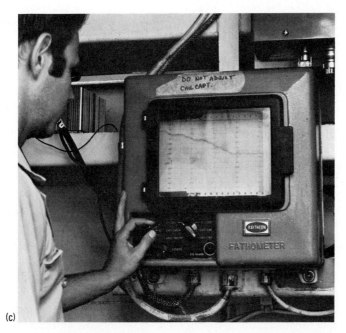

(c)

FIGURE 8.12   Methods of determining ocean-floor topography. (a) Before the 1920's the only method was the lowering of the weighted lines (left); since then, increasingly sophisticated echo-sounders (right) have been used to map the ocean floor. (b) A weighted line being used for sounding a shallow, uncharted area. (c) A recording echo-sounder showing a profile of the underlying topography. (b: U.S. Coast Guard; c: Ocean Science Laboratory.)

FIGURE 8.13 Idealized drawing of a portion of the mid-Pacific ocean floor with water removed, showing two flat-topped guyots in the distance. The canyon in the foreground is cut into a guyot, most of which does not show. (Painting by Chesley Bonestell, from Hamilton, "Geological Society of America Memoir," 64, 1956.)

of these early surveys was the discovery of a great many rounded, flat-topped mountains, called **guyots**, on the floor of the northern Pacific (Figure 8.13). The tops of many guyots are covered by many thousands of feet of water, yet the only known mechanism for producing their broad, flat tops is the erosional action of waves at the surface of the sea. Because their flat tops could have been produced only at sea level, either sea level had risen many thousands of feet since they were formed or, more probably, the ocean floor on which they stand was somehow lowered several thousand feet. Guyots thus provided the first suggestion of large-scale movements of the ocean floor.

Another significant result of early ocean-bottom surveys was the location and mapping of several **oceanic trenches** —long, narrow zones where rocks of the ocean floor, investigators were puzzled to find, are depressed many thousands of meters *below* the surrounding terrain (Figure 8.14). Most of these trenches are parallel to continental margins and are usually bounded on their landward side by curving chains of offshore volcanic mountains that extend above the ocean surface to form **island arcs** (Figure 8.14). These unusually

FIGURE 8.14 (a) The principal oceanic trenches (dark color) and island arcs (light color). (b) Cross section through the Tonga Trench, with Mt. Everest superimposed for scale. The vertical scale is exaggerated 10 times in the upper sketch; the true scale is shown below. ("The Trenches of the Pacific" by Robert L. Fisher and Roger Revelle. Copyright © 1955 by Scientific American, Inc. All rights reserved.)

deep depressions immediately adjacent to high volcanic mountains also suggested that dynamic processes are taking place in the rocks of the ocean floor.

Since 1945, additional surveys of bottom topography have been undertaken in many areas: the Atlantic, Indian, Arctic, and eastern Pacific oceans have been intensely surveyed, and other oceans are known in less detail. These surveys have shown that the ocean floor, although relatively flat over large areas, also includes the longest, highest, and most continuous mountain ranges on earth. These ranges make up the **oceanic ridge-rise system**, a world-encircling belt of ridgelike mountains and broad rises that is of extraordinary importance for understanding movements of the ocean floor (Figure 8.15).

Crest of ridge or rise

Large faults crossing ridges

FIGURE 8.15   The oceanic ridge-rise system. ("The Origin of the Oceans" by Sir Edward Bullard. Copyright © 1969 by Scientific American, Inc. All rights reserved.)

FIGURE 8.16   A portion of the Midatlantic Ridge showing the location of earthquake epicenters (orange dots). The cross section below shows the rift valley at the crest of the ridge. (After Heezen, vol. 203, copyright © 1960 by Scientific American, Inc. All rights reserved.)

The most intensively studied part of the oceanic ridge-rise system is the Midatlantic Ridge, a chain of mountains lying almost exactly in the center of the Atlantic Ocean (Figure 8.16). The existence and general position of the ridge has been known for many years because it comes to the surface in several places in the form of oceanic islands such as Iceland and the Azores. Furthermore, it has long been known that the ridge overlies a zone of rather shallow earthquakes. In the 1950s, detailed studies of the topography of the ridge and the distribution of earthquakes under it revealed two important relationships. First, although the total width of the ridge averages several hundred kilometers, the earthquakes are concentrated in a narrow band under only the highest part or *crest* of the ridge. Second, the crest itself does not make up a single long ridge but is instead composed of two parallel, steep-sided ridges separated by a deep valley. Similar but smaller and less continuous valleys, called rifts, are also seen on the surface of the continents, where they can be shown to have formed from normal faulting caused by a tension or *pulling apart* of the faulted rocks on each side of the valley (Figure 8.17). This immediately suggested that the Midatlantic Ridge might represent a similar but much larger zone of crustal tension in which the Atlantic Ocean floor on both sides of the ridge is moving away from the rifted ridge; the rift valley at the crest of the ridge and the earthquakes underlying it would mark the line of separation. Other lines of evidence also pointed to the same conclusion. Where the tops of the ridge are exposed as islands and the rocks of the ridge can thus be sampled, they were found everywhere to be basaltic or ultramafic rocks, as would be expected if the ridge represented a fracture zone in which basaltic lavas had poured out from the underlying mantle to build up the ridge. Furthermore, the entire width of the rift valley itself is exposed above the sea in Iceland, where tension cracks and other evidence of movement can be directly observed [Figure 8.17(a)].

After the significance of the Midatlantic Ridge was discovered, interest quickly spread to similar features in other ocean basins. On the basis of topographic information combined with data on the distribution of oceanic earthquakes, it was proposed that the Midatlantic Ridge is only one segment of a much longer world-encircling system of oceanic mountains that represents a fundamental zone of fracture and movement of the earth's crust. This is the oceanic ridge-rise system that extends, with several side branches, down the center of the Atlantic Ocean, through the Indian Ocean, south of Australia, and up the eastern Pacific Ocean. Although the system mostly occurs in ocean basins, it does extend into the continents in a few places such as the Red Sea, eastern Africa, and the Gulf of California.

(a)

FIGURE 8.17   Rifts. (a) A part of the rift valley of central
Iceland. (b) A small rift in east Africa. (a: Sigurdur Thorarinsson; b: Sidney P. Clark, Jr.)

(b)

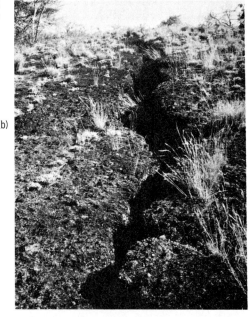

The discovery of the oceanic ridge-rise system, with its associated earthquakes and, in many areas, central rift valleys, coupled with the discovery of generally high-heat flow to the earth's surface, strongly suggested that horizontal movements take place in the crustal rocks beneath the sea floor on a tremendous scale. The elevation of this hypothesis of **ocean-floor spreading** to a theory and then to a scientific principle was accomplished by using magnetic studies of the rocks of the ocean floor.

In Section 7.6 we saw that measurements of the strength of the magnetic field at the earth's surface are affected by two components: one, the earth's main magnetic field, originates from motions in the liquid iron of the core; the other originates from the distribution of magnetic minerals in rocks of the crust. There are no magnetic effects from mantle rocks lying between the crust and the core because the minerals making up the mantle are heated beyond the *Curie point* (the temperature at which they lose their magnetism). By subtracting the large component contributed by the main magnetic field, it is possible to study differences in the magnetic minerals of crustal rocks by making magnetic surveys of large areas with shipboard or airborne magnetometers. Such surveys have been conducted over land areas for many years and have shown complex magnetic patterns that are caused primarily by differences in the amount of the mineral magnetite present in the underlying crustal rocks. The first systematic magnetic surveys of the ocean floor were undertaken off the coast of California in 1955. Surprisingly, these showed patterns that are *far more regular than any from continental areas* (Figure 8.18). In particular, the oceanic magnetic patterns showed a series of extremely long, narrow bands extending for hundreds of kilometers approximately parallel to the coastline. One additional feature of these banded magnetic patterns is of great significance: In certain areas the patterns are broken and offset for hundreds of kilometers along huge faults extending at approximately right angles to the present coastline. Some of these faults were already known because they make large submarine cliffs that had been previously discovered by echo sounding. The fact that oceanic rocks had moved for hundreds of kilometers along these faults was first shown, however, by the offset patterns of magnetic measurements. Here again was strong evidence for large-scale movements of the ocean floor.

Once the linear oceanic magnetic pattern was discovered, the next question was: What caused it? In continental areas the much

San Francisco

Los Angeles

0 100
km

FIGURE 8.18 Contrasting linear magnetic patterns of oceanic rocks and irregular patterns of continental rocks. (After Raff, "Journal of Geophysical Research," vol. 71, 1966; Sauck and Summer, "Aeromagnetic Map of Arizona," 1971.)

less regular magnetic pattern could be shown, by geologic mapping, to be caused by differing amounts of magnetic minerals in the underlying rocks. There was, however, another more likely cause for the regular oceanic patterns. This was related not to differing *amounts* of magnetic minerals but to differences in their *direction of magnetization*.

Rocks of the ocean floor are almost exclusively basalts containing a large and relatively constant amount of the mineral magnetite (Fe_3O_4), which makes them strongly magnetic. When lavas cool to form basalt, this magnetite crystallizes from the liquid lava and then eventually cools to the **Curie temperature**. As this temperature is reached, the magnetic crystals become magnetized in the direction of the earth's magnetic field. Now suppose for a moment that the direction of the earth's magnetic field is not constant but shows regular changes. If this were true, lavas forming at different times would have different directions of magnetization, reflecting the earth's magnetic field at the time the lavas cooled. (The original patterns would dominate because magnetic minerals permanently retain much of their original magnetic orientation gained on passing the Curie point and do not become completely reoriented to later changes in the earth's field.) Most significantly, at about the same time that the puzzlingly regular magnetic patterns were discovered in the oceans, additional studies of vertical sequences of magnetic mineral orientation in lava flows on land and in samples of sediments from the sea floor (fine sedimentary grains of magnetic minerals also become oriented to the earth's magnetic field when they are deposited by water) showed that the earth's main magnetic field

has undergone frequent and rapid **reversals in magnetic polarity,**
the north magnetic pole becoming the south pole and vice versa
(Figure 8.19). The cause of these sudden magnetic reversals is still
unknown, but they must somehow be related to changes in flow
patterns in the liquid iron of the earth's core, where the main magnetic field originates.

Soon after the regular oceanic magnetic patterns were discovered, it was suggested that they might reflect sudden reversals in
the earth's magnetic field in the following way: If basaltic lavas

FIGURE 8.19   A time scale for magnetic reversals
during the last 4.5 million years. Intervals of normal
polarity are shown in color; reversed polarity in
white. (Modified from Cox, "Science," vol. 168,
1969.)

poured onto the ocean floor from a long crack in the crust, then cooled to form basalt, and were then somehow separated down the middle and moved away in opposite directions from the crack before new lava was extruded, and furthermore, if a reversal in the earth's magnetic field took place between the lava outpourings, the result would be *a series of parallel bands of basalt each having minerals with a different magnetic orientation* (Figure 8.20). These differences in magnetic direction might account for the regular, parallel patterns of ocean-floor magnetism, since the normally oriental basalt would *add* slightly to the present field of the earth, and the reversed basalt would *subtract*. Unfortunately, this idea still cannot be directly tested because it is impossible to determine the direction of magnetization without having carefully oriented samples of the magnetic rocks, and these are extraordinarily difficult to obtain for oceanic basalts covered by thousands of meters of water and hundreds of meters of sediments.

Strong evidence that spreading basaltic bands *are* the cause

FIGURE 8.20   Interpretation of symmetrical magnetic patterns observed on a portion of the Midatlantic ridge south of Iceland (color). Lavas from the mantle pour out along the ridge axis and then move laterally outward on both sides of the ridge forming symmetrical bands that are progressively older (lighter color) away from the ridge. Bands of reversed polarity are shown in gray; normal polarity in color. (Magnetic pattern from Vine, in "The History of the Earth's Crust," 1968.)

of the oceanic magnetic pattern was obtained, however, from another source in 1966, when the first detailed magnetic analysis was made of the Midatlantic Ridge. This study showed parallel magnetic patterns similar to those previously found off California, but this time the bands were found to be *identical on each side of the Midatlantic Ridge*, just as would be expected if lavas were pouring from the earthquake rift zone, solidifying into basalt, then being broken along the rift and moving away from it on both sides (Figure 8.20). Furthermore, the width of the parallel magnetic bands was found to match closely the relative times between reversals in the earth's magnetic field over the past several million years as established independently from magnetic studies of dated sedimentary rocks and lava flows. This discovery showed that the spreading basaltic rocks of the oceanic crust have behaved like a great moving magnetic recording tape, clearly reflecting changes in the direction of the earth's magnetic field. Basaltic rocks of the oceanic crust must rise from the mantle along the oceanic ridge-rise system, solidify, and then be carried horizontally away from the ridges by powerful forces acting from below, within the hotter and less rigid rocks of the mantle. The oceanic crust thus becomes progressively older at farther distances from the ridge-rise system.

Following the dramatic indication of ocean-floor spreading from analyses of magnetic patterns, two other lines of evidence contributed further confirmation of the motions involved. One, a careful study of earthquake motions, has shown that large-scale crustal movements at the ridges take place with precisely the tensional patterns suggested by the magnetic evidence. The other, an important program of drilling from shipboard into the deep ocean floor, has revealed that the thin sediments lying upon the oceanic crust show a regular increase in age farther away from the ridge-rise system, as would be expected if the underlying basalts similarly varied in age (Figure 8.21).

FIGURE 8.21 Confirmation of ocean-floor spreading from deep-sea drilling. Sediments lying just above the ocean-floor basalts become progressively older away from the axis of the Midatlantic Ridge. (After Maxwell et al., "Initial Reports of the Deep Sea Drilling Project, vol. 3, 1969.)

Eurasian Plate

North American Plate

Eurasian Plate

Cocos Plate

Caribbean Plate

Arabian Plate

Philippine Plate

Pacific Plate

Mid-Atlantic ridge

Nazca Plate

African Plate

Indian Plate

East Pacific rise

South American Plate

Antarctic Plate

▲▲ —Subduction zone   ————— Uncertain plate boundary

——— Transform faults
and Spreading ridges   ——▶ Direction of relative plate motions (Africa held motionless)

FIGURE 8.22   Twelve major lithospheric plates.

PLATE TECTONICS

Success of the ocean-floor spreading model quickly led to a reconsideration of *all* crustal motions, for the discovery of the movement of large blocks of the ocean floor indicated dynamic crustal processes on a scale that had never been obvious from studies of the more accessible continental crust. In particular, the position of earthquake belts and oceanic ridges now showed the crust to be divided into twelve major (and several minor) moving **plates**, each relatively rigid within itself but bounded by zones of profound crustal movement (Figure 8.22). Differential motion of these huge plates of lithosphere is now believed to account for most of the dynamic features seen in the earth's crust, and their study is called **plate tectonics**. Recall that *tectonics* refers to large-scale movements of the earth.

8.5
PLATE TECTONICS AND STYLES OF LITHOSPHERIC INTERACTION

As introduced in Chapter 1, there are three types of boundary zones that mark the edges of the lithospheric plates. These are: (1) *spreading ridges* (or *rises*), (2) *subduction zones,* and (3) *transform faults*.

All of these zones are marked by earthquake activity. We are not sure why lithospheric plates move, but we know they do, and we can describe some of their motions. Furthermore, we know that individual plates change both their direction and their velocity from time to time. New plates can be created, and old ones can be destroyed. Although it is very difficult to determine the absolute motion of a plate, in contrast to knowing how it is moving relative to another plate, certain reasonable assumptions allow estimates that are probably close to correct. Results of these estimates indicate individual plate velocities varying from almost motionless to 11 or 12 cm/yr. Thus the fastest moving plate is currently traveling at a rate that will carry it about 30 feet during an average human's lifetime. Our best and newest thoughts concerning the forces that make plates move are discussed in Box 8.1.

BOX 8.1

The Driving Mechanisms Behind Plate Tectonics

Recall that one of the main reasons for the nonacceptance of Alfred Wegener's hypothesis of continental drift in the early 1900s was that he could not provide a satisfactory mechanism for *how* drift could occur. Since that time, the models of sea-floor spreading and plate tectonics have provided a partial explanation, but we still are unable to produce a thorough description of the forces responsible for movements of lithospheric plates. Most research in recent years has focused on describing the geometry of plate movements and fitting these movements into geologic history. Little has been done to resolve the more fundamental question, "What is the driving mechanism behind plate motion?" Let us consider a few "candidates" [see Figure (a)] for such a driving force. (This approach was first published in 1975 by D. Forsyth and S. Uyeda.*)

1. *Ridge push*: Since the ridges are topographically higher than the surrounding terrain, they have more potential energy, and therefore spread laterally, thus pushing the entire plate along.

2. *Plate pull*: The lithospheric plate becomes cooler the farther it has traveled from its origin, and as it cools, it shrinks from contraction. So when it reaches a subduction zone, it is more dense than the underlying mantle rock; thus the entire plate is pulled downward by gravity.

3. *Convective drag*: If convective movement within the asthenosphere is taking place in the direction of plate movement, frictional drag between the convectively moving material and the base of the lithosphere could account in part for the plate's motion.

*Forsyth, D,. and S. Uyeda, "On the Relative Importance of the Driving Forces of Plate Motion." *Geophysical Journal,* Royal Astronomical Society, v.43, no. 1, 1975, pp. 163–200.

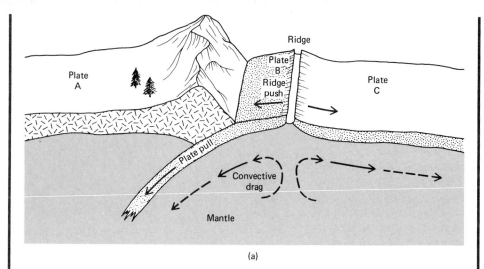

(a)

FIGURE (A) Three possible driving mechanisms for the movement of *Plate B*: (1) ridge push, (2) plate pull, and (3) convective drag. See text for discussion. [after S. Uyeda, see additional readings for reference]

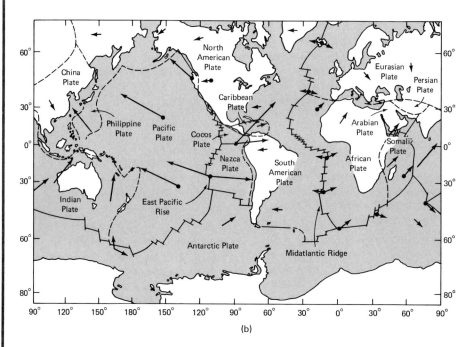

(b)

FIGURE (B) Present motions of plates over hot spots. The relative motions were determined from fault strikes and spreading rates on rise boundaries; with an appropriate constant rotation added.

MOUNTAINS AND PLATE TECTONICS

How might we attempt to discover which, if any, of these three possible driving mechanisms is likely? The velocity at which each plate moves can be compared to other characteristics of that plate in an attempt to find helpful correlations. The presence or absence of correlations will indicate greater or lesser importance of each of the forces mentioned above. Reference to Figure B shows, for example, that the plates moving at the greatest velocity (Pacific, Cocos, and Nazca) are all bounded by long subducting slabs of lithosphere (that is, of their total circumference, 25 percent to 30 percent is subduction zone), as compared to the slowest moving plates (Eurasian, North American, and South American), which are bounded by very little subducting lithosphere. This suggests that *plate pull* may be very important as a driving mechanism, since it appears that the greater the percentage of "dangling" lithosphere, the greater the velocity of plate movement.

Correlations between plate velocity and spreading ridge length or plate area do not exist, thus indicating that *ridge push* and *convective drag* are probably not major factors in generating a plate's velocity. They may exert a minor influence, but apparently not nearly so much as that of *plate pull*.

Another look at Figure (b) suggests another important correlation: The correlation is between plate velocity and whether the plate is composed primarily of oceanic lithosphere, or has a continent embedded in it. When continents project into the mantle, perhaps there is a frictional slowing of plate movement. The Indian Plate, however, is particularly instructive in this regard: It is fast-moving and has a high percentage of subducting boundary (about 20 percent), as would be expected, yet it also possesses a large continent. This suggests that *plate pull* exerts a greater influence on increasing a plate's velocity than the slowing effect of a continent protruding down into the mantle.

Although this is an instructive beginning, there is still much to be learned before we will have a genuinely satisfactory understanding of this fundamental aspect of plate tectonics. We still lack a well-developed theory to explain the driving mechanisms of plate tectonics.

New lithospheric crust is constantly being created at spreading ridges. These regions are characterized by earthquake activity generated from **normal-slip faulting** as tensional spreading stresses eventually cause newly formed lithosphere to break. Because the rock is young and therefore still warm, large-magnitude earthquakes are infrequent along zones of spreading. All magnitude (M_s) values are less than 7, and usually are much lower than that. These earthquakes result from pulling apart of the lithosphere. Thus all foci are shallow because enough strain to cause an earthquake can occur only near the surface where the rocks are rigid. Sometimes we speak of a **ridge** (Midatlantic Ridge) and sometimes reference is made to a **rise** (East Pacific Rise). (See Figure B in Box 8.1.) Why the difference? If topography is rugged, the site of spreading is called a **ridge,** and if the topography is subdued, the term **rise** is used.

There are other important differences between ridges and rises that will help us to understand what the causes are that create these two different kinds of spreading zones. First of all, heat flow to the earth's surface is higher at rises. Also, rises are characterized by smaller earthquakes, and there is no grabenlike rift valley above the zone of spreading. All of these differences between rises and ridges can be explained by the fact that rises are zones where the rate of spreading is fast, whereas ridges are formed above boundaries having a slow rate of spreading (see Figure B in Box 8.1). When spreading is fast, the newly formed lithosphere doesn't have time to become thick and rigid above the boundary where new material is being added to the diverging plates. It follows, then, that heat flow will be higher, and since the rocks are plastic, earthquake activity will be less, and topography will be more subdued (Figure 8.23). Thus the answer to our initial question, "Why the difference?" is that *ridges develop above zones where the spreading is slow*, and *rises form in regions of fast spreading*.

Let us now consider plate boundaries having *convergence*. When either of the converging plates is composed of oceanic lithosphere, a deep trench in the ocean floor is dragged down as an oceanic plate descends beneath the other plate, be it either oceanic or continental. Recall, also, that magmas are generated within and

FIGURE 8.23   Contrast between spreading *ridges* and *rises*. See text for discussion.

Slow	← Rate of spreading →	Fast
Low	← Heat flow →	High
Central rift graben	← Topography →	Subdued
Many 'quakes	← Seismic activity →	Few 'quakes
Thick	← Lithosphere →	Thin

adjacent to the subducting lithosphere; thus volcanic eruptions are commonplace above subduction zones. In Chapter 7 we discussed the seismic evidence for the descending slabs of lithosphere and should note here that these inclined zones of earthquake foci, called **Benioff Zones,** were recognized more than ten years before the notion of subduction was included within the plate tectonics framework. The following two important characteristics of these Benioff Zones were noted in the 1950s, but without the plate tectonics model they could not be incorporated into a theoretical understanding at that time.

1. The dip of the Benioff Zone was shallower when the boundary was between oceanic crust and continental crust than when oceanic crust was subducting beneath another slab of oceanic crust. (Typical dips are about 30° vs. 60° for these two places, respectively.)

2. In some places, earthquake foci were very deep (up to 700 km); whereas in others, foci extended down to only intermediate depths (71–300 km).

Consideration of Figures 8.24 and 8.25 will help explain these two phenomena in terms of modern plate tectonic theory. First compare the Tonga region (A–A') while the Chile region (C–C'). At the Tonga subduction there is one oceanic slab of lithosphere beneath another oceanic slab, whereas at Chile subduction is between oceanic and continental lithosphere. Oceanic lithosphere is more rigid and more dense than continental lithosphere, so it seems reasonable that the subducted plate will be deflected at a greater angle at Tonga than at Chile, where the weaker continental lithosphere will cause less bending of the descending slab in the downward direction [Figure 8.25(a) and (c)]. Notice that beneath South America [Figure 8.25(c)], at a depth of about 300 km, the lithospheric plate changes its dip to a greater angle, no doubt because it comes into contact with significantly more rigid rock at that depth. In other words, the maximum depth at which rocks reflect characteristics of an overlying continent appears to be about 300 km.

Why is it that earthquake foci are not nearly as deep in the Alaska region (Figures 8.24 and 8.25; B–B') as in the Chile region? Both are sites of oceanic lithosphere subducting beneath continental lithosphere. And both have Benioff Zones dipping at a shallow angle. Why, then, the difference in the depth of foci? The explanation lies in the difference between their rates of convergence in their respective subduction zones. Since the Pacific Plate and the North American Plate are converging at about 5.5 cm/yr in the region of B–B', and the Nazca Plate is converging with the South American Plate at about twice that rate (C–C'), it seems reasonable that in

Depth of earthquake foci

■ Shallow, 0–70 km

□ Intermediate, 71–300 km

▨ Deep, 301–700 km

↗ 8 cm/yr
Rate of convergence in subduction zone

⚓ Subduction zone

✕ Spreading ridge

FIGURE 8.24   Three subduction zones. A-A′ in the Tonga region; B-B′ in the Alaska region; and C-C′ in the Chile region. See text for discussion.

FIGURE 8.25   Cross sections to correspond to the three regions shown in Figure 8.24. See text for discussion.

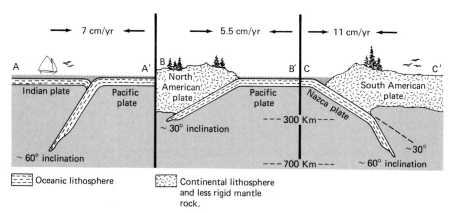

⊟ Oceanic lithosphere

▨ Continental lithosphere and less rigid mantle rock.

the Chile region, subducting lithosphere can extend deeper into the earth before it loses its rigidity (hence its ability to cause earthquakes) due to heat effects within the upper mantle. Indeed, it is also possible to conceive of convergence between two plates that is so slow that subduction would not occur at all.

Comparison of Figures 8.25(a) and (c) shows that subducting lithosphere reached about the same depth (650–700 km) in both the Tonga region and the Chile region, yet convergence in the Chile region is one and one-half times as fast as at Tonga. The steeper angle of subduction (about 60°) at Tonga explains why the lithosphere can reach the same depth there as at Chile, even though convergence is slower. It's analogous to descending a steep stairway, where each step allows you to go down more than if the stairway had a gentler slope. The lower tip of still rigid lithosphere in the Tonga region has been within the hot interior of the earth for essentially the same duration as the tip of lithosphere beneath Chile, in spite of the fact that convergence is faster between the Nazca Plate and the South American Plate. This is because the angle of descent is also gentler in the Chile region than in the Tonga region. Thus the rate at which lithosphere descends into the earth is about the same for both Chile and Tonga. We should expect, therefore, that they will both have earthquakes extending to comparable depths.

Box 8.2 describes how we can recognize ancient spreading ridges that were plastered against continents by subduction.

BOX 8.2

Recognizing Ancient Plate Boundaries

There are regions around the world where distinctive suites of rock called **ophiolites** are located within ancient zones of mountainous structure. The great significance of these occurrences lies in the fact that the rocks composing ophiolite suites were formed originally at spreading ridges in the deep ocean environment, yet now we find them incorporated within continental lithosphere. The figure below shows an idealized ophiolite suite: ultramafic igneous rocks and serpentine, associated with gabbro and other distinctive igneous materials emplaced in an intricately mixed intrusive fashion, overlain by basaltic lavas having a pillow structure because of submarine eruptions. All these rocks, in turn, are overlain by deep marine sediments such as chert, limestone, and shale. When rock-types are associated together in this way, they constitute an **ophiolite suite.**

As subducting oceanic lithosphere converges toward a continent, coarser-grained sediments, such as sandstones (particularly turbidity current deposits), are deposited above the more organic-rich sedimentary rocks formed when the plate was beneath deeper water. These rock materials are frequently mixed together in a chaotic, granulated, and sheared fashion. This occurs near the place where one plate bends beneath the other at the margin of the subduction zone. Such a mixture, called a **mélange,** is testimony to the past existence of a subduction zone plate boundary, even though no such boundary exists in the region today. Ophiolites are commonly among the large unbroken rock masses, called **tectonic inclusions,** contained within the extensively sheared mélanges. Thus, when we recognize ophiolites and mélanges in regions such as the Urals, the Appalachians, the western part of California, and others, we believe these were settings of plate convergence in the geologic past, even though subduction zones are not active in these regions at the present time.

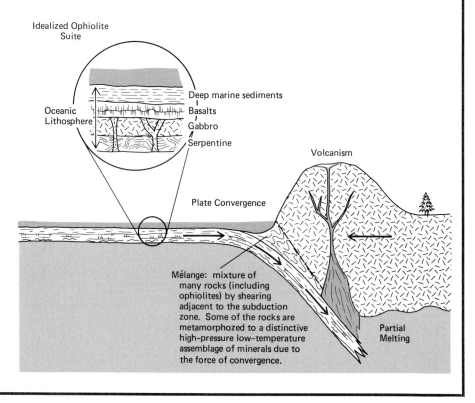

Idealized Ophiolite Suite

Oceanic Lithosphere

Deep marine sediments
Basalts
Gabbro
Serpentine

Plate Convergence

Volcanism

Mélange: mixture of many rocks (including ophiolites) by shearing adjacent to the subduction zone. Some of the rocks are metamorphozed to a distinctive high-pressure low-temperature assemblage of minerals due to the force of convergence.

Partial Melting

The only plate boundary where there is neither convergence nor divergence is called a **transform fault.** Because these boundaries are where plates are shearing past each other, rather than spreading or subducting, volcanism is not a characteristic of transform faults. Earthquake activity, however, is commonplace, and its style is instructive regarding the development of our plate tectonics model. J. Tuzo Wilson (a Canadian geophysicist) first proposed in 1965 that these faults are not like our common strike-slip faults. He argued then that they should have a different name (i.e., *transform fault*) in order to underscore their difference. At the time of Wilson's suggestion, there was still a great deal of confusion surrounding these major ocean-floor faults. In Figure 8.26(a), part of the Midatlantic Ridge is shown, with many offsets. Consider the fault that is labeled A–B: Although there is a great deal of left-lateral offset, the fault seems to terminate abruptly without continuing on to the South American or African continents. How can so much left-lateral offset disappear? Wilson noted that this problem would be solved if the ridges were centers of spreading that mark the *original fractures* between continents. Thus the left-lateral *offset* along A–B is *not* the result of left-lateral *slip* at all, but instead remains from very early in the separation of South America from Africa. Wilson predicted that careful seismic investigations of these faults would discover two surprising things: (1) faulting would be confined to the region *between spreading ridges only*, and (2) faulting would have lateral movement in directions *opposite* to the directions of ridge offset [Figure 8.26(b)]. The almost immediate confirmation of these predictions did a great deal to establish and develop the new plate tectonics model for crustal movements.

Box 8.3 summarizes the important geologic processes that occur at each of the three plate boundaries.

FIGURE 8.26 Transform faults. (a) Mid-ocean ridge and transform faults. (b) close-up of a spreading ridge. (See text for discussion.)

BOX 8.3

Summary of geologic processes at plate boundaries

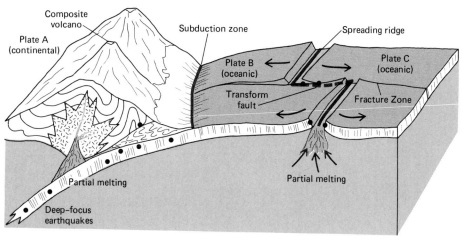

Composite volcano
Plate A (continental)
Subduction zone
Spreading ridge
Plate B (oceanic)
Plate C (oceanic)
Transform fault
Fracture Zone
Partial melting
Partial melting
Deep-focus earthquakes

● Earthquake Foci

▬ Plate Boundary

Formation of Magma

Type of Plate Boundary	Type of Stress	Type of Faulting	Seismicity	Igneous Activity	Topographic Features
Subduction Zone [between plates A and B]	Compression (due to convergence)	Reverse Slip (minor normal slip at hinge where lithosphere bends downward)	Only zone with foci deeper than thickness of lithosphere World's largest quakes (Ms > 8.4)	Intermediate and silicic volcanism on overlying plate Plutonic and metamorphic rocks formed beneath volcanics	Thick sedimentary fill in trench Folded sedimentary rocks form mountains at plate margin
Ridge (slow spreading) **or Rise** (rapid spreading) [between plates B and C]	Tension (due to divergence)	Normal Slip	Shallow focus only Always of intermediate to low magnitude (Ms < 7)	Basalt and ophidites create new lithosphere	Graben development creates a rift valley

Type of Plate Boundary	Type of Stress	Type of Faulting	Seismicity	Igneous Activity	Topographic Features
Transform Fault [segment of faulting *between* spreading ridges that separate plates B and C]	Shear (movement is parallel to rupture)	Strike Slip	Shallow focus only	None	Scar is developed by transform movement As movement extends beyond the spreading ridge no more faulting occurs—the aseismic scar is then called a *fracture zone*

In Section 8.1 we introduced the geosynclinal model for mountain building and indicated that it suffers from an inability to account for strong compressional forces and the scores of miles of crustal shortening that are known to have occurred. Using the plate tectonics model, these problems are resolved since the dominant mechanism for deformation is the horizontal impinging of one plate against another, thus deforming marginal sedimentary accumulations (previously called **geosynclines**) into **fold mountain** ranges such as the Appalachians [see Figure 6.25]. **Fault-block mountains,** such as those seen in the Great Basin of the western United States, may also be explained as resulting from large-scale tensional forces within a tectonic block that were induced by transform faulting along one of its margins. [This tectonic process is discussed in the appendix at the end of this chapter.] The structure of continental rocks is therefore far more complex than that of the ocean floor because the continents persist indefinitely and are repeatedly moved and deformed at the earth's surface. In contrast, the rocks of the ocean floor are created, moved, and destroyed relatively quickly and uniformly, and thus are both generally younger and less complex than continental rocks.

On a smaller scale, many of the complex structural features seen in continental deformation (discussed in Chapter 6) can be related to plate motions. Thus many *compressional* features such as folds, thrust faults, and folded mountain ranges probably originate where a continent and an adjacent plate are pushed together at subduction zones [Figure 8.27(a)]. On the other hand, many *ten-*

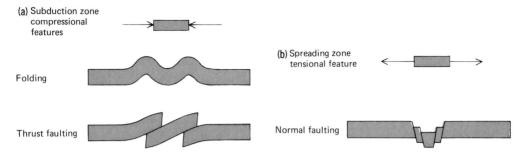

FIGURE 8.27 The relation of the most common structures of continental deformation to moving plate margins.

sional features, such as large-scale normal faults and fault-block mountains, form when continents are stretched and broken over or near new crust zones or transform faults [Figure 8.27(b)].

The discovery of plate motions clearly indicates that the basaltic rocks of the oceanic crust originate from local melting of the upper mantle, as described in Section 3.4, but this still leaves unresolved the question of the origin of the lighter, silicic rocks of the continents. Because volcanic rocks associated with subduction zones along continental margins are usually silicic andesites rather than oceanic basalts, some geologists have suggested that continents grow continuously along their margins by the addition of silicic materials that somehow separate from the mafic rocks of the descending plate or underlying mantle. An equally likely proposal suggests that the andesites result only from a deep melting of preexisting continental rocks, or of sediments derived from them, and thus shed no light on the *ultimate* source of the silicic continents. The question of origin of continents themselves thus remains a fundamental puzzle of the earth's crust.

SUMMARY OUTLINE

CONTINENTAL MOUNTAINS

8.1 Mountains and geosynclines: Most mountain ranges are made up largely of folded sedimentary rocks that originally accumulated along continental margins in thick sequences called *geosynclines;* near the axis of many mountain ranges the sediments have been melted to form elongate masses of granite.

8.2 Continental drift: The jigsaw puzzlelike fit of the continents and geologic, fossil animal, and paleoclimatic data combined with studies of "fossil rock-magnetism" have suggested that the continents have moved or "drifted"; this phenomenon is now known to be related to still more fundamental movements involving the ocean floor.

8.3 Topography of the ocean floor: The ocean floor is the site of the earth's longest and most continuous mountain chain, called the *oceanic ridge-rise system.*

8.4 Magnetism and motions of the ocean floor: The regular magnetic patterns of ocean-floor rocks show that basaltic lavas have been continuously poured out at the ridge-rise system and then moved laterally to create parallel bands of new crustal rocks; this process is called *ocean-floor spreading.*

PLATE TECTONICS

8.5 Plate tectonics and styles of lithospheric interaction: There are three types of plate boundaries—spreading ridges (divergent), subduction zones (convergent), and transform faults (shearing); angle on descent and depth reached by subducting lithosphere are controlled by plate velocities and plate compositions; mountain-building deformations of continental margins are caused by plate motions.

ADDITIONAL READINGS

* Cox, A. (ed.): *Plate Tectonics and Geomagnetic Reversals,* W. H. Freeman & Company, Publishers, San Francisco, 1973. An anthology of research articles with excellent introductions by the editor.

Dickinson, W. R.: "Plate Tectonics in Geologic History," *Science,* 174 (1971), 107–13. A brief, authoritative review article.

Dott, R. H., Jr., and R. L. Batten: *Evolution of the Earth,* 3rd ed., McGraw-Hill Book Company, New York, 1980. A textbook incorporating the plate tectonics role in the evolution of the earth.

*Keen, M. J.: *An Introduction to Marine Geology,* Pergamon Press, Inc., Elmsford, N.Y., 1968. An introductory survey with good discussions of ocean-floor topography, rocks, and structures.

*Press, F., and R. Siever (eds.): *Planet Earth, Readings from Scientific American,* W. H. Freeman & Company, Publishers, San Francisco, 1975.

*Uyeda, S.: *The New View of the Earth,* W. H. Freeman & Company, Publishers, San Francisco, 1978. An excellent introduction to plate tectonics.

*Wilson, J. T. (ed.): *Continents Adrift, Readings from Scientific American,* W. H. Freeman & Company, Publishers, San Francisco, 1972. Popular review articles on earth structure, continental drift, and plate tectonics.

* Available in paperback.

The High Cascades
vs. the Sierra Nevada
and Basin and Range Province

The western United States is very active tectonically. Recall that one of the basic tenets of plate tectonics is that plate boundaries are where the geologic "action" is, and such certainly is true for

FIGURE 8.28   Plate interaction in the region of Western North America. See text for discussion.

(a)

(b)

FIGURE 8.29 Cross-sections along lines A-A' and B-B' shown on Figure 8.28. See text for discussion.

this region (Figure 8.28). Active *volcanism* is the dominant geologic process occurring north and east of the *triple junction* where the Gorda, Pacific, and North American plates are in contact with each other, whereas active *faulting* is more characteristic for the region south and east of this point. Figure 8.28 shows the position of the Mendocino Triple Junction, which is the place where the Gorda, Pacific, and North American plates are in contact with each other. Plate tectonic theory enables us to explain why there is volcanism in the High Cascades (remember Mt. St. Helens), in contrast to normal faulting that has created horst and graben structure in the Basin and Range Province, and the impressive fault scarp on the east side of the Sierra Nevada. The explanation depends on differences in stresses exerted between the plates that are located in the two different regions.

Figure 8.29(a) shows a cross section of the Gorda Plate being subducted beneath the North American Plate. This is a boundary of convergence and thus is the setting in which partial melting of the descending lithosphere and the adjacent asthenosphere produces magma. As the magma ascends to the surface, some differenti-

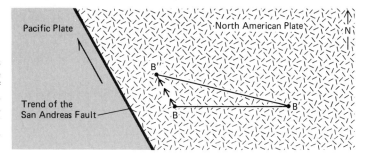

FIGURE 8.30 Tensional stresses within the North America Plate due to the northwestward shearing of its western region in the same direction as the Pacific Plate's movement. B-B′ is lengthened to B″-B′ as point B is sheared northwestward to point B″.

ation takes place within it. There is also some assimilation of silicic rock material from the continental lithosphere through which it rises. These two processes allow for eruptions of lavas that are primarily andesitic, and sometimes they are even more silicic than that. All the great composite volcanoes located around the circumpacific are of this origin. Those that compose the High Cascades are no exception.

South of the Mendocino Triple Junction, plate interaction between the Pacific Plate and the North American Plate is along a zone of transform faulting, with the San Andreas Fault being the principal surface of faulting within the zone. The total rate of right-lateral displacement between the Pacific and North American plates is between 5.5 and 6.0 cm/yr, yet the San Andreas Fault, itself, appears to have accommodated only 35 percent to 40 percent of this slip for a long period of geologic time. Where has all the remaining offset gone? Much of it, to be sure, has occurred along a system of branching and secondary faults that are subparallel to the San Andreas. All these faults, together, constitute the San Andreas Fault *Zone*, in contrast to the San Andreas *Fault*, which refers only to the *master trace* of transform movement.

Even so, a significant amount of right-lateral slip between the Pacific Plate and the North American Plate occurs elsewhere within the western United States. It seems likely that most of this offset is accommodated by normal slip-faulting in a region extending from the eastern scarp of the Sierra Nevada to the eastern edge of the Basin and Range Province [Figure 8.29(b)]. Imagine the effect of northwestward drag on the Pacific Plate occurring not just on the San Andreas Fault but extending all across the region shown along line B–B′. If the faulting in this region were parallel to the San Andreas, the slip would be purely right-lateral, but most of the faults in the Basin and Range Province are oriented in a more nearly north-south direction, thus requiring dip-slip movement to accommodate the tensional stresses.

Why tensional stresses? Consider Figure 8.30. As the western region of the North American Plate is sheared to the northwest (parallel to the direction in which the Pacific Plate is moving), point B will move toward point B′, thus lengthening the distance to point B′. Any faulting that occurs in this region along north-south trends will have to express this lengthening; thus the movement will require *normal slip* [Figure 8.29(b)].

Now we see why regions that are separated by the Mendocino Triple Junction are so different from each other. Both the Cascades and the Sierra Nevada–Basin and Range regions are very active, yet compressional tectonics and volcanism are manifested in the Cascades, and shearing and tensional stresses give rise to active faulting as the dominant tectonic activity south and east of the Mendocino Triple Junction. Plate boundaries are the places where dynamic geologic activity occurs, but when the nature of plate interactions at these boundaries differs, the style of tectonism responds accordingly.

Weathering and Water on the Land

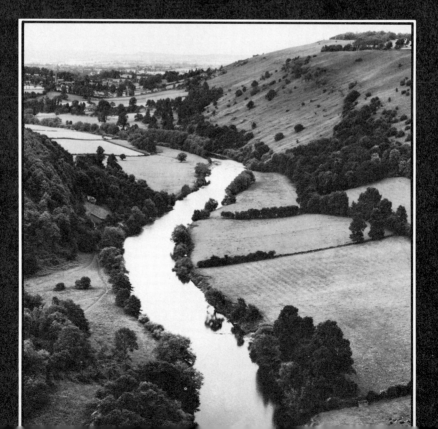

N PREVIOUS CHAPTERS WE HAVE considered the materials of the earth and the tectonic processes that cause them to move from their environments of origin into new positions, such as when a marine sandstone formation is folded into a mountainous region. We shall now discuss the destructional processes of weathering and erosion that operate on these rocks and minerals.

WEATHERING

WEATHERING PROCESSES

Weathering concerns the static (in-place) alteration of rock material, an initial result of which is the production of soil. **Erosion,** on the other hand, involves the dynamic process of transporting rock debris (boulders, sand grains, soil, etc.) from one place, commonly called the *source terrane*, to another, the *environment of deposition* where sedimentation occurs. As a general rule, weathering precedes erosion.

There are two principal processes by which air and water act to change the structure and composition of rocks at the earth's surface. The first are **mechanical weathering** processes, the most important of which is known as **frost wedging.** Most rocks exposed near the surface have many small cracks and cavities filled with rainwater. Because water expands in volume as it freezes, it can exert tremendous pressures on the surrounding rock as temperatures fall below freezing. When freezing and thawing alternate, as often occurs as the land surface is warmed during the day and cooled at night in polar and cool-temperate regions, the repeated stresses of frost wedging are a significant cause of the breakup of massive rocks into smaller fragments (Figure 9.1).

Of still greater importance than mechanical weathering are the many processes, grouped together under the term **chemical weathering,** whereby both the structure *and* the chemical composition of rocks are changed. Most of these processes center on the chemical actions of the earth's surface waters. Absolutely pure water is chemically rather inactive, but natural surface waters are normally

FIGURE 9.1 The reduction of a massive limestone boulder to small fragments by mechanical frost wedging. (From Thornbury, "Principles of Geomorphology," 1969; photos by Alan Pratt.)

slightly acidic due to the presence of dissolved CO_2 from the atmosphere, some of which combines with hydrogen in the water to form a weak solution of carbonic acid. Dead and decaying plant and animal remains also contribute acids to surface waters. Like most weak acids, these surface waters are good solvents and slowly dissolve many minerals; they also enter directly into chemical reactions to form new minerals. See Box 9.1.

We saw in Chapter 3 that most of the earth's crust is composed of either silicon-rich granite or magnesium- and iron-rich basalt. The minerals of these two igneous rocks are therefore the primary materials subjected to weathering as they are exposed to acid waters at the earth's surface. Such waters ultimately convert the feldspars of granite and basalt to the fine-grained sheet silicate **clay minerals,** which contain a relatively large amount of water in their crystal structures and are much more stable than are most igneous minerals under the temperatures and chemical environments of the earth's surface (Figure 9.2). Quartz, which is extremely resistant to chemical attack, is preserved without chemical alteration.

During alteration, much of the potassium, sodium, calcium, magnesium, and silicon of the original igneous minerals goes into

BOX 9.1

Weathering by the chemical attack of weak acid in ground water

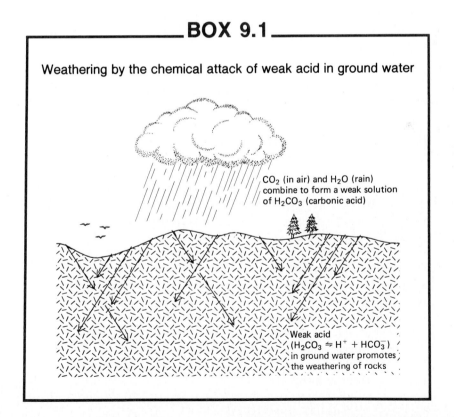

CO_2 (in air) and H_2O (rain) combine to form a weak solution of H_2CO_3 (carbonic acid)

Weak acid $(H_2CO_3 \leftrightharpoons H^+ + HCO_3^-)$ in ground water promotes the weathering of rocks

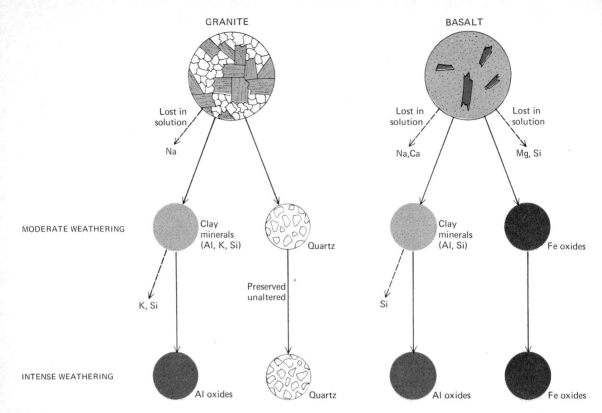

FIGURE 9.2 Schematic summary of the breakdown of granite and basalt by chemical weathering. Feldspar alters to clay minerals which under very intense weathering may, in turn, alter to aluminum oxides. Pyroxene and olivine alter to iron oxides. Quartz is preserved without chemical alteration.

solution and is removed from the place of origin by flowing water. Eventually, these elements are either deposited elsewhere in new sedimentary minerals or added by rivers to the oceans, which contain huge quantities of land-derived dissolved materials. Of the half-dozen or so common elements in igneous rocks, only iron and aluminum are relatively insoluble and tend to persist in solid form under the attack of chemical weathering. The iron is quickly converted to insoluble, rustlike oxide minerals, and the aluminum forms a principal constituent of the clay minerals. When chemical weathering is especially intense, even the silicon-oxygen tetrahedra of the clay minerals themselves may be removed by solution, leaving only a silicon-free residue of aluminum oxide (Figure 9.2).

The attack on fresh rock by weathering agents often creates rounded and smoothly curved surfaces, a process known as **spheroidal weathering** [Figure 9.3(a)]. Chemical decomposition of rock-forming minerals proceeds from all joints and cracks in the rock where air and water are allowed to migrate. As can be seen in

WEATHERING AND WATER ON THE LAND

(a)

Chemical attack on all surfaces is deepest and most intense at a corner.

(b)

FIGURE 9.3 Spheroidal weathering and exfoliation. (a) Spheroidal weathering. (b) Schematic diagram. (c) Exfoliating granite dome in Yosemite. (a:E. A. Hay; c: R. Strauss.)

(c)

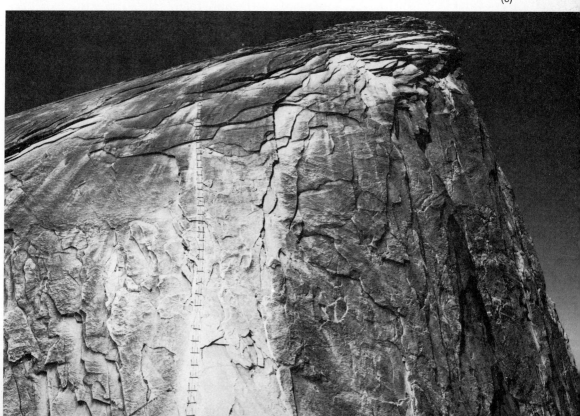

Figure 9.3(b), this accentuates the depth and intensity of attack at any edge or corner, thus causing a spheroidal surface to evolve. On a much larger scale, the process of **exfoliation** yields similar-appearing curved surfaces of rock [Figure 9.3(c)]. It is believed that the mechanism of exfoliation, however, is distinctly different from spheroidal weathering. Massive rocks, such as some sparsely jointed granites and sandstones, are believed to expand slightly as the pressure on them is reduced by erosional removal of overlying rocks, much in the manner a balloon expands as it rises into regions of less pressure. Expansion of the rock causes fractures to form that are approximately parallel to the surface of erosion, giving rise to the onionskinlike layered appearance known as *exfoliation*. Then weathering, both chemical and mechanical, begins to attack the rock along its newly formed fractures, causing slabs of rock to break away and yielding the layered look seen in Figure 9.3(c).

9.2
SOIL

The result of mechanical and chemical weathering is to cover much of the land surface with a thin veneer of altered rock debris known as **soil**. Soil, as we might predict from our discussion of the products of weathering, is made up primarily of tiny particles of various clay minerals mixed in varying proportions with larger particles of quartz. Because quartz is the only really stable igneous mineral under the action of chemical weathering, most of the gravel and sand-sized particles of the earth's surface are in large part composed of it.

In addition to the clay and quartz fragments produced by rock weathering, most soils also contain from 1 percent to as much as 50 percent organic carbon compounds derived from the decay of plants and animals supported by the soil. These organic constituents are extremely important components of soils, for they are closely interrelated with soil texture, structure, and composition. Plants, in particular, profoundly affect soils in many ways. By using dissolved elements left over from weathering—particularly potassium, sodium, and calcium—in their metabolic processes, plants tend to retain these elements near their site of formation instead of allowing them to be dispersed by moving water. These components are returned to the soil as the plants die and decay and are then used by new plants in an endless cycle. Only when this cycle is broken—for example, by harvesting the plants instead of allowing them to die and decay—are these nutrient elements permanently removed from the soil. It is for this reason, of course, that supplemental nutrients in the form of fertilizer are necessary for most cultivated soils.

WEATHERING AND WATER ON THE LAND

Plant roots and burrowing animals also tend to facilitate weathering by making the soil porous so that surface water can penetrate to unweathered, underlying rocks. In addition, the presence of organic acids from plant decay adds to the chemical activity of surface waters, as we have already noted. These processes tend, in general, to sharply increase the rate of chemical weathering on those portions of the land surface that are covered by plants. At the same time, plants facilitate the accumulation of weathered debris as soil by binding together the particles with their roots and by protecting the soil surface from the erosive effects of wind and water.

In those many parts of the land surface where plants are present and where the soil consequently contains significant organic matter, soils tend to have a definite cross-sectional structure known as a **soil profile.** Typically, such profiles show three horizons of changing composition and structure with depth (Figure 9.4). The uppermost

FIGURE 9.4   A generalized soil profile.

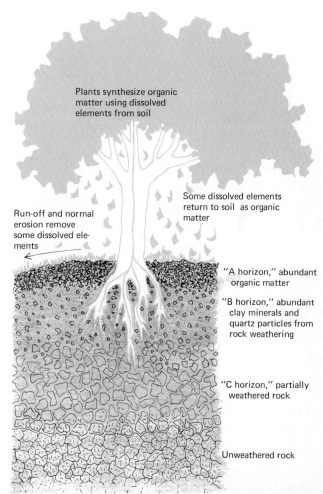

Plants synthesize organic matter using dissolved elements from soil

Some dissolved elements return to soil as organic matter

Run-off and normal erosion remove some dissolved elements

"A horizon," abundant organic matter

"B horizon," abundant clay minerals and quartz particles from rock weathering

"C horizon," partially weathered rock

Unweathered rock

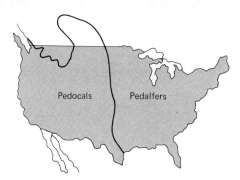

FIGURE 9.5 Generalized distribution of major soil types in temperate North America. Pedalfers result from greater chemical weathering in regions of higher rainfall and temperature. (See text for discussion.)

and thinnest horizon contains abundant decaying organic matter from the overlying plants and a minimum of inorganic constituents that are quickly removed by intense chemical weathering near the surface. Immediately below this is a thicker zone with less organic matter, where many of the weathered constituents, such as clay materials, quartz sand, and dissolved elements, are concentrated. Below this is a still thicker horizon of only partially weathered underlying rock that generally lacks organic matter but that is in the process of being converted to soil by slow chemical weathering. Superimposed on this basic threefold structure are numerous variations that permit soil scientists to define and classify seemingly endless minor soil types.

The kinds and intensity of weathering processes, and the soils that result from them, are closely controlled by climate. In the United States, for example, two major soil types are geographically distributed primarily as a function of average annual rainfall (Figure 9.5): **pedalfers** are relatively rich in aluminum and iron, whereas **pedocals** contain abundant calcium carbonate. The former is favored by a warm, humid climate, and the latter develops in regions of less rainfall. A third major soil type develops in tropical climates where chemical weathering is increased by abundant surface water and high temperatures. Because of intense weathering, tropical regions commonly have silicon-poor soils composed mostly of iron and aluminum oxides (Figure 9.6). Where iron oxides predominate, the soils are red and are known as **laterite;** where aluminum oxides dominate, the soils are usually yellow or gray and are known as **bauxite** (Figure 9.7). The intense weathering and abundant vegetation of tropical regions cause an extensive soil development; tropical soils commonly reach thicknesses exceeding 30 m (90 ft) and have an average thickness of over 3 m (9 ft).

Chemical weathering is the dominant process in both tropical and temperate climates, but in the latter, the generally lower rainfalls and temperatures make the process less intense. In temperate soils, enough silicon normally remains to make clay minerals, rather

WEATHERING AND WATER ON THE LAND

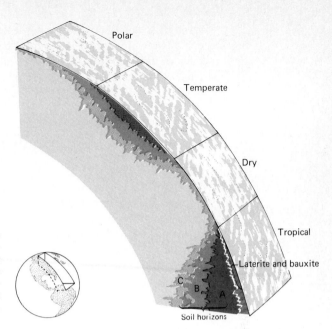

FIGURE 9.6 Interrelations of soil and climate. Thick soils develop only under temperate and tropical climates where vegetation is abundant. The high temperature and rainfall of tropical regions lead to intense chemical weathering, deep soils, and residual iron and aluminum oxides (laterite and bauxite). The vertical scale is exaggerated.

FIGURE 9.7 Bauxite: the result of intense chemical weathering. (Reynolds Aluminum Company.)

than oxides, the dominant constituents. In contrast to tropical soils, temperate soils have an average thickness of only about 1 m (3 ft) (Figure 9.6).

In both tropical and temperate regions, the presence of a permanent protecting cover of vegetation permits a relatively thick soil layer to accumulate. In polar and dry climates, on the other hand, vegetation is sparse, and the products of rock weathering are exposed to continuous removal by wind and water. Under such conditions, normally only a very thin soil cover, with abundant exposure of bare rock surfaces, develops. In polar regions, mechanical frost wedging of the exposed rock supplements chemical breakdown as an important weathering process.

WATER ON THE LAND

Weathering is the first step in the sequence of events that shapes landscapes, for weathering reduces massive rock to small particles that can be removed from their place of origin by flowing water, wind, and ice. Because of weathering and removal of rock debris, the land surface is constantly being worn away. Indeed, were it not for the opposing internal forces of isostasy, mountain building, and volcanism, the land surface would have long ago been reduced to a flat, featureless plain by these processes of erosion.

Weathering, we have seen, is closely controlled by climate; the same is true of the other processes that shape the land surface. The most powerful agent of land sculpture is *moving water*; and under tropical and temperate climates, it is the principal agent in shaping landscapes.

Each year, when averaged over the entire surface of the earth, a layer of water about 1 m (3.3 ft) deep is evaporated into the atmosphere, and each year the same meter of water is precipitated somewhere on the earth's surface as rain or snow. The amounts evaporated and precipitated differ, however, over the land and ocean. Over oceans, more water is evaporated than is precipitated; this excess falls on the land surface where, on the average, precipitation exceeds evaporation (Figure 9.8). In order to complete the cycle, this excess ocean-derived water dropped on land must ultimately return to the ocean; this occurs primarily as streams flow across the land and empty into the sea. The energy of this relatively small quantity of excess water, propelled by gravity as it moves over the land surface toward the sea, is the principal agent of land sculpture.

Most of the water falling on land does not pass immediately into moving streams for the return trip to the ocean. Only about one-eighth reaches streams directly as runoff from the land surface; the remaining seven-eighths is absorbed into soil and rocks to become **ground water.** Even this ground water ultimately reaches streams and returns to the ocean, but its progress is far slower and less direct than that of surface runoff.

In addition to streams and ground water, there is one additional form in which liquid water occurs on land—that is, as lakes, which are relatively stationary concentrations of surface water. Neither

FIGURE 9.8 The hydrologic cycle. More water is evaporated than precipitated over the ocean; the excess is transported and precipitated over land and is ultimately returned to the ocean by streams and rivers. These relatively small quantities of water moving across the land are the principal agent of land sculpture.

land precipatation

ocean evaporation

lakes nor ground water plays a significant role in shaping the land surface when compared with the far more energetic action of moving streams. Consequently, we shall only briefly consider some of the principal characteristics of the former before looking more closely at streams.

9.3
LAKES

Viewed over millions of years of geologic history, lakes are extremely transient features of the earth's surface. They form when obstructions of rock or soil temporarily block the path of flowing water, and they disappear as the obstructions are worn away and as deposition of sediments fills the depression occupied by the lake. During their relatively short existence, lakes, particularly very large ones, manifest many of the same phenomena as the ocean—for example, surface waves and temperatures that decrease downward due to surface warming and mixing. Most lakes differ profoundly from the ocean, however, in lacking a high concentration of dissolved materials.

Normal ocean water contains about 3.5 percent dissolved elements. A few "saline lakes" in dry regions where rains are infrequent and evaporation is intense—lakes such as the Dead and Caspian seas and Great Salt Lake—also have high concentrations of dissolved materials, although not ordinarily in the same proportions as in the ocean. Most lakes, however, have only an insignificant fraction of 1 percent dissolved matter. Because of this negligible salinity, lakes differ from the ocean in several other important properties. In the ocean, differences in both temperature and salinity are important in causing density differences that lead to current movements. In lakes, only thermal differences occur, and density-induced currents are thus less pronounced than in the ocean. Another result of the lack of dissolved materials is that lake water freezes at 0°C (32°F) rather than having the indefinite freezing properties of seawater. As a consequence, lakes in very cold regions commonly freeze solid to depths of 100 m (330 ft) or more, whereas ice on the ocean (other than in land-derived icebergs) seldom exceeds 3 m (10 ft) in thickness.

9.4
GROUND WATER

Under the influence of gravity, most of the water falling on the land surface sinks into the underlying soil and rock to become **ground water**. As a result, except for a relatively thin outer layer that dries between rainfalls, all cracks, voids, and pores in continental rocks that are located above the depth (commonly thousands of feet) where they are closed by pressure are permanently saturated with water. The upper surface of this zone of saturation, which separates it from the periodically dried layer above, is known as the **water table**. In any one region the depth of the water table below the surface varies with topography, which it follows by rising under hills and dropping along the sides of valleys [Figure 9.9(a)]. When the water table intersects the land surface, *springs* result.

Ground water is not usually stationary; rather it moves very slowly under the influence of gravity until it ultimately reaches the surface at some lower elevation. Permanently flowing streams of tropical and temperate climates normally move in valleys whose bottoms lie *below* the local water table [Figure 9.9(a)]; much ground water ultimately reaches the surface by slow seepage into these **perennial streams**. In dry climates, on the other hand, this process is reversed. There, temporary, **ephemeral streams**, formed after the infrequent rainfalls, lose water to the ground and ultimately disappear until the next rainfall.

Ground water is a valuable natural resource in many parts of the world. A body of rock that holds and can yield large volumes of water is known as an **aquifer** [Figure 9.9(b)]. To serve as an aquifer, a rock unit must be both porous and permeable—that is, it must have a significant volume of void space (*porosity*) and it must also have large enough openings between its grains to allow water to pass through (*permeability*). Sandstones whose voids between grains are not filled with cement or clay are very good aquifers, for example; shales, on the other hand, are poor sources of water even though

(a)

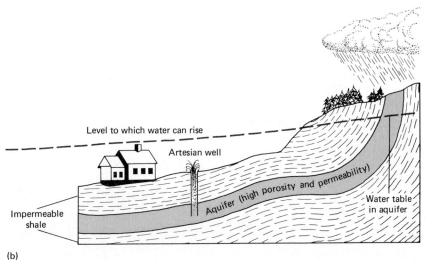

(b)

FIGURE 9.9 Ground water. (a) The relationship of ground water to climate and stream flow. (b) Conditions for an artesian well.

they have high porosity (sometimes as much as 40 percent void), for in a shale the grains are so small that water molecules cannot easily pass between them.

In situations where a good aquifer is overlain by an impermeable rock unit, as shown in Figure 9.9(b), free-flowing conditions may exist for wells that penetrate down to the aquifer: these are known as **artesian wells**.

Although ground water has great importance to man, besides its crucial role in weathering and soil formation, it plays a relatively minor part in shaping landscapes—with one very important exception, which occurs in regions underlain by limestone. Limestone alone among the common rocks of the earth's crust is readily dissolved by dilute acids. Waters of the land surface are usually slightly

(a)

Sinkholes

Water table

Caverns

(b)

(c)

FIGURE 9.10 Karst topography. (a) Caverns, sinkholes, and related features commonly form in regions underlain by limestone, which is readily dissolved by acidic ground water. (b) Karst topography in central Kentucky. (c) Close-up of a small, deep sinkhole in northern England. (b: John S. Shelton; c: Geological Survey of Great Britain.)

acidic both because of dissolved atmospheric carbon dioxide and because of the addition of acids from decaying plants. For this reason, ground water commonly dissolves significant amounts of the underlying rock in regions where limestone is exposed at or near the earth's surface. This dissolution leads to large underground cavities, channels, and passageways, which may open to the surface as *sinkholes*. Regions showing these distinctive features are said to exhibit **Karst topography**, named after the Karst region of Yugoslavia, where solution features are particularly well developed (Figure 9.10). Most of the earth's large dramatic underground caverns are developed in such regions.

9.5
STREAMS

The third, and geologically most important, form in which liquid water occurs on land is as **streams**, relatively long, narrow concentrations moving downward across the land surface under the influence of gravity. In everyday language we normally make a size distinction between smaller "streams" and larger "rivers," but geologists, recognizing that all gradations exist between the smallest flowing trickle and the largest rivers, generally refer to *all* flowing waters on the land surface as "streams."

Streams in tropical and temperate regions derive their water from two sources. Roughly half their flow comes directly from surface runoff of rain or of water from melting snow. The other half comes from slow seepage of ground water into the stream channel, which normally lies below the local water table—at least in perennial, or permanently flowing, streams. It is this slow, continuous influx of ground water along stream channels that maintains their flow between rainfalls. Conversely, stream flooding during periods of heavy rainfall is a result of the greatly increased surface runoff. In dry climates the water table is generally so deep that ephemeral streams receive none of their water from ground-water seepage. Instead, they are fed only from surface runoff after the infrequent rainfalls and are dry for much of each year (Figure 9.11).

Gravity is the principal driving force of stream (and groundwater) movements; it begins to act whenever solar energy moves water from the ocean into the atmosphere and deposits it above sea level on the land surface. The gravitational force then comes into play and moves the water downward, toward sea level, but it is opposed by complex frictional forces as the water impinges on solid rock and sedimentary particles. The net result of the impelling gravitational force and the opposing frictional forces is to impart a particular speed or *velocity* to the moving water.

(a)

(b)

(c)

FIGURE 9.11 Varieties of streams. (a) Perennial stream in southern England. (b) Ephemeral stream in southern Arizona in dry stage and (c) in flood. (a: Geological Survey of Great Britain; b,c: Tad Nichols.)

In seeking to analyze the dynamics of stream flow, geologists in recent years have made intensive studies of many secondary factors that influence the two primary forces of gravity and friction in stream flow. The force of gravity is primarily a function of two such secondary factors: the volume of the flowing water, which is called the *stream discharge*, and the *slope* of the surface over which it moves. The opposing frictional forces, on the other hand, are primarily related to two other factors: the amount of sediment moved by the flowing water, known as the *sediment load*, and the *shape of the channel* through which the water flows. These four

WEATHERING AND WATER ON THE LAND

secondary factors—discharge, slope, sediment load, and channel shape—are closely and complexly interrelated with one another and with their ultimate result, the velocity of the moving water.

Analyses of records of velocity, discharge, slope, sediment load, and channel shape from hundreds of streams have shown that the interaction of these factors is not random but varies in a systematic way; that is, the factors are so balanced that changes in one lead to surprisingly regular and predictable changes in the others (Figure 9.12). If, for example, the discharge at some point along a stream is doubled after a rainfall, the stream velocity will increase by a factor of 1.3, the channel shape will change by a small but predictable amount as the water rises and the channel width and depth increase, and the amount of sediment carried by the stream will increase by a factor of 8. The mere fact that such increases take place is not surprising. Streams are easily seen to become wider and deeper when discharge increases during floods. Likewise, the fact that large quantities of sediment are moved during floods is clear because most streams flow on **flood plains** (Figures 9.13 and 9.14)—valleys partially filled with loose sand and clay that have been transported during periods of high discharge and dropped as the stream recedes into its normal channel. It is not the fact that such changes in shape and sediment load take place that is so astonishing, but that the *quantity* of such changes are regular and predictable, as established by careful observation and analysis.

FIGURE 9.12 The dynamics of stream flow at a single point along a stream. Sediment load, water velocity, and channel shape all increase regularly, but at different rates, with increasing discharge. (Modified from Leopold et al., "Fluvial processes in Geomorphology," 1964.)

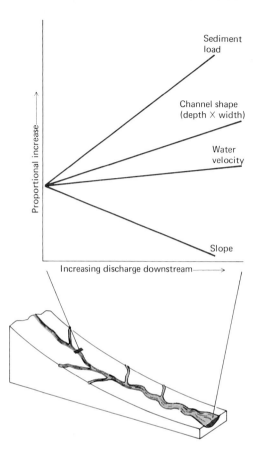

FIGURE 9.13 Stream flow. The dynamics of stream flow with increasing distance downstream. Sediment load, channel shape, and water velocity increase and slope decreases, with increasing discharge. Although steep mountain streams appear to flow faster than those in relatively flat alluvial valleys, careful measurements show that this is not normally true. (Modified from Leopold et al., "Fluvial Processes in Geomorphology, 1964.)

Labels on figure:
- Sediment load
- Channel shape (depth × width)
- Water velocity
- Slope
- Proportional increase
- Increasing discharge downstream

FIGURE 9.14 Typical meanders of a small stream across a floodplain in Colorado. (Tad Nichols.)

WEATHERING AND WATER ON THE LAND

So far we have considered only changes at a single point along the course of a stream. If, instead, we consider the interrelations of discharge, velocity, channel shape, and sediment load through the entire length of the stream, we find equally regular, but somewhat different, relationships (Figure 9.13). In perennial streams, discharge normally increases downstream as water is added from run-off, ground-water seepage, and the inflow of tributary streams. Sediment load and channel width and depth increase regularly as discharge increases downstream. At the same time, slope—the one factor that (obviously) cannot be considered at a single point on the stream—decreases regularly downstream, so that in longitudinal section the channel has a concave-up profile that flattens in the lower part of the stream course (Figure 9.13). One of the most surprising results of modern stream analyses was the discovery that these factors interact to cause a small but regular velocity *increase* downstream. This conclusion had not been expected since rushing mountain streams flowing on steep slopes *appear* to move faster than large rivers flowing on flat flood plains (Figure 9.13). Measurements show, however, that this is not usually true, for the downstream decrease in slope is more than compensated for by the decreased friction of a larger channel and the increase in volume.

Before moving on to consider how stream flow shapes the land, there is one rather puzzling characteristic of streams to be considered. When viewed from above, as from an airplane or on a map, large streams almost never flow in straight linear channels but instead follow a regular zigzag series of loops known as meanders (Figure 9.14). These have the effect of increasing the channel length and thus adding to the distance through which frictional forces can act; they also decrease the channel slope, with the result that the gravitational impelling force is lessened. For these reasons, meanders are believed to be somehow related to the dynamic balance of frictional and gravitational forces in stream flow, but as yet there is no satisfactory explanation of their exact cause.

LAND SCULPTURE

Shaping of the land surface takes place as rock debris produced by weathering is moved downward by gravity toward its ultimate resting place, the ocean. These movements of rock debris usually involve flowing water, but they may begin under the influence of gravity alone, as when soil slides down a steep hillside, or when a block of rock, loosened by weathering, falls from the face of a cliff. Such direct movements of weathered debris by gravity are called mass wasting (Figure 9.15). When mass wasting combines with

FIGURE 9.15 Erosion of the land surface. Weathering and mass wasting deliver rock debris to streams where it is transported as sediment.

weathering and stream transportation, the result is the formation of *valleys*, empty spaces formerly filled with rock, bounded by *hillslopes*, curved surfaces underlain by rock that is still undergoing weathering and erosion.

9.6
MASS WASTING

Soil and other rock debris formed by weathering move downward under the influence of gravity, just as water does, whenever the gravitational impelling force overcomes opposing frictional forces. On slopes steeper than about 40 degrees, gravity exceeds frictional resistance for *all* kinds of rock debris, and therefore only massive bedrock, exposed as cliffs, occurs on such steep slopes. Mass wasting also continuously takes place, however, on more gentle, soil-covered slopes. This mass wasting is of two sorts. Most commonly the frictional resistance is so great that downslope movements are very slow, from one to a few centimeters per year; such movements are known as **creep.** All soil-covered slopes undergo creep, which is a principal cause of tilted fences, cracked sidewalks, bent tree trunks, and other common hillslope phenomena (Figure 9.16).

More rapid downslope movements by mass wasting are known collectively as **landslides.*** The speed at which rock debris moves in landslides varies from several meters per *day* to several meters per *second*, but is always much more rapid than the centimeters-per-year movement of creep. Rapid landslides are especially common on slopes where frictional forces are reduced by the lubricating effects of unusual amounts of ground water. Such lubrication often occurs where soil is underlain by an impermeable layer of clay or, in polar climates, frozen ground water, both of which limit and concentrate the downward penetration of surface water (Figure 9.17). Although landslides are often large and spectacular and can

---

* Chapter 12 contains a more complete discussion of landslides as they relate to man and his structures.

FIGURE 9.16 Soil creep. (William C. Bradley.)

(a)

FIGURE 9.17 Examples of mass wasting. (a) Small landslides. (b) Large landslide. (c) Rockfall and talus. (a: Wisconsin Conservation Department; b: W. R. Cotton; c: R. Strauss.)

(c)

(b)

cause great destruction, they are less important in shaping landscapes than are the slower but more nearly continuous movements of creep. Often, particularly in regions of strong mechanical weathering, rock fragments will loosen and fall a considerable distance under the influence of gravity alone. These fragments are called **talus**, and in some places they sometimes form steep and jumbled talus slopes [Figure 9.17(c)].

9.7
STREAM EROSION

Mass-wasting processes account for most of the *initial* movement of rock debris, but it is transportation of this debris by streams that normally carries it from its immediate area of origin and thus makes possible a continuous wearing away of the land surface. Solid debris particles are moved by flowing water in either of two ways: They may be completely surrounded and supported by the moving water as **suspended load;** or they may be rolled, slid, or bounced along the stream bottom as **bed load** (Figure 9.18). In general, larger and heavier particles move as bed load and smaller and lighter particles as suspended load. In addition to solid debris, streams also transport a **dissolved load** of ions weathered from rocks of the crust.

In the last section we noted that the total amount of sediment moved by a stream increases very rapidly as the discharge and velocity of the stream increase (Figures 9.12 and 9.13). For this reason, most sediment movement takes place at times of high water, when the transporting capacity of the stream is at a maximum. Between periods of flood, the sediment is temporarily deposited in the stream channel or on the adjacent flood plain. Most stream valleys are at least partially filled with such sediment, called **alluvium**, that is temporarily at rest on its downslope journey. The ultimate resting place of this alluvial debris is the ocean, for sea level marks the lowest

Movement of a
suspended load
particle

FIGURE 9.18 Transportation of debris by moving water.

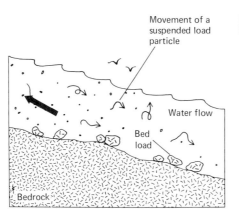

Water flow

Bed
load

Bedrock

point to which streams can ordinarily flow. On entering the ocean, the stream-transported sediments are moved, sorted, and reworked by waves and currents; ultimately they come to rest in beaches and other *depositional* landscape features.

The combined effect of mass wasting and stream transportation is to shape the land surface into valleys and hillslopes. Valleys result from the erosional action of the streams that flow through them. In general, two types of valley-stream relationships occur. In rugged mountainous regions where slopes are steep, the sedimentary debris supplied by mass wasting is readily transported, and streams commonly flow directly on the underlying rock. When this occurs, chemical solution and mechanical abrasion cause the stream to cut actively into the rock to form steep-walled **V-shaped valleys** [Figures 9.19(a) and 9.20(a)].

In contrast, on the more gentle slopes that characterize the lower reaches of most streams, valleys are floored by large quantities of alluvial debris that make up the relatively flat flood plain over which the stream flows. Even during flood, such streams generally erode only these flood-plain sediments rather than cutting downward into the underlying rock. The resulting flat-floored **alluvial valleys** [Figures 9.19(b) and 9.20(b)] usually show characteristic patterns of temporary lakes, terraces, and other topographic features

FIGURE 9.19 Types of valleys. (a) V-shaped and (b) alluvial valleys. Alluvial valleys, which characterize the lower reaches of most streams, commonly show abandoned channels, cut banks, terraces, and other features caused by the shifting channel and moving alluvium.

Eroded directly by stream down cutting

Eroded by mass-wasting and subsequent stream transport

(a)

Valley wall

Abandoned channels

Terrace

Cut bank

Lake or swamp in abandoned channel

Alluvium

Flood plain

(b)

(a)

(b)

FIGURE 9.20 (a) V-shaped valley in Colorado. (b) Alluvial valley in Hawaii. (R. Strauss.)

Convex

Concave

FIGURE 9.21 A typical hillslope profile.

caused by the intermittent erosion and deposition of the underlying sediment. Some of these features are illustrated in Figure 9.19(b).

V-shaped and alluvial valleys are easier to characterize than are the hillslopes that bound them. When viewed in cross section, most hillslopes have a *profile* that is convex in the higher parts and concave in the lower (Figure 9.21). The upper, convex slope is thought to be shaped primarily by weathering and creep, whereas the lower, concave portion results from fluid transportation by concentrated surface water runoff, leading to a more rapid removal of debris. Beyond this, the exact shape and form of hillslopes are a result of a complex and poorly understood interaction between the various processes of erosion, the structure and composition of the underlying bedrock, and the length of time the rock has been exposed to weathering and erosion.

When viewed from a larger perspective, streams develop drainage patterns that reflect regional structure and the relative erodibility of the bedrock across which they flow. Contrast, for example,

FIGURE 9.22 Diagrammatic composite of stream drainage patterns. (a) Trellis pattern resulting from structural control. (b) Dendritic pattern, indicating a lack of structural control. (c) Radial pattern developed on a volcano.

the three drainage patterns shown in Figure 9.22. What can each tell us about the underlying bedrock? The *trellis pattern* in Figure 9.22(a) suggests a strong *structural influence* on the stream's position. It has cut the deepest valleys along the trend (strike) of more easily eroded layered rocks, hence the trellislike pattern reflecting the regular geometry of the bedrock. The *dendritic pattern* in Figure 9.22(b), in marked contrast, lacks geometric regularity altogether; it appears to be random, and therefore lacking in any structural influence on the part of the underlying rock. Flat-lying sedimentary or volcanic rocks, or nonlayered plutonic rocks, would all erode in this manner. Finally, a *radial pattern* [Figure 9.22(c)] is commonly developed on domal or cone-shaped structures. Large volcanoes provide our best example of radial drainage patterns.

9.8
THE GRADED STREAM
AS AN EQUILIBRIUM CONCEPT

Let us now reconsider the factors controlling the effectiveness of stream erosion and analyze them in more detail in order to learn how changes in a stream's erosional activities can be predicted.

First, it can be noted that erosion, and hence transportation of debris, requires *work*; furthermore, work requires the expenditure of *energy*. There are two kinds of energy of primary concern to our understanding of stream erosion: potential energy and kinetic energy (*potential energy* is energy of position, and *kinetic energy* is energy of motion). In a somewhat oversimplified manner, we may conceive of stream transportation as being a geologic process whereby the potential energy of water derived from rain and snow at high elevations is converted to a moving force (hence kinetic energy) capable of doing the work of rock transportation.

The amount of potential energy locked up in stream water is determined by two variables: mass and elevation. It is easy to see that the potential for water to do work will increase if (1) the amount, or mass, of water increases, and also if (2) a given amount is raised to a higher elevation so that it can fall farther. By way of analogy, consider the potential in an axe for doing the work of splitting logs: Neglecting the force of the axe wielder, it is clear that the heavier-headed axe raised higher above the log can do the work most rapidly. This work on the log cannot actually be accomplished, however, until the force of gravity acts on the axe, causing it to convert its energy of position into energy of motion. The work is achieved by the *moving* mass, not the *elevated* mass. By applying this example to stream water, we can see the importance of gravity acting on water masses at high elevations.

Imagine a mass of water perched at position A in Figure 9.23. By the time that water reaches sea level at position B, it will have expended all the potential energy it possessed by virtue of its position 600 m (2,000 ft) above sea level (at A). It is theoretically conceivable, but not actually possible, that the water could convert all its potential energy into downslope acceleration (velocity increase), in which case the water emerging at B would be a smooth flow moving at an incredible speed. Instead, what always happens in nature is that as the potential energy is converted into acceleration, the moving water soon impacts the stream bed with enough force to dislodge

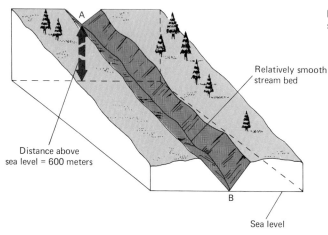

FIGURE 9.23 Block diagram of a stream valley. (See text for discussion.)

Relatively smooth stream bed

Distance above sea level = 600 meters

B

Sea level

WEATHERING AND WATER ON THE LAND

fragments. This hypothetical event brings about two highly significant changes in the stream: first, the newly roughened surface causes turbulence; and second, the fragments begin the process of being transported as part of the **bed load** (Figure 9.18). The newly created turbulence, a condition wherein water is moving in random directions rather than smoothly in the downslope direction, allows the stream now to transport small particles in the **suspended load**. The overall effect of roughening the channel, therefore, is to increase the work done by the stream at the expense of decreasing the rate of downslope acceleration.

Let us now consider a stream that eventually achieves a condition of equilibrium between its potential for erosion and its potential for deposition, and what takes place when this equilibrium is disrupted. Our model for such a stream in equilibrium is called a **graded stream**. Even though it is unlikely that a perfectly graded stream can be found in nature, the concept is nevertheless universally useful. Consider the map in Figure 9.24, which shows a stream network of Lizard Creek (A–B) and its tributaries. The long profile (side view of the straightened-out stream bed) of Lizard Creek might have a generalized appearance as shown in Figure 9.25.

What does it mean to call Lizard Creek a graded stream? It means that it is neither eroding nor depositing sediment—it is in *equilibrium*. It has achieved a delicate adjustment of its channel shape, roughness, and slope with the amount of water that flows through it, so that all the sediment that enters is carried through its entire length, with no excess of energy available to erode addi-

FIGURE 9.24 Map of Lizard Creek drainage system. (See text.)

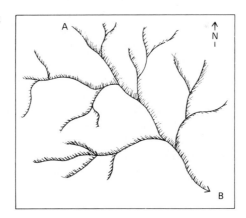

FIGURE 9.25 Long profile of Lizard Creek. (See text.)

tional bedrock. This concept of equilibrium carries with it the notion that any alteration of the equilibrium causes an immediate reaction in the stream in the direction of restoring equilibrium conditions. Referring back to Figures 9.24 and 9.25, let us consider how Lizard Creek would respond to local mountain-building forces tilting the earth's crust in a manner that steepened the long profile to the A'–B position shown in Figure 9.26.

Notice that A' is higher than A, and therefore water flowing in Lizard Creek now has more potential energy and hence a greater capacity to do the work of erosion. This can also be seen graphically by the steepening of A'–B with respect to the old profile A–B, causing the water to flow faster and cut down more at the stream bed. The effect of this increased energy will be to erode back toward A–B until the slope has been flattened enough to allow transportation of only the debris carried into A–B by its tributaries, thus restoring equilibrium. Although the stream is a nonthinking entity, it acts as if it said to itself, "Which must I do—erode or deposit—in order to achieve the ability to transport all the debris I receive, no more and no less? Well, I must flatten my slope, because I now have more velocity than is needed; and the way I can flatten my slope is to cut it down by erosion."

Thus any disruption of equilibrium for a stream segment will be met automatically with a response that works to reestablish the graded condition: Deposition will steepen the slope and erosion will flatten it.

The equilibrium of a stream segment may be altered by a variety of geologic processes. Climatic changes, for example, might cause downcutting or deposition in response to an increase or a decrease in rainfall, respectively. The degree of weathering and other elements of the bedrock's erodibility must also be considered when analyzing a stream's equilibrium.

In truth, the delicate balance of stream erosion involves a complex interaction of all these variables and more. Throughout geologic time perhaps the most important one, though, has been that of upward crustal movement. Again and again we find evidence of stream **rejuvenations** (Figure 9.27), which appear to have resulted from raising of the land with respect to the sea, thereby endowing streams with increased potential energy, which they have expended in more vigorous downcutting.

FIGURE 9.26 Uplift of Lizard Creek. (See text.)

WEATHERING AND WATER ON THE LAND

FIGURE 9.27 The process of rejuvenation as brought about by uplift of the land.

Uplift of the land

Prior valley shape

Active downcutting

RATES AND CYCLES OF WATER SCULPTURE

The landscapes of the earth's surface at any one time represent a balance between uplift of the land by the internal forces of crustal movement and destruction of the land by the external forces of erosion. Both of these processes act slowly—though at varying rates—over long periods of time. Therefore, in order to fully understand landscapes, we must know something of the historical sequence of uplift and erosion. Today, however, we can observe and study these processes at only a brief moment in the earth's long history, since interpretations of their interactions over millions of years involve many uncertainties.

The first and most basic question concerning the history of land sculpture is: How quickly does it take place? In other words, what is the rate at which the land surface is being lowered by erosion? Various schemes have been devised for estimating such rates, but none is fully satisfactory. Perhaps the most nearly accurate one is based on estimates of the amount of rock debris that is carried to the ocean each year by streams. Such estimates suggest that the United States, for example, is being lowered at an overall rate of about 8 cm (3 in.) per 1,000 years. Since the average height of the land surface on the entire earth is about 800 m (2,600 ft), such an erosion rate would reduce all the continents to sea level in about 10 million years. Geologically speaking, this is a very short time. There are, however, many difficulties in such estimates. One relates to the activities of man: The clearing of much of the land surface for agriculture during the last few hundred years has greatly increased rates of erosion—and by amounts that are difficult to estimate. In addition, the opposing internal forces that cause uplift of the land must be considered. Measurements of present-day rates of uplift suggest that the continents are now rising several times faster than they are being eroded. Moreover, the continents apparently stand higher today than they did through much of earth history; this suggests that rates of uplift and erosion may have been more nearly balanced in the past.

Perhaps the most serious problem in estimating erosion rates is caused by climatic change. Climate has a profound influence on erosion: Under dry and polar climates, local erosion rates have been measured that are many times greater than the 8 cm/1,000 years average for the temperate United States. As yet, however, too little is known about overall erosion patterns under such conditions to permit close comparisons with rates derived from temperate regions.

Along with these difficulties in measuring merely the *rate* at which the land is being lowered, there are, as you might expect, even greater problems in reconstructing the exact *sequence* of landscape changes that result from the land being lowered by erosion and raised by internal forces over millions of years. Because no one has seen landscapes evolve over such a long period, all attempts at such reconstruction must be based on indirect evidence and intuition. One such intuitive scheme for reconstructing landscape history dominated the study of landscapes for many years. It was developed around the turn of the century by several American geologists, the most influential and articulate of whom was W. M. Davis of Harvard University. Davis visualized landscape development in temperate climates, where flowing water is the dominant erosional agent, as commencing on relatively flat surfaces, such as former sea floors, that were raised above sea level by tectonic forces (Figure 9.28). At first, he believed, streams would cut steep V-shaped valleys without flood plains into the surface; later the valleys would widen, and broad flood plains separated by steep hillslopes would dominate; local relief would be at a maximum in this stage. Finally the hillslopes would be reduced by erosion to a relatively flat rolling surface that he called a **peneplane** (*pene* = almost, *plane* = flat). Landscapes showing each of these characteristics exist today in temperate zones, and Davis and his followers devoted much effort to classifying them according to their "stage of evolution" in his theoretical scheme of landscape development. This scheme, which involves such concepts as *youth*, *maturity*, and *old age*, described the degree to which the land had been destroyed by erosion.

Most geologists now feel, however, that Davis's scheme was very much oversimplified. Under certain conditions the sequence he envisioned might take place, but the complications of climatic change and the interaction of uplift and erosion probably lead to the formation of valleys and hillslopes by many complex sequences of events not included in Davis's appealingly simple analysis. There

WEATHERING AND WATER ON THE LAND

(a)

(b)

(c)

(d)

FIGURE 9.28 The cycle of land sculpture as postulated by W. M. Davis.

nevertheless remain general benefits to be gleaned from this simple "stage of landscape evolution" concept. High-standing crustal masses resulting from either deformation or volcanism and only slightly destroyed by stream erosion can correctly be recognized as "youthful"; others that display the effects of considerable denudation have greater maturity (Figure 9.29). It should be remembered, however, that such terms are relative and may be used only in a very broad sense.

Landscape features called **water gaps** [Figure 9.30(a)] result from special erosional conditions. They are formed by the development of **superposed streams**, as shown in Figures 9.30(b) and (c). The stream course is established originally in a rock unit that overlies the future water gap. Eventually the younger rock is eroded deeply, forcing the stream to cut through the previously buried resistant rock. The stream becomes entrenched in its valley and has no place else to go, even though ordinarily it would not continue to flow across the more resistant rock.

(a)

(b)

(c)

FIGURE 9.29 Stages of landscape evolution. (a) Youthful (relatively little modification of terrain by stream erosion). (b) Early maturity (streams have fully established their drainage system; most of the original surface has been destroyed). (c) Late maturity (streams have widened valleys greatly by lateral erosion; topography is relatively subdued). (a: Tad Nichols; b: Sante Fe Railway; c: Geological Survey of Great Britain.)

(a)

FIGURE 9.30 The formation of a *water gap* by development of a *superposed stream*. (See text for discussion.) (a: U.S. Army Air Corps photo. From Leet, et al., Physical Geology, 6th ed., Prentice Hall, Inc., Englewood Cliffs, N.J., with permission.)

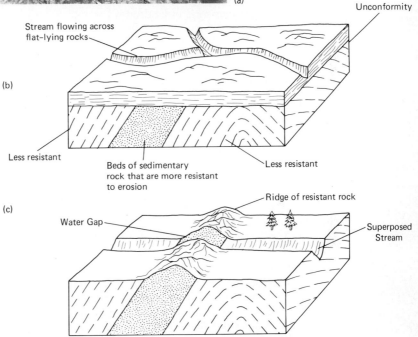

SUMMARY OUTLINE

WEATHERING

9.1 *Weathering processes*: Exposure to air and water at the earth's surface causes massive crustal rocks to break up into small particles and change composition by both mechanical and chemical processes.

9.2 *Soil*: Weathering produces an accumulation of altered rock debris—

mostly clay minerals, oxide minerals, and quartz fragments—that is thickest under tropical climates, thinnest under polar and dry climates, and of intermediate thickness under temperate climates.

WATER ON THE LAND

9.3 Lakes: Lakes are temporary stationary accumulations of land water that show some properties of the ocean but have relatively little influence on land sculpture.

9.4 Ground water: Much of the water on the land is in cracks, pores, and voids in soil and rocks; it directly influences landscapes only in limestone terrain.

9.5 Streams: Streams are the principal agent of land sculpture; the velocity and erosive effect of stream flow are controlled by a shifting balance among discharge, channel shape, channel slope, and sediment load.

LAND SCULPTURE

9.6 Mass wasting: Soil and rock debris first move downslope under the direct influence of gravity—either slowly, by creep, or more rapidly, by various sorts of landslides.

9.7 Stream erosion: Debris ultimately reaches flowing stream water that moves it from the area of origin; where slopes are steep, the debris is removed rapidly and the stream actively cuts a V-shaped valley; on more gentle slopes the debris accumulates to form an alluvial valley.

9.8 The graded stream as an equilibrium concept: The graded stream concept provides a basis for predicting changes in a stream's tendency to erode or deposit sediment in response to changes in its discharge or its channel shape, roughness, or slope.

9.9 Rates and cycles of water sculpture: Stream erosion of the land surface is offset by mountain building and internal uplift; precise cycles of erosion and uplift are difficult to reconstruct.

ADDITIONAL READINGS

* BLOOM, A. L.: *The Surface of the Earth*, Prentice-Hall, Inc., Englewood Cliffs, N.J., 1969. A brief introduction to landscapes.

GAURI, K. L.: "The Preservation of Stone," *Scientific American*, June 1978.

*GORDON, R. B.: *Physics of the Earth*, Holt, Rinehart and Winston, New York, 1972. Chapter 5 provides a good introduction to land sculpture.

LEOPOLD, L. B., M. G. WOLMAN, and J. P. MILLER: *Fluvial Processes in Geomorphology*, W. H. Freeman & Company, Publishers, San Francisco, 1964. An intermediate text on streams and their relation to landscapes.

*MORISAWA, M.: *Streams: Their Dynamics and Morphology*, McGraw-Hill Book Company, New York, 1968. A brief introductory text.

SCHUMM, S. A.: *The Fluvial System*, John Wiley & Sons, Inc., New York, 1977. An intermediate to advanced treatment of stream processes.

SHELTON, J. S.: *Geology Illustrated*, W. H. Freeman & Company, Publishers, San Francisco, 1966. An excellent introductory text stressing landscapes; extraordinary photographs.

* Available in paperback.

10

Oceans and Coastal Processes

A

S LAND-DWELLERS, WE TEND to think of the dry surfaces of the continents as the feature most characteristic of the earth. An observer in space, however, is most impressed not with the earth's land areas but with the enormous volume of ocean water covering more than seven-tenths of the earth's surface. Among the planets of the solar system, only the earth appears to have such huge quantities of liquid water. Water is present on earth not only in the ocean basins but also in smaller amounts on land, where it occurs in lakes, rivers, streams, and as ground water saturating the uppermost levels of rock and soil. All of these waters make up a world-encircling sphere of liquid that is often referred to as the **hydrosphere** to distinguish it from the rocks of the underlying solid earth (lithosphere) and the gases of the overlying atmosphere. About 97 percent of the water in the hydrosphere occurs in the ocean, which, through evaporation and rainfall, is also the ultimate source of the 3 percent of water occurring on land.

OCEAN MOVEMENTS

Rapid and dynamic movements of ocean water are of two sorts: **currents,** which are motions that transport water from one part of the ocean to another, and **waves,** moving disturbances traveling on or through the water, like wind ripples crossing a field of wheat, which do not directly transport water from one place to another. Currents will be discussed first; the following sections then treat ocean wave movements, **tides,** and the infrequent but devastating seismic sea waves that are sometimes (incorrectly) called **tidal waves.**

10.1
CURRENTS

Current movements are closely related to the ocean's layered structure. The most obvious take place in the surface layer, the upper hundred meters or so of water where solar energy and interaction with the atmosphere are concentrated. Most knowledge of surface currents—as horizontal water movements occurring in this surface layer are called—has come from records of their effect on the movement of ships. From thousands of such observations, navigators have compiled **current charts** showing the general patterns of surface currents around the world. The first comprehensive charts of this kind were made in the midnineteenth century as aids to navigation; a simplified modern version is shown in Figure 10.1.

An examination of the surface current patterns in Figure 10.1 shows certain similarities of the two largest oceans. The principal features are large circular patterns of flow called **gyres**. The Atlantic and Pacific oceans each have three such gyres: a small gyre flowing to the left (counterclockwise) in their northernmost extensions, and two much larger gyres on each side of the equator, the northern one flowing to the right (clockwise) and the southern one to the left (counterclockwise). Flowing along the equator between these large gyres in the opposite direction is a simple, one-directional current called the **equatorial countercurrent**. The Indian Ocean extends only a little bit north of the equator and has only the southernmost, left-flowing gyre well developed. The Antarctic Ocean has no gyres but merely a continuous eastward current, circling the entire earth around the continent of Antarctica. All of the major gyres persist in direction and undergo only relatively small-scale changes in position with the changing seasons; the smaller currents

FIGURE 10.1   Principal surface currents of the ocean. Cold currents are shown in darker color, and areas of faster cold and warm currents by heavier shading.

north of the equator in the Indian Ocean, however, completely reverse their directions in summer and winter.

The large gyres do not have formal names, but can be informally referred to as the "North Atlantic," "South Pacific," etc., gyres (Figure 10.1). Certain segments of each large gyre, however, have been given separate geographic names. For example, the western part of the large North Atlantic gyre is called the Gulf Stream, the northern part the North Atlantic Drift, the eastern part the Canary Current, and the southern part the North Equatorial Current. Usually only the parts with relatively rapid water movements are called currents; parts with slower movements are called drifts. Within each gyre is a large region of relatively stable and immobile surface water called an eddy. (The eddy within the North Atlantic gyre is called the Sargasso Sea because large quantities of the floating seaweed (*sargassum*) accumulate within its relatively quiet and stable waters; the eddies within the other major gyres do not have common names.) One other important fact concerning the ocean's surface currents is that all of the gyres tend to be asymmetrical to the west. Instead of having their centers in the middle of the ocean basins, the centers tend to be shifted to the left or westward in both the northern and southern hemisphere. As a result, the currents of each gyre tend to be narrowest and swiftest along their western sides. This is particularly evident in the Gulf Stream and the Japan Current—the *western boundary currents* (as they are called) of the North Atlantic and North Pacific gyres, respectively.

Of all the currents making up the gyres of the oceans, the Gulf Stream at the western edge of the North Atlantic has been by far the most extensively studied. Like other western boundary currents, it is made up of warm water flowing away from the equator at a relatively high speed, 6 km/hr (3.7 mi/hr); it somewhat resembles a "river" of warm water moving in a "channel" of cooler water. The "river" varies greatly in size but is typically very large, averaging about 80 km (50 mi) in width and several hundred meters in depth. Its boundary is often sharply marked by changes in water color or transparency. The Gulf Stream was long thought to be relatively constant in structure and position, but recent surveys have shown that, in fact, it is not a single mass of moving water, like a large river, but more like a series of small, rapidly flowing interconnected "streams" separated by stable water. The positions of the "streams" change rapidly, sometimes as much as 150 km in only a few days. It is the average flow of many such filamentlike streams over the wide region shown in Figure 10.1 that makes up the rapid northward movement of water in the Gulf Stream. Limited observations on the western boundary currents in other gyres suggest that they have structures similar to this.

Currents transporting water from one part of the ocean to another are not the only movements that take place in the ocean. Other movements occur that do *not* involve large-scale displacements of water but merely the passage of moving patterns of disturbance, called **waves**, on or through the water. In watching surface waves on the sea, it at first appears that the water itself *does* move rapidly in the direction of wave travel. However, closer observation of small objects floating in the water, such as a cork or a piece of seaweed, shows that it is merely the *form of the wave*, rather than the water itself, that progresses. As a wave passes, the cork and the individual water particles in which it floats move not forward but in a vertically circular pattern that results in their ending up in approximately the same position as before the wave passed (Figure 10.2). Ocean wave movements therefore differ in a most fundamental way from the current movements we have already considered, for they do not involve large-scale transportation of water from one part of the ocean to another.

There are four principal ocean wave movements, each of which is caused by different dominant forces. The most familiar are **wind waves**, formed at the ocean surface by action of the wind, and **tides**, world-encircling waves caused by the gravitational attraction of the sun and moon. Somewhat less familiar are **seismic sea waves** (also

FIGURE 10.2   Water motion in wave passage. An object floating in passing waves does not progress with the wave but inscribes an in-place circle (color) with each wave.

Direction of wave motion

called **tsunamis** and, incorrectly, **tidal waves**) caused by earthquakes, volcanic eruptions, or other disturbances of the ocean floor. **Internal waves,** the final type, move beneath the surface of the ocean and are the most difficult to observe and interpret; their exact cause is still unknown.

WIND WAVES

The waves produced on the ocean's surface by the action of winds, called **wind waves,** are among the most fascinating and easily observed phenomena of the ocean. Rather surprisingly, though, they are still not fully understood. The simplest of any regular sequence of moving waves can be described by three properties: the length of the waves or *wavelength*, the *height* of the waves, and the *period* of the waves, which is merely the length of time it takes one complete wave to pass a fixed point [Figure 10.3(a)]. From two of these parameters, wavelength and period, the *velocity* of the waves can easily be computed. Likewise, the ratio of wavelength to wave height determines the *steepness* of the wave [Figure 10.3(b)]. Wind waves typically have wavelengths varying from less than 3 cm (1 ⅛ in.) to more than 600 m (2,000 ft). The maximum steepness is reached when the wavelength is about seven times as great as the wave height. At or below this ratio, the wave form becomes unstable and the water plunges from the top to form a "whitecap" or "breaker."

Wavelength, height, and period are useful concepts for describing and discussing waves, but natural wind waves are usually far too complex and irregular to be understood by these properties alone. If you watch waves generated by a strong wind, you will see that it is impossible to follow single crests moving over long distances. Instead, the waves tend to grow and subside in complex patterns that defy simple recognition of wavelength and period. In considering such complex waves it is convenient to look at a completely smooth ocean surface over which a gentle wind has just

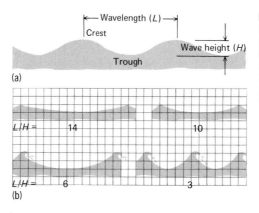

(a)

(b)

FIGURE 10.3 Wave properties. (a) Wavelength and wave height. (b) The ratio of wavelength to wave height determines the steepness of a wave. When the ratio is less than 7, the crest becomes unstable and plunges to form a "whitecap" or "breaker."

OCEANS AND COASTAL PROCESSES

begun to blow. The first effect is the production of very small surface irregularities less than 3 cm (1 ⅛ in.) across, known as **capillary waves** (Figure 10.4). These capillary waves are so small that they quickly disappear if the wind subsides. If the wind speed increases and the winds become more turbulent and gusty, much larger and more irregular waves, ranging in length and height from several centimeters to a meter or more, begin to form (Figure 10.4). Unlike small capillary waves, these larger waves will continue to move under the influence of gravity even after the wind subsides; for this reason they are called **gravity waves**. With further increases of wind velocity, the larger gravity waves, for reasons that are poorly understood, tend to gain energy at the expense of the smaller ones, with the result that the smaller waves are destroyed soon after they appear, whereas the larger waves continue to grow. The maximum height of these larger waves has been observed to depend on three characteristics of the generating wind: its *velocity*; its *duration*, or the length of time it blows; and its *fetch*, which is the distance over which it blows. The height increases as each parameter—wind velocity, duration, and fetch—increases. The maximum observed height of wind waves is rarely greater than 6 m (20 ft), although exceptional storm waves as high as 36 m (120 ft) have been reported (Figure 10.5). Even 6-m (20-ft) waves are unusual, for they require

FIGURE 10.4 Sequence of wind and wave formation. (a) Small capillary waves; wind velocity 4 km/hr. (b-f) Gravity waves at increasing wind velocities: (b) 10 km/hr; (c) 30 km/hr; (d) 45 km/hr; (e) 80 km/hr; (f) 95 km/hr. (Photographs courtesy of Dr. Krugler, Hamburg.)

(a)   (b)   (c)

(d)   (e)   (f)

FIGURE 10.5 Unusually large waves in a storm off northern California. The ship, a Coast Guard Cutter on a rescue mission, is 100 m (327 ft) long. (U.S. Coast Guard.)

winds blowing at velocities greater than 80 km/hr (50 mi/hr), lasting for several days, and blowing over hundreds of kilometers of open water. It has been estimated that 45 percent of ocean waves are under 1 m (3.3 ft), 35 percent from 2 to 6 m (6.5 to 20 ft) high, and only 10 percent have heights greater than 6 m (20 ft).

Complex natural wind waves are considered to result from the interaction of many superimposed simple wave patterns (Figure 10.6). For a given set of wind conditions, a statistical combination of many such simple wave patterns permits a calculation of the resulting distribution of energy in complex waves of differing sizes. From this energy distribution, the general shape of the sea surface can then be estimated. These calculations agree rather closely with observations of natural waves and have formed the basis for an extremely useful scheme for predicting the maximum wave size to be expected under different conditions of wind velocity, duration, and fetch.

The complex wave patterns that we have been discussing occur in the **generating area,** the region where strong winds produce wave motions (Figure 10.7). Waves may, however, travel far beyond the generating area into calmer regions where large waves are no longer

OCEANS AND COASTAL PROCESSES

FIGURE 10.6 Wave averaging. A series of simple wave forms are statistically "added" to simulate complex natural waves (bottom).

Generating area

Wind →

FIGURE 10.7 Development of waves in a "generating area" of strong winds. The waves may move far beyond the generating area; as they do they become more regular and are known as "swell."

"Sea" wave profile in generating area

"Swell" wave profile beyond generating area

being produced by the wind. In this way, large storm waves often travel across hundreds or thousands of kilometers of open ocean with relatively little loss of energy. In the process of spreading from the generating area, the waves become more regular and are easier to describe by the simple properties of wavelength, height, and period. Such waves are called ocean **swell** to distinguish them from the more complex waves of the generating area, which are known as a **sea**.

Waves traveling across the open ocean as swell continue to move with little loss of energy until they reach shallow coastal waters, where their energy is dissipated by interactions with the ocean floor. There is a simple relationship for calculating the water depth at which surface waves begin to "feel bottom" and lose energy (Figure 10.8). As a wave passes a given point, the motion of water particles extends downward, with decreasing energy, to the **wave base**, a depth about half as great as the wavelength of the passing wave. Thus a wave 300 m (1,000 ft) long begins to "touch bottom" in water 150 m (500 ft) deep. When this happens, the form of the wave begins to change because the bottom restricts the movement of water particles in the wave: The velocity decreases, the wavelength becomes shorter, and the wave height increases. This steepening of the wave continues as the water becomes shallower until the wave reaches an unstable height and "breaks" to form surf, an action that dissipates most of its energy (Figure 10.9). Breaking normally occurs when the water depth is about 1 ⅓ times the wave height.

Depth = ½ wavelength

FIGURE 10.8 Wave motions in shallow water. At water depths less than ½ wavelength, the wave motion intersects the ocean floor causing the wave to move more slowly and, ultimately, to steepen and "break."

FIGURE 10.9 Waves steepening and breaking in shallow water along the northern California coast. (R. Strauss.)

A second fundamental ocean wave motion is seen in the **tides**, world-encircling ocean movements caused by the gravitational attraction of the sun and moon. The rhythmic rise and fall of the tides seen along the coastlines of the earth are the most regular and, next to surface waves, the most easily observed of all ocean movements. Since at least the seventeenth century, men have known that these movements are related to astronomical forces, for they observed that regular tidal changes accompany the changing phases of the moon. Even though it has long been clear that tides are caused by the changing positions of the moon and sun, however, the exact manner in which the gravitational forces produce varying tidal patterns is still not completely understood.

To visualize the origin of ocean tides it is helpful to think first of the effect of the moon alone on an idealized earth completely covered by oceans. On such an earth, ocean water should bulge slightly outward in the direction of the moon because of the moon's gravitational attraction. At first it would seem that only a single bulge would exist directly under the moon, and indeed this would be the case if gravity were the only force involved. The mutual gravitational attractions of the earth and moon, however, are balanced by *centrifugal* forces caused by slight motions of the earth around the mutual center of gravity of the earth-moon system. This centrifugal motion creates a force in a direction *opposite* to the moon and results in another tidal bulge on the side of the earth *farthest away from* the moon (Figure 10.10). The result of this bal-

FIGURE 10.10 Origin of the tides. The gravitational interactions of the earth and moon produce a low, world-encircling wave with two crests (high water) and two troughs (low water). The earth rotates "under" these waves each 24 hours, producing two intervals of high water and two of low water at each point on the ocean surface.

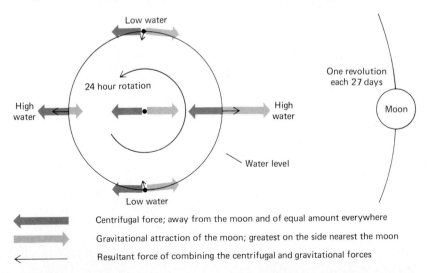

Low water

One revolution
each 27 days

24 hour rotation

High water — High water

Moon

Water level

Low water

Centrifugal force; away from the moon and of equal amount everywhere

Gravitational attraction of the moon; greatest on the side nearest the moon

Resultant force of combining the centrifugal and gravitational forces ance of centrifugal and gravitational forces is to permanently deform the ocean surface into a slightly ovate (egglike or football-like) shape, with the long axis extending in the direction of the moon. This deformation can be thought of as world-encircling waves with only two "crests," one at each tidal bulge, and two "troughs" in between. The forces involved in producing the tides are so small that the height of these waves is usually less than 1 m (3.3 ft) in the open ocean, but their wavelength is extraordinarily long, for they extend halfway around the earth from one bulge to the other.

Daily tidal changes result from the fact that the tidal bulges remain in a relatively fixed position—that is, aligned with the moon—as the earth rotates on its axis every 24 hours. Thus, points on the earth's surface tend to rotate under both tidal bulges, and their intervening "troughs," every 24 hours. This is the reason that tidal records typically show two periods of high water and two intervening periods of low water each day. The tidal bulges themselves also move, however, as the moon rotates around the earth every 27 days. The effect of this movement is to make the tides, like the time of moonrise, come about 50 min later each day, thus completing one cycle and occurring at the same time once each 27 days (Figure 10.10).

This simple explanation of tides has neglected many complicating factors, the most important of which is the sun, whose gravitational attraction causes about *half* as much tidal deformation as does the moon. The principal effect of the sun is to cause tides to have their greatest range twice each month at **spring tides*** (near the times of full and new moon) when the sun and moon are aligned and their forces act together; conversely, tidal ranges are lowest at **neap tides** (near the first and third quarter of the moon) when the solar and lunar forces are in opposition and act at right angles to each other (Figure 10.11).

FIGURE 10.11   Spring and neap tides. Because of the gravitational attraction of the sun, tide ranges are greatest when the moon and sun are aligned (spring tides) and least when they are opposed (neap tides.)

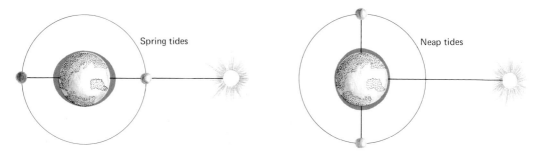

Spring tides

Neap tides

* *Spring*, in this usage, has nothing to do with the season of the year.

OCEANS AND COASTAL PROCESSES

There are still other factors that complicate natural tidal patterns. The earth is not, of course, completely covered by water, and thus the movement of the tidal "bulges" around the earth each day is strongly influenced by the shape and interconnections of the ocean basins. Furthermore, the extremely long wavelength of the tides causes them to "feel bottom" and behave as shallow water waves even in the deepest ocean basins. As a result, free movement of the tidal deformations is slowed down by frictional drag on the sea floor. Because of these and other complications, it has so far proved impossible to predict local tidal patterns from purely theoretical considerations. Instead, tidal predictions are based on long observation of local patterns, which tend to be repeated in regular ways along the coastlines of the earth.

Tidal observations taken over many years at thousands of stations around the world have shown that many regions, including most of the Atlantic Ocean, show a regular twice-daily tidal pattern with high and low tides of equal magnitude, just as predicted by our simple analysis. Such tides are called **semidiurnal** (Figure 10.12). In other areas, however, various complicating factors lead to two additional tidal patterns. Most common are *mixed tides*, having two highs and two lows of unequal magnitude each day. Such tides dominate most of the shores of the Pacific Ocean. In a few places, such as the Gulf of Mexico and Southeast Asia, there occur *diurnal tides*, with only one high and one low water per day.

FIGURE 10.12 Tidal patterns. (a) Schematic diagram of a recording tide gauge. (b) The three principal types of tides, as recorded on a tide gauge. Semidiurnal tides have two high and two low waters of approximately equal magnitude each day. In mixed tides, some of the highs and lows are unequal. Diurnal tides show a single high and low each day.

In the open ocean, the amount of rise and fall of water with the changing tides is difficult to measure, but tidal observations on isolated oceanic islands suggest that the water seldom varies in height by more than 1 m (3.3 ft). In contrast, along the coasts of the continents much greater tidal ranges may occur when water movements become concentrated and focused by the shape of the land and by interaction with the shallow sea floor. The maximum tidal ranges so produced are found on the shores of the North Atlantic, particularly in Nova Scotia and around the English Channel, where the maximum range is about 15 m (50 ft). On most shores, however, the maximum tidal range is less than 3 m (10 ft).

10.3
SEISMIC SEA WAVES

All of the ocean movements we have discussed so far have been caused by either atmospheric forces (currents and wind waves) or external gravity forces (tides). Another ocean wave motion occurs that derives energy directly from earthquake movements taking place in the rocks of the solid earth. Such waves are commonly called seismic sea waves, but they are also often referred to by their Japanese name, tsunamis, or by the misnomer tidal waves. Seismic sea waves have no relation to tide-producing forces; they do, however, resemble tides in that they have very low heights and very long wavelengths. In the open ocean they commonly have wavelengths of hundreds of kilometers, and velocities of hundreds of kilometers per hour, but heights of less than 3 m (10 ft), which is so low that the crests pass unnoticed by ships in midocean. Unlike tides, however, the height of seismic sea waves may be greatly intensified as the waves move into shallow water. This topic will be developed more fully in our consideration of geologic hazards to man in Chapter 12.

COASTAL EROSION

Whereas the properties of ocean water and of its waves, tides, and currents discussed so far in this chapter are important to an understanding of the earth, of primary concern to the geologist are the erosional landforms that develop along coastlines and the story they have to tell about crustal deformation and sea level changes. The principal agent in the production of coastal landforms is surf action.

As sea waves approach a shoreline where the water shallows, waves build up and eventually "break" to become a rush of water onto the land. Waves undergoing this process produce surf. *Surf action* is the dominant factor in coastal erosion. The principal mechanisms of surf erosion are the *abrasive action* of sand, silt, and pebbles against the coastal bedrock and the *hydraulic impact* of the water itself as it generates extreme pressures within the many small bedrock joints. Waves, to a lesser extent, contribute to the abrasional process by slowly grinding clastic grains back and forth in the zone where the wave base touches bottom.

This relentless attack on the land by the sea causes any high-standing or emergent coastal terrain to undergo predictable erosional changes. First, a **marine terrace**, consisting of a surf-cut bench and a surf-cut cliff, forms rather rapidly [Figure 10.13(a)]. Along coastlines where the land has recently undergone repeated upward movements relative to the sea, several marine terraces can be seen extending hundreds of feet above the present surf zone (Figure 10.14). These relationships are common along the western coast of the United States. How would it be possible to know if such elevated marine terraces had resulted primarily from uplift (deformation) of the land rather than from sea level lowering? Although

FIGURE 10.13 Shoreline profiles. (a) Marine terrace. (b) Beach profile. Winter berm is narrower, higher, and composed of larger fragments. (After Bascom, 1964.)

FIGURE 10.14 Elevated marine terraces (San Clemente Island). (John S. Shelton.)

FIGURE 10.15 A warped terrace, south of San Francisco. (N. T. Hall.)

combinations of these two factors can give rise to complex relationships, there is one straightforward test that can be used to *exclude* a purely sea level-change mode of origin. When sea level lowers, it drops the same amount everywhere, so we would expect to find terraces formed by sea level lowering to be perfectly horizontal. However, along the western coast of North America such horizontality is almost never attained. Instead the terraces are warped, and some are severely deformed, thus proving the important role played by deformation in their origin (Figure 10.15).

10.5
THE BEACH AND LONGSHORE TRANSPORT

The **beach** is a coastal zone within which fragments are actively moved both onshore and offshore, as well as parallel to the shore. It extends from the base of the surf-cut cliff seaward to some variable position controlled by the wave base [Figure 10.13(b)]. Because winter waves and surf are more energetic than summer waves, we should expect the beach's appearance to vary with the seasons. Indeed, not only is the summer **berm** (the layman's notion of "beach") wider and lower than in winter, as shown in Figure 10.13(b), but also we frequently observe dramatic differences in fragment sizes exposed in the berm from season to season (Figure 10.16). High-

FIGURE 10.16   La Jolla Beach. (a) Summer. (b) Winter. (Photos courtesy John S. Shelton. From, "Geology Illustrated" by John S. Shelton. W. H. Freeman and Company, Copyright © 1966.)

(a)

(b)

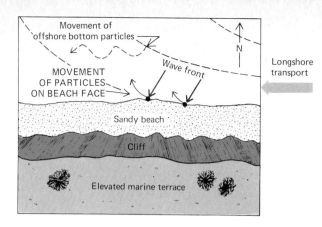

FIGURE 10.17 Map view showing longshore transport resulting from waves and surf with a westward component of movement.

energy winter surf not only moves more material offshore, it also selects all but the coarsest grain sizes for transport. During summer, the lower-energy waves and surf slowly push the fine-grained material back up toward and onto the shore.

In defining a beach, we suggested that its fragments move parallel to the shoreline, as well as inward and outward from it. This **longshore transport**, as it is called, results from the fact that waves seldom approach a coastline from straight out at sea. Wave fronts usually approach the coast at an angle, and although they are typically refracted by being slowed in shallow water so as to become almost parallel, a small longshore-transport component persists (Figure 10.17). Longshore transport often combines with local

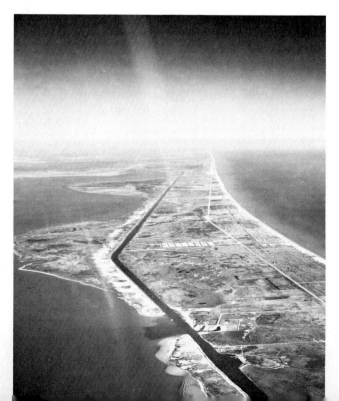

FIGURE 10.18 A barrier island along the Texas coast. (John S. Shelton.)

FIGURE 10.19 Effects of surf action. (a) Wave energy from AB is focused on the promontory at A"B", while BC energy is dispersed along B"C" segment. (b) The net effect of wave refraction plus time is to produce a straightened coastline.

currents in shallow coastal waters to redistribute coastal sediments and to shape them into characteristic **barrier islands** (Figure 10.18).

The process of wave refraction contributes to another important aspect of a coastline's development. Suppose an irregular coastline comes into being, perhaps by deformation or sea level changes. How will such a coastline evolve? Will it become more or less irregular through surf attack? In view of the patterns of wave refraction shown in Figure 10.19(a), it is apparent that the net effect will be to reduce the irregularities and straighten out the coastline by focusing energy at promontories and dispersing energy in embayments [Figure 10.19(b)]. (Recall that we can predict the direction of wave refraction in this manner: The wave will bend in the direction of whichever end of the wave front is slowed first.) Other aspects of longshore transport and surf attack that more directly affect man will be discussed in Chapter 13.

10.6
CONTINENTAL MARGINS

Seaward from the narrow coastal zone, the continental margins slope gently downward and are covered by progressively deeper ocean water. At the edges of these submerged continental margins, which are called the **continental shelves**, there is usually a much steeper zone, called the **continental slope**, leading downward to the deep ocean basins (Figure 10.20). At their outermost edges, most stable continental shelves today are covered by about 200 m (660 ft) of ocean water; in tectonically active areas this depth is highly variable. Quite significantly, however, the size of the continental shelves has changed dramatically with the climatic fluctuations of Pleistocene time because the large continental ice sheets locked up enough

Beach
Cliffed coast
Barrier island
Old beach and barrier deposits
Longshore current
Submarine canyon
Continental shelf
Continental Slope
(actual slope is
less than 10°)

FIGURE 10.20 Characteristic landscape features of coasts and continental shelves. Vertical scale is greatly exaggerated.

water to lower worldwide sea levels by at least 100 m (330 ft) and, possibly, by as much as 200 m (660 ft). During intervals of maximum glaciation, much or all of the present continental shelves were therefore exposed above sea level, and the coastline lay offshore at points now deeply submerged. Conversely, it is estimated that if the present Greenland and Antarctic ice sheets were to melt, enough water would be added to the oceans to *raise* sea level about 50 m (165 ft), thus flooding much of the earth's present coastal regions. The ice sheet fluctuations of Pleistocene time have therefore led to numerous past migrations of the shoreline back and forth across the continental margins; the most important result has been to deposit beachlike sediments over much of the shelf region.

Although depositional processes have dominated the continental shelves, the outermost margins of many of them show dramatic erosional canyons that are deeper and steeper than any occurring above sea level (Figure 10.20). The exact origin of these **submarine canyons** is still uncertain; some geologists believe they were formed, in their uppermost parts at least, by streams flowing on dry land during intervals of maximum glaciation when sea level was much lower. Others think it more likely that they have been carved entirely by sediment-laden bottom currents of ocean water moving down the steep continental slope.

Beyond the steep margins of the continents, the deep ocean basins are regions in which the "land" surface is little affected by erosion. Instead, the construction of new crustal rocks by volcanic action and ocean-floor spreading, and the accumulation of land-derived sediments, are the dominant processes. Nevertheless, active erosion does occur whenever volcanic rocks of the ocean build above sea level to form oceanic islands. Over many years the tops of volcanic islands may be eroded and leveled by wave action. Such wave-eroded, flat-topped volcanic mountains, called **guyots** (see Section 8.3 and Figure 8.13), are a common feature of the ocean floor. The tops of the youngest guyots stand near present sea level, but older ones have been deeply submerged by the movement of ocean floor away from midocean ridges.

SUMMARY OUTLINE

OCEAN MOVEMENTS

10.1 Currents: Currents are best known in the surface layer, where they move in large, circular gyres; the swiftest motions occur in the asymmetrical western portions of the gyres.

10.2 Waves and tides: Wind waves are moving disturbances formed on the ocean surface by wind action; they increase in size as wind velocity, duration, and fetch increase and may move far beyond their generating areas to produce swell; tides are world-encircling waves caused by the gravitational attraction of moon and sun; points on the ocean surface normally have two high and two low tides daily, but this pattern is complicated by the shapes and limited interconnections of the ocean basins.

10.3 Seismic sea waves: These are large waves caused by undersea earthquakes.

COASTAL EROSION

10.4 Surf action: Surf action is the dominant factor in coastal erosion; marine terraces are formed by prolonged surf attack.

10.5 The beach and longshore transport: The beach is kept in constant motion by longshore transport.

10.6 Continental margins: Continental shelves and slopes connect the beach with the deep ocean basin.

ADDITIONAL READINGS

* BASCOM W.: *Waves and Beaches*, Doubleday & Co., Inc., Garden City, N.Y., 1964. A popular and entertaining introduction.

BIRD, E. C. F.: *Coasts*, The M.I.T. Press, Cambridge, Mass., 1969. A brief intermediate-level review of coastal landforms.

*MOORE, J. R. (ed.): *Oceanography, Readings from Scientific American*, W. H. Freeman & Company, Publishers, San Francisco, 1971. Many excellent popular articles.

ROSS, D.: *Introduction to Oceanography*, 3rd ed., Prentice-Hall, Inc., Englewood Cliffs, N.J., 1982. A well-written treatment of oceanography.

*TUREKIAN, K. K.: *Oceans*, Prentice-Hall, Inc., Englewood Cliffs, N.J., 1968. An authoritative and readable introduction, emphasizing ocean chemistry.

*VANANDEL, T.: *Science at Sea: Tales of an Old Ocean*, W. H. Freeman & Company, Publishers, San Francisco, 1981. A very well-written weaving together of oceanography, plate tectonics, and earth history.

* Available in paperback.

11

Deserts and Glaciers

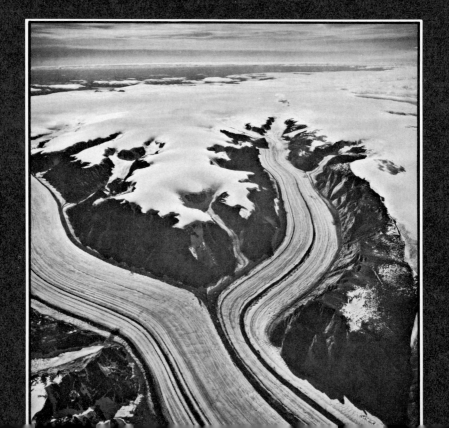

I N CHAPTERS 9 AND 10 WE discussed what might be called the "normal," or most common, modes of erosion and the landforms they create. Stream processes are indeed the principal agents of land sculpture, and surf and wave action take their toll wherever the land meets the sea. In this chapter we shall consider erosional processes and effects that are characteristic of two climatic extremes: deserts and glacial regions.

DESERTS

Worldwide zones of dry climate tend to develop in the belt of descending air that lies between the moist rising air of the tropics and the turbulent midlatitude belts of cyclones and anticyclones. These zones of dry climate are characterized by an annual amount of surface evaporation that equals or exceeds the annual amount of rainfall. Under these conditions, most of the scant precipitation returns rather quickly to the atmosphere, and there is no excess to form permanent streams or to support extensive vegetation. The results are **deserts**, areas with little or no moisture or vegetation, which today occupy about one-fourth of the land surface (Figure 11.1).

Although we normally think of deserts as being warm, high temperatures play a role in the origin of deserts only through increasing the annual amount of evaporation. For example, regions on the warm, equatorial side of the dry climate zone may receive 75 cm (30 in.) of rainfall a year, about as much as falls in Chicago or Seattle, and still remain deserts because of their high average temperatures

FIGURE 11.1 The principal present-day desert regions.

■ Deserts   ▨ Areas of sand accumulation

and consequent high rates of evaporation. In contrast, on the cooler poleward side of the dry zones, rainfall must normally be less than 35 cm (14 in.) per year to cause complete evaporation and desert conditions.

11.1
DESERT LANDSCAPES

Although the rain that falls in desert regions evaporates relatively quickly—usually in a few hours or days—it nevertheless plays a dominant role in shaping desert landscapes. Because there is little soil or vegetation to absorb the rainfall, it tends to remain on the surface where, particularly in desert mountains, it may be concentrated in normally dry channels to cause *flash floods*, which subside in a few hours. Such flood waters commonly have an enormous discharge and velocity and thus transport large volumes of sedimentary debris to the base of desert mountains, where it is deposited in fan-shaped wedges called **alluvial fans.***

Figure 11.2 shows the relationship between an eroded fault scarp in Death Valley, California, and alluvial fans formed at its base. Several features typical of arid mountainous regions are apparent in this photograph: (1) little or no vegetation; (2) an absence of thick soils over the bedrock; (3) a sharp break in angle between the eroded bedrock and the surface of the overlapping fans, which are forming an alluvial apron, or **bajada;** and (4) white evaporite deposits in the valley bottom. Each of these features owes its existence, directly or indirectly, to the arid condition of the terrain.

The absence of moisture directly causes sparse vegetation and thin soils (water is necessary to weather rock chemically). The reduced chemical breakdown of bedrock creates a situation wherein only relatively large mechanically weathered rock is exposed at the surface, which accounts for the steep bedrock slopes. The evaporite deposits result from the absence of through-flowing streams, which, in more humid regions, would carry dissolved ions to the oceans and allow them to concentrate there. In arid regions, intermittent **playa lakes** are formed by infrequent downpours and quickly dry up, leaving an accumulation of evaporites [see Figures 4.27 and 4.28(b)]. It is noteworthy that such *interior drainage* is testimony to the fact that deformational forces have defeated erosional forces. It seems likely that rates of mountain building in more humid regions

---

* These and other sedimentary deposits of desert origin were described in Section 4.6.

FIGURE 11.2   Alluvial fans and an eroded fault scarp. (John S. Shelton.)

are not any slower than in deserts, but that more precipitation allows greater rates of erosion to carve through-going drainage systems.

Figure 11.3 shows what is believed to be the evolutionary sequence of landforms observed in the arid Great Basin of western United States. (These changes are reminiscent of the stages of landscape evolution by streams discussed in Section 9.9.) Figure 11.4 introduces terminology that is applied to many of the features typically seen in such regions. As is apparent in Figures 11.3 and 11.4, the **piedmont** (*pied* = foot, *mont* = mountain) slope is underlain by two distinctly different kinds of material, although their line of contact is frequently imperceptible. The **pediment** is eroded bedrock, often covered by a very thin veneer of slope-washed alluvium; and the **bajada** is many alluvial fans that are joined together to form a broad alluvial apron. The precise erosional mechanism responsible for cutting pediments and maintaining their abrupt angle with the mountain face is not well understood at this time.

(a)

(b)

(c)

FIGURE 11.3 Arid cycle of erosion. (a) Youth (with relatively fresh scarps and individual fans). (b) Maturity (with mountain outliers and well-developed bajada). (c) Old age (with inselbergs). (a,b,c: John S. Shelton.)

FIGURE 11.4 Desert landscape features in the Great Basin.

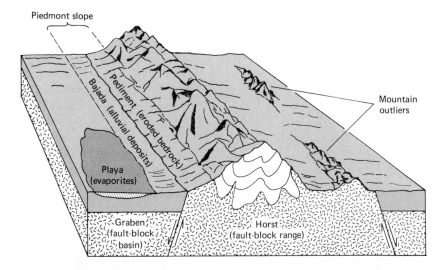

Piedmont slope

Bajada (alluvial deposits)

Pediment (eroded bedrock)

Playa (evaporites)

Mountain outliers

Graben (fault-block basin)

Horst (fault-block range)

Among the most distinctive characteristics of desert landscapes are those caused not by flowing water but by the wind. Winds in desert areas are not stronger or more persistent than in most other regions; but because of the lack of vegetation and water, exposed desert sand, silt, and clay are more readily transported by wind action. Under such circumstances, wind provides a more nearly constant and widespread eroding agent than does moving water. Just as in flowing water, sedimentary particles may be carried by the wind as either suspended load or bed load. Because air is a far less viscous fluid than water, however, only very fine sand, silt, or clay particles can normally be carried in suspension. Strong winds blowing across desert alluvium can carry fine sand, silt, and clay several thousand meters into the air in *dust storms*, and later deposit them hundreds of kilometers away as sheets of fine dust (Figure 11.5).

The removal of fine particles in this manner, called **deflation** (from Latin, meaning "to blow away"), leaves distinctive features

FIGURE 11.5 Dust storm. (John S. Shelton.)

FIGURE 11.6 (a) Formation of desert pavement and ventifacts. (b) Desert pavement. (c) Ventifacts. (b: E. A. Hay; c: Sheldon Judson.)

behind. Figure 11.6 depicts the role played by deflation in the origin of **desert pavement** and the **ventifacts** (*venti* = wind, *fact* = face) that are commonly associated with it. **Sand dunes** are formed by the accumulation of clastic grains that are small enough to be moved but too large to be blown away completely. Figure 11.7 displays some of the variety of dune forms and the conditions responsible for their origin. Although we normally think of sand dunes as particularly characteristic of deserts, they occupy a relatively small fraction of the earth's dry regions. Nevertheless, such sand concentrations can be impressive; the largest terrain of dunes, in the Sahara of North Africa, occupies an area larger than Texas.

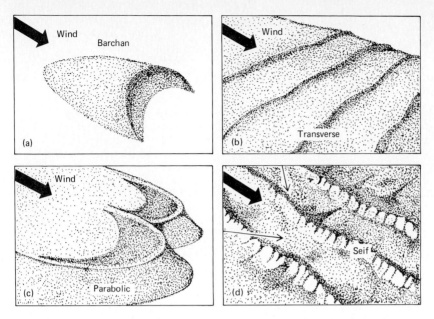

FIGURE 11.7 Sand dune forms. (a) Barchans, which occur on hard, flat surfaces with limited sand supply and a steady wind direction. (b) Transverse dunes, with abundant sand supply and constant wind direction. (c) Parabolic (U-shaped) or "blowout" dunes, which are partially stabilized by vegetation. (d) Longitudinal or seif dunes, which result from variable wind directions.

GLACIATION

As noted above, deserts form in regions where evaporation equals or exceeds precipitation. In tropical and temperate areas where evaporation does *not* exceed precipitation, the yearly excess of water, being liquid, does not accumulate but moves downward to the ocean under the influence of gravity. In polar regions, on the other hand, most of the precipitation falls as solid water—snow; when the average yearly snowfall exceeds the yearly loss from evaporation and summer melting, the snow continues to accumulate from year to year to form **glaciers** (Figure 11.8). Because of decreased temperature and increased precipitation, glaciers can exist in high mountains even in the tropics. Mount Kilimanjaro in East Africa rises to an elevation of 5,800 m (19,000 ft) and has permanent glaciers even though located almost on the equator.

Although very high mountains everywhere and most mountains of cool-temperate and polar regions today have extensive glaciers, it is important to emphasize that much of the earth's polar regions is *not* ice-covered. In many low-lying areas there is too little

FIGURE 11.8   An ice sheet (background) on Baffin Island in the Canadian Arctic giving rise to two converging valley glaciers (foreground). (Canada, Department of Energy, Mines, and Resources.)

FIGURE 11.9   Distribution of present-day valley glaciers (dots) and ice sheets (dark colored: Greenland and Antarctica). The maximum extent of Pleistocene glaciers is shown in lighter color.

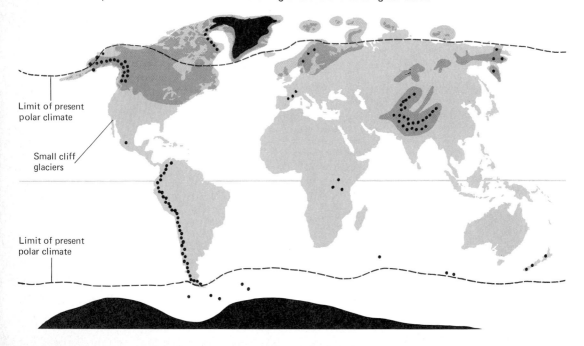

snowfall to accumulate even under extreme polar climates. For example, most of northern Alaska is ice-free, whereas glaciers are common in milder southern Alaska where there is more precipitation. In all, about 10 percent of the present land surface of the earth is covered by glaciers or ice sheets. During the maximum extent of Pleistocene ice, about 30 percent of the land was covered by glaciers and ice sheets (Figure 11.9).

11.3
GLACIAL MOVEMENT

Glaciers are massive bodies of moving ice. As layers of snow accumulate to build glaciers, the structure and texture of the ice change (Figure 11.10). Falling snow normally consists of delicate, lacy ice crystals; when these crystals first accumulate on the surface, they make up a porous, powdery mass containing only about 20 percent ice and 80 percent air. Within a few days or weeks, the combined effects of evaporation from the surface of the snowflakes, daytime melting and nighttime refreezing, and compaction by the weight of overlying snow all act to convert many powdery flakes into larger, roughly spherical ice particles with the texture of coarse sand; these particles are known as firn. At this stage the accumulated snow is concentrated to about half ice and half air. As the firn is buried more deeply by subsequent snowfalls, the trapped air either escapes to the surface or is concentrated in large bubbles; at the same time the adjacent grains of firn tend to fuse. The final result is a solid mass of glacier ice containing only about 10 percent air. In addition

FIGURE 11.10 Structural changes during the transformation of snow to glacier ice.

Snow   Firn   Ice

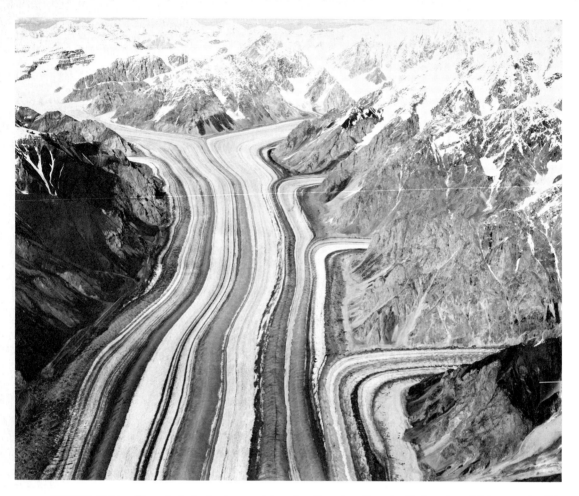

FIGURE 11.11 Flow of glacier ice in mountains of northwestern Canada. Sedimentary debris on and within the moving ice clearly shows the patterns of glacial flow. (Bradford Washburn.)

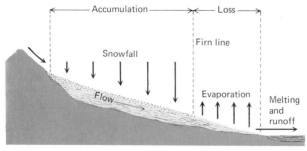

FIGURE 11.12 Flow and dissipation of glacier ice. As the ice flows downward it eventually reaches lowlands where loss exceeds accumulation. Fresh snow and firn are absent and the older moving ice is dissipated by evaporation, melting, and runoff.

to ice, most glaciers and ice sheets contain varying amounts of sedimentary particles; wind, mass wasting, and summer meltwater commonly deposit clay, sand, and gravel on the ice surface, which then become buried by the next snowfall and incorporated, in layers, into the ice.

The mechanisms that permit solid glacier ice to flow like a very viscous fluid have been much investigated in recent years; these studies show that at least three separate mechanisms are important in glacier flow. Some movement is caused simply by *slipping* of the entire ice mass over the underlying bedrock. Because of the small but constant outflow of the earth's internal heat at the earth's surface, the basal portion of most glaciers is not solid ice but a slightly melted mixture of ice and water. As a result of this basal melting, glaciers are seldom "frozen to" the underlying rock, but instead they move over it on a lubricating film of water. A second factor in glacial movement is simple *fracturing* and *sliding* of large blocks of ice past one another. This fracturing takes place primarily near the surface, where the ice behaves as a brittle solid. Deep within the glacier the pressure of the overlying ice prevents brittle deformation; instead, the ice deforms by still a third process—*plastic flow*. We have seen that under high pressures and over long periods of time, the solid rocks of the earth's crust slowly deform as if they were viscous liquids. Ice crystals under pressure behave similarly, but they have far less inherent strength than do the silicate crystals of rocks; for this reason, ice flows even more readily, and under far lower pressures, than does rock. As a rule, once the ice attains a thickness of about 30 m (100 feet), flowage occurs. This internal plastic flow is probably the most important factor in glacial flow; it is known to involve several molecular mechanisms that permit slow changes of shape in both single ice crystals and larger ice crystal aggregates.

Careful measurements show that glaciers move at average rates of a few centimeters to a few meters per day; the steeper the bedrock gradient and the thicker the ice, the more rapid the flow. Under exceptional (and still poorly understood) circumstances, the rate may be still faster—the maximum observed movement is several hundred meters per day. When glaciers occupy mountain valleys (Figure 11.11), rates of movement are easily measured by observation of surveying markers placed on their surface; but huge ice sheets, such as those covering most of Greenland and Antarctica, are not confined by valleys, and their flow is therefore not unidirectional but radially outward from their high, dome-shaped centers. Because of their thickness (as great as 4,000 m or 13,000 ft) and size, flow measurements are far more difficult to make on the Greenland and Antarctic ice sheets than on valley glaciers, although it appears that ice sheets flow much more slowly (Figure 11.12).

11.4
VALLEY GLACIERS

Valley glaciers range widely in size from those fed by large ice sheets in arctic regions (Figure 11.8) to very small "glacierettes" or **cliff glaciers** found at high elevations in temperate zones (Figure 11.13).

All glacially modified valleys are **U-shaped** and headed by bowl-like basins called **cirques** (Figure 11.14). These features owe their

FIGURE 11.13   Cliff glacier in the Sierra Nevada. (E. A. Hay.)

FIGURE 11.14   Cirques. The melting of valley glaciers exposes these bowllike features of glacial sculpture. (John S. Shelton.)

existence to the unique capabilities for erosion inherent in glaciers. Ice, being a solid, is able to *pluck* and *quarry* large rock fragments as it moves. Further, these fragments and other debris falling into the ice become powerful abrasives as a glacier scrapes them against the bedrock it is overriding, imparting a polished and grooved surface to it (Figure 11.15). Thus it is easy to visualize how a glacier is able to deepen the valley and steepen the valley walls through which it moves, causing a typically V-shaped stream canyon to become U-shaped (Figure 11.16). But why do cirques have a steep headwall (upslope cliff)? Not much ice exists in that region to scour and cut such a precipice. The answer lies in the existence of the **bergschrund,** an air gap formed between the bedrock and the glacial ice due to the constant downslope movement of the ice (Figures 11.13 and 11.17). This is a zone of intense frost wedging, facilitated by the ready availability of water that seeps into rock fractures during the day and freezes at night. The headwall of the cirque is thus steepened by mass wasting into the bottom of the bergschrund, where the angular rock fragments are used to scoop out the depressions that, upon melting of the ice, are occupied by small lakes, called **tarns,** found in the bottoms of most cirques. Glacial **horns,** such as the famous Matterhorn in the Alps, are erosional remnants from cirque and U-shaped valley development around the flanks of mountaintops (Figure 11.18).

We have seen that glacial modification of a stream valley imparts a U-shaped cross profile to it. A natural consequence of this

FIGURE 11.15   Glacial polish and grooves. (E. A. Hay.)

(a)

(c)

Stream erosion: down–cutting at arrow; mass wasting of sideslopes maintains Canyon shape as stream erosion deepens it from A to B to C.

(b)

(d)

Glacial erosion: all–around abrasion and plucking widens as well as deepens valley from A to B to C.

FIGURE 11.16 Conversion of U-shaped valleys by glaciation. (a) V-shaped valley. (b) U-shaped glaciated valley. Glaciers do not initiate valley cutting; they modify previously existing stream valleys. Note straightening of valley by truncating of ridge-ends. (c) Stream erosion. (d) Glacial erosion. (a: Geological Survey of Great Britain; b: Tad Nichols.)

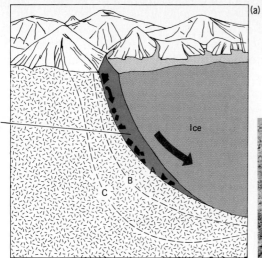

(a)

water
(freezing)

Ice

FIGURE 11.17 (a) Bergschrund: the zone of intense frost-wedging activity at the head of a valley glacier. Valley head is modified from A to B to C. (b) Small glacier, showing bergschrund, in Sierra Nevada. (E. A. Hay.)

(b)

FIGURE 11.18 Glaciated mountains with horns, cirques, tarns, U-shaped valleys. Wind River Range, Wyoming. (John S. Shelton.)

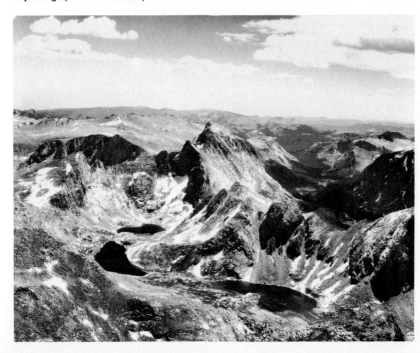

367

valley wall-steepening is the formation of **hanging valleys** and the impressive waterfalls that frequently pour over them (Figure 11.19). Although the main valley glacier has the energy to effectively deepen, straighten, and steepen its valley, smaller tributaries are occupied by much thinner masses of ice and are therefore unable to downcut at so great a rate. A comparison of the main glacier and its tributaries in Figure 11.11 makes this discrepancy apparent. When all the ice eventually melts away, the tributaries are left "hanging" above the major valley.

Waterfalls of another origin are also common in glaciated valleys. The waterfalls in Figure 11.20 occupy irregularities, or "steps," in the long profile of the glaciated valley, in contrast to hanging valleys that enter *into* such a valley. The origin of these irregularities resides in a glacier's unique ability to pluck and quarry large jointed fragments of bedrock in a manner beyond the capability of stream processes of erosion. Figure 11.21 depicts the manner in which jointing influences the glacier's excavation of a valley and the long profile steps that result. On a smaller scale, **roches moutonnées** (fleecy rocks)

FIGURE 11.19   A hanging valley, Bridalveil Falls in Yosemite. (E. A. Hay.)

DESERTS AND GLACIERS

FIGURE 11.20   Steps in the long profile, Devil's Staircase in Yosemite. (E. A. Hay.)

DESERTS AND GLACIERS

Smooth long profile resulting from stream erosion. Note variation in density of jointing in bedrock.

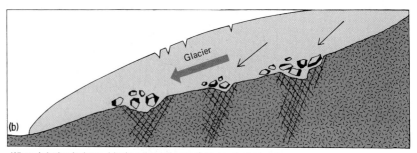

Where jointing is dense, blocks are small enough to be plucked out.

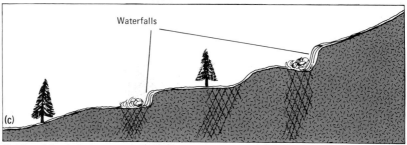

Melting of the glacier leaves stream valley with irregular long profile.

FIGURE 11.21   Development of steps in a long profile by glaciation.

are asymmetric erosional remnants of similar origin that are frequently observed along the flanks and bottoms of glaciated valleys (Figure 11.22). The direction of glacial movement can be determined from their asymmetry because the upstream side is polished and the downstream side is plucked and steepened due to thir different angles of exposure to the glacier's force.

(a)

(b)

FIGURE 11.22 Roches moutonnées. (a) Small feature in central Sierra Nevada. (b) Lembert Dome in Yosemite. (c) Diagrammatic sketch. At A, plucking and steepening occur because the angle between the surface and the glacial force is small and favors prying. At B, polishing occurs because of the large angle between the surface and the glacial force. (Photos by E. A. Hay.)

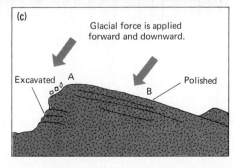

(c)

Glacial force is applied forward and downward.

Excavated   A
Polished
B

Erratic deposits of large rocks exist on the central plains of Europe in positions such that their sources are not apparent. In the early nineteenth century, the widely held view was that these deposits were floated (or drifted) by icebergs to their present positions, then dropped through the ocean water to the earth's surface as the ice melted. In 1837, Louis Agassiz proposed that they could be explained better as having been deposited from the melting of great glaciers that once extended vast sheets of flowing ice onto the plains of central Europe. His model for glacial origin of these deposits was based on many relationships discovered only by years of careful field observations. Some terms used to describe glacial deposits are holdovers from terminology used prior to the work of Agassiz.

Material deposited directly from ice is called **till** [Figure 11.23(a)], and all glacially derived sediment—including stratified outwash from meltwater, lakes, and streams—is known as **drift**. Erratics [Figure 11.23(b)], as mentioned, were thought to have been floated (or drifted) over the central plains of Europe by icebergs and then deposited as the icebergs melted. An important and diagnostic characteristic of glacial till is its chaotic appearance. Glaciers are so viscous (thick) that they transport a great variety of sizes of rock with equal ease, and when they melt, all these fragments are immediately dumped. The result is, as can be seen in Figure 11.23(a), a completely unsorted and unstratified pile of debris. To glacial deposits that accumulate in various distinctive forms, the term **moraine,** used with an appropriate modifier, is applied: *terminal* moraines, *lateral* moraines, *recessional* moraines, and *ground* moraines are those most commonly seen (Figures 11.24 and 11.25). The ability of a glacier

FIGURE 11.23   (a) Glacial till (near Lake Tahoe); note the poor stratification and sorting. (b) Glacial erratics (Yosemite): out-of-place boulders dropped by a glacier as it melted. (a: N. T. Hall; b: W. R. Cotton.)

(a)   (b)

FIGURE 11.24   Origin of glacial moraines.

(a)

(b)

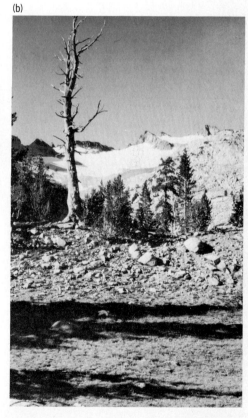

FIGURE 11.25   Glacial moraines. (a) Terminal moraine out of the east side of the Nevada (note its horseshoe-like shape). (b) Recessional moraine looking at Lyell Glacier, Sierra Nevada. (a, b: E. A. Hay.)

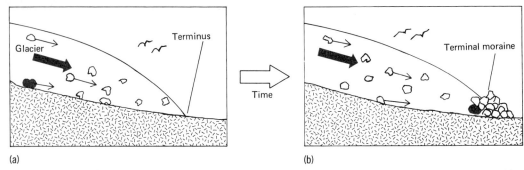

(a)   (b)

FIGURE 11.26   Development of a terminal or recessional moraine. (a) Equilibrium conditions: advance of ice equals rate of melting. (b) Note change in position of the dark boulder.

FIGURE 11.27   (a) Esker; (b) Drumlin. (From Leet et al; Physical Geology, 5th ed., by permission of Prentice-Hall, Inc, Englewood Cliffs, N.J., © 1978.)

(a)

(b)

to be moving forward with a large sediment load and yet have its front margin (terminus) maintain a fixed position, or even be retreating slowly (Figure 11.26), is what gives rise to the impressive ridgelike moraines shown in Figure 10.25.

Regions where extensive continental glaciation occurred during the Pleistocene epoch commonly display a variety of distinctive depositional forms. **Eskers** are elongated ridges of stratified till deposited by meltwater in contact with the base of a glacier [Figure 11.27(a)]. The ridges are either straight or sinuous, and they are roughly parallel to what was the direction of ice movement. **Kames** are of similar origin but are more or less isolated mounds composed chiefly of stratified sand and gravel. As glacial outwash deposits are forming, occasionally large chunks of ice are carried onto the outwash plain along with morainal debris. Later when the ice melts, large depressions, called **kettles,** become visible.

Drumlins are formed by moving ice, but their origin may be both erosional and depositional [Figure 11.27(b)]. They usually occur in swarms and typically are enlongate mounds, although rounded hills and low, gentle swells are also recognized. Both bedrock *and* till are constituents of some drumlins, suggesting a complex origin involving both glacial carving and subglacial deposition.

THE GLACIAL EPOCH

Today glaciers are restricted to arctic regions and high elevations, but as recently as 20,000 years ago, 30 percent of the earth's land surface was covered by huge ice sheets (Figure 11.9). The Pleistocene epoch, which began about 2.5 million years ago, is also known as the glacial epoch because during these past 2.5 million years the earth has experienced several extreme cycles of glaciation. Early study in Europe and North America during the nineteenth and early twentieth centuries suggested that there were four major advances and retreats of glacial ice during the Pleistocene. These different **glacial ages,** as they were called, were recognized primarily by analysis of different deposits of glacial till that show greatly variable degrees of weathering, the most highly weathered deposits obviously being older (Figure 11.28). More recent investigations have used deep-sea cores that distinguish between cold-water and warmwater deposits, carbon-14 dating of organic materials contained in various tills, and potassium-argon dating of volcanic rocks interlayered with morainal deposits in order to establish a chronology of glacial and interglacial episodes. The results have been startling: There have been several (perhaps eight or ten, or more) major fluctuations of climate during the last two or three million years.

FIGURE 11.28 Sherwin Till, on the east side of the Sierra Nevada, with a hammer imbedded in a boulder, indicating that the deposit is relatively old. This is because the minerals in the boulder have weathered extensively (become rotten). Weathering like this must have taken a long time (hundreds of thousands of years). (E. A. Hay.)

It is only natural to wonder why these unusual conditions have occurred and what controls them. Before seeking a cause for the Pleistocene climates, however, let us inquire whether there were other such episodes at much earlier times in earth history? Have other major glaciations existed in the past? The answer is yes, but geologists are not sure exactly how many there were or precisely when they occurred. Recall from Section 8.2 and Figure 8.9 that there is excellent evidence for a period of late Paleozoic glaciation in the southern hemisphere. Somewhat sketchier indications of an Ordovician-Silurian glacial episode also exist in Africa. Many parts of the world have provided outstanding evidence for a late Precambrian glaciation, but without recourse to fossils, geologists have found it difficult to determine if all these very old tillites (till that has been converted to solid rock) are of the same age; they could conceivably differ in age by 100 million years or more.

In any case, it is clear that glacial epochs have not been commonplace. They have occurred infrequently, without apparent periodicity, and were characterized by the affected areas undergoing several relatively abrupt temperature fluctuations between extremes varying from glacial conditions to environments perhaps somewhat warmer than those of today. What natural mechanism can account for these characteristics?

11.6
HYPOTHESES FOR GLACIAL EPISODES

So many hypotheses have been proposed to explain glaciations that we shall not attempt to cite them all. The difficulty faced by all such efforts is that they deal with extremely long-term processes and with mechanisms that may or may not be operating today. In the Introduction, we observed that geology is a historical science and as such is confronted with problems that do not lend themselves to strategies of hypothesis testing by conducting controlled laboratory experiments. Our present problem is a classic example of this geologic condition. Since hypotheses concerning processes taking place over thousands or even millions of years cannot be easily tested, neither can they be easily rejected and dismissed. This is why so many of them "stay on the books," so to speak.

The most venerable of glaciation hypotheses are concerned with past fluctuations of solar energy output and the possible effects of mountain building in redirecting patterns of atmospheric and oceanic circulations. The obvious difficulties with these views are that they are not subject to testing, and they do little to explain the many short-term variations that have been documented for the Pleistocene.

Other hypotheses, such as those concerned with variations of atmospheric carbon dioxide, salinity changes in the upper oceans (thus changing the rate and amount of evaporation), and astronomical jugglings of earth motions and solar distances, are all stimulating but untestable.

Even plate tectonics has entered this arena. There are fairly good meteorological arguments suggesting that glacial advances are slightly favored if a geographic polar region is either wholly continental or wholly oceanic, a condition in which *both* polar regions found themselves throughout the Pleistocene. Might it be that the moving about of continents by plate tectonics positioned them in appropriate positions with respect to the poles during the late Precambrian and late Paleozoic glaciations? There are no reliable data available for a Precambrian reconstruction, but the late Paleozoic position of Pangea is compatible with this hypothesis (compare Figures 8.8 and 8.11). Even so, the only prudent statement we can make at this time is that no *hypothesis* (model) has thus far been tested sufficiently to be considered a satisfactory *theory* for glacial episodes.

11.7
IS THE PLEISTOCENE OVER?

Let us close this chapter on climatic extremes by pointing out that we do not know whether our earth is about to embark soon on another glacial advance or retreat. Considerations of sea-level change alone make this a very important question. There is good evidence that during the major advances of Pleistocene glaciers, sea level was approximately 130 m (400 ft) below its present position. Crude estimates of the volume of water now locked up in the Greenland and Antarctica ice sheets indicate a likely rise of sea level of 40 to 50 m (130–165 ft) if this ice melts. Both of these potential changes, resulting either from glacial advances or retreats, present unsavory prospects to our coastal communities. The status quo is desirable, but any assurance that the status quo will persist, as well as the ability to influence the nature of any change in it, is beyond our present understanding.

SUMMARY OUTLINE

DESERTS

11.1 Desert landscapes: Periodic flash floods and the dominance of mechanical weathering give rise to distinctive desert landforms; alluvial fans and playa lakes are common in the arid Great Basin of western United States.

11.2 The role of the wind: Constant wind erosion in the desert accumulates sand dunes and creates desert pavement by the process called *deflation*.

GLACIATION

11.3 Glacial movement: Glaciers move by slipping over bedrock, by fracturing internally, and by plastic flow in response to high pressure from overlying ice.

11.4 Valley glaciers: Many new landforms result when a stream valley is glaciated: A U-shaped cross profile, hanging valleys, horns, cirques, and irregular long-profiles are common.

11.5 *Glacial deposits*: Deposits from a glacier's melting ice are typically poorly sorted and poorly stratified; some distinctive landforms such as terminal and recessional moraines mark a position where the rate of ice melting was the same as the glacier's rate of advance.

THE GLACIAL EPOCH

11.6 *Hypotheses for glacial episodes*: No wholly satisfactory hypothesis has yet been proposed to account for the earth's history of glaciations.

11.7 *Is the Pleistocene over?*: Worldwide sea-level changes of plus or minus 40 to 50 m could result from renewed melting or advancing of present glaciers; either event would cause serious problems for our coastal communities.

ADDITIONAL READINGS

* BLOOM, A. L.: *The Surface of the Earth*, Prentice-Hall, Inc., Englewood Cliffs, N.J., 1969. A brief introduction to landscapes.

FLINT, R. F.: *Glacial and Quarternary Geology*, John Wiley & Sons, Inc., New York, 1971. A standard advanced text.

*IMBRIE, J., and K. P. IMBRIE: *Ice Ages: Solving the Mystery*, Enslow Press, Short Hills, N.J., 1979. An exploration of approaches to explain ice ages.

SHELTON, J. S.: *Geology Illustrated*, W. H. Freeman & Company, Publishers, San Francisco, 1966. An excellent introductory text stressing landscapes; extraordinary photographs.

* Available in paperback.

12

Geology and Human Concerns

AS IN ALL SCIENCE, MUCH OF the geological knowledge summarized in this book was gathered to help quench man's intellectual curiosity rather than to satisfy his physical needs. There are, nevertheless, two areas of vital human concern that draw heavily on geological information.

The first of these involves the discovery and use of mineral and water resources. Metals, fuels, fertilizers, industrial chemicals, and building materials are all found as local concentrations of specific minerals within the rocks of the earth's crust. The search for and the efficient exploitation of these resources require sophisticated geological understanding and occupy the full attention of most of the world's trained geologists. Likewise, man's essential supplies of fresh water, whether occurring as streams, rivers, lakes, or buried ground water, are a kind of special mineral resource whose proper use depends heavily on geological knowledge.

The second major area in which geology makes a direct contribution to man's well-being involves the recognition and prevention of potential hazards wherever the construction of houses and other buildings, roads, and other man-made structures takes place in regions subjected to earthquakes, volcanoes, or unusually active erosional processes such as landslides.

All these and related topics are the concern of *engineering geology*, an active and growing subdiscipline of the science. In this chapter we shall briefly review these two principal applied aspects of geology—the search for mineral resources and the prevention or reduction of geologic hazards.

MINERAL RESOURCES

Hundreds of different rocks and minerals are of direct value to man as mineral resources. These range from common sedimentary building materials, such as gravel and clay, which cost only a few dollars per ton, to rare metals and gemstones, such as gold, platinum, diamonds, and emeralds, whose value may be hundreds or even thousands of dollars per *ounce*. Even though many such rocks and minerals are useful to man, only a relatively few are consumed in large quantities by industrialized societies. These, in turn, fall into three large categories: (1) *metals*, the most important of which are iron, manganese, aluminum, magnesium, copper, lead, and zinc; (2) *non-metallics*, principally fertilizers, industrial chemicals, and building materials; and (3) *fuels*, principally coal, petroleum, and uranium. Although coal and petroleum are technically not minerals, because of their organic origin, it is customary to consider them as mineral resources. The principal rocks and minerals from which these major resources are extracted are summarized in Figure 12.1.

FIGURE 12.1   Table of major mineral resources and their principal sources.

Major Mineral Resources		Principal Rock or Mineral Sources
Metals	Copper	Rare igneous and hydrothermal concentrations of native copper and copper-bearing sulfide minerals
	Lead	Rare igneous and hydrothermal concentrations of lead-bearing sulfide minerals
	Zinc	Rare igneous and hydrothermal concentrations of zinc-bearing sulfide minerals
	Iron	Sedimentary concentrations of hematite, magnetite, goethite; less common igneous or metamorphic concentrations of magnetite or hematite
	Manganese	Weathering (residual) deposits of concentrations of uncommon manganese oxide minerals
	Aluminum	Weathering (residual) deposits of aluminum oxide ("bauxite")
	Magnesium	Extracted directly from sea water; also from sedimentary dolomites
Fuels	Coal	Sedimentary coal deposits interlayered with sandstones, shales, limestones
	Petroleum	Extracted from interstitial spaces in sedimentary sandstones, limestones
	Uranium	Rare sedimentary concentrations of uranium-bearing minerals
Building materials	Sand and gravel	Sedimentary deposits of quartz sand or pebbles
	Brick clay	Sedimentary deposits of mud, shale
	Limestone	Sedimentary limestones
	Gypsum	Sedimentary evaporite deposits
	Building stone	Sedimentary limestones, sandstones, igneous granites; metamorphic schists, marbles
	Cement	Sedimentary limestones or metamorphic marbles, and sedimentary shales
Fertilizers	Potassium	Sedimentary evaporite deposits
	Phosphorus	Phosphorus-rich sedimentary rocks associated with limestones, dolomites
Industrial chemicals	Halite (common salt)	Sedimentary evaporite deposits
	Sulfur	Native sulfur formed by alteration of sulfate minerals in sedimentary evaporite deposits

Continental rocks supply most of the essential minerals. The only mineral removed in any quantity from the ocean floor is petroleum, and even that comes from wells drilled into rocks submerged under shallow waters along the continental margins rather than from the deep ocean basins. This is partially because of the inaccessibility of the ocean floor, which has precluded large-scale exploration for mineral resources there; but there are also good reasons for believing that the basaltic rocks of the ocean floor generally lack the large concentrations of easily extracted minerals that occur in the more complex silcic rocks of the continents. If so, the continents will *always* supply the bulk of man's resources.

On the continents, the thin veneer of sedimentary rocks contributes a disproportionate share of minerals. Most of the building materials (other than granite used as building stone), the fuels, the fertilizers, and the minerals for industrial chemicals are extracted from sedimentary rocks or soils, as are the principal supplies of iron, aluminum, and manganese. The much greater volume of continental igneous and metamorphic rock is of primary importance in the distribution of only three major metals, which in any event are scarce: copper, lead, and zinc.

12.1
METALS

COPPER, LEAD, AND ZINC

These three important metals are closely related in their geologic occurrence, although they differ in their uses to man. (Copper is used primarily by the electrical industry and in the making of brass; the majority of lead is used for automobile storage batteries; zinc is used in various metallic mixtures and in anticorrosion treatment of iron and steel.) Each of the three metals occurs as a fractional trace element in many different minerals, but the quantities involved are normally too small for profitable extraction. Under exceptional circumstances, however, the three elements have become locally concentrated in rich deposits of otherwise rare sulfide minerals (Figure 12.2). These deposits are usually associated with present or former igneous activity and appear to form as the gases and liquids associated with molten magmas move through cracks in overlying solid rocks. There, the gases and liquids carrying volatile compounds of copper, lead, zinc, and sulfur cool and crystallize as solid sulfide minerals. Because both heat and water-rich gases and liquids appear to be involved in their origin, such concentrations are known as **hydrothermal ore deposits.**

Hydrothermal ore deposits do not occur at random on the continents but tend to be concentrated in linear belts called **metallogenic provinces** (Figure 12.3). The exact cause of such concentration is uncertain, but the recent discovery of lithospheric plate motions

(a)

FIGURE 12.2 Copper mining. (a) Drilling into copper ore in an underground mine, Montana. (b) An open pit copper mine in Arizona. (c) Close-up view of an open pit copper mine. (a: The Anaconda Co.; b: Tad Nichols; c: Cities Service Co.)

(b)

(c)

FIGURE 12.3   Distribution of principal world copper deposits (dots) and major earthquake zones (shaded). The close correspondence suggests that the copper originates in the mantle and is transported into the crust along plate margins. (Copper deposits from a compilation by Paul Eimon, 1970.)

suggests that metal-rich vapors should be most abundant at plate margins where volcanic magmas from the mantle pour out onto the earth's surface. Where such a zone occurs under or immediately adjacent to continental rocks, conditions should be ideal for the escape of gases and fluids into cool overlying rocks, where they might crystallize as hydrothermal ore deposits.

Iron has long been the essential resource of industrialized societies,   IRON
where it is used principally to make steel for construction, transportation equipment, and industrial machinery. Iron today accounts for about 95 percent of the total production of metals. Indeed, a significant fraction of the remaining 5 percent is composed of manganese and other metals produced principally to be added to iron in order to increase the strength and corrosion resistance of the resultant steel.

Iron is relatively easily extracted from any of its oxide minerals—such as magnetite, hematite, or goethite—by intense heating in the presence of carbon (charcoal or coke) (Figure 12.4). During this "smelting" process, the carbon combines with the oxygen of the oxide mineral to form carbon dioxide gas, leaving behind an accumulation of relatively pure metallic iron. Man has produced iron by this process for at least 4,000 years, and modern steel mills differ from their earlier counterparts only in scale, efficiency, and refinements rather than in the fundamental process employed.

Because of the large volumes of both iron ore and coal (for

Iron ore and
carbon (coke)

Hot carbon
dioxide

Hot air

Slag

Iron

FIGURE 12.4 A modern blast furnace for the production of iron from iron oxide ore minerals.

coke) consumed in iron production, the traditional centers of iron and steel manufacture have been regions—such as the English Midlands, the Ruhr Valley of Germany, or the American Great Lakes—where iron ore and coal are found in close proximity. In recent years, however, the development of cheap, large-scale ocean transport has upset this pattern by making it possible to ship the raw materials long distances to be processed. In this way such countries as Japan and the Netherlands have become important producers of iron and steel.

For many years, iron was produced principally from ores that contained at least 50 percent iron—mostly relatively rare igneous concentrations of magnetite or goethite-rich soils. More recently, however, refinements in processing have made it profitable to mine hematite occurring in *banded iron formations*—thick sedimentary accumulations in which layers of iron-rich hematite alternate with layers of chert—most of which contain only 15 to 40 percent iron (Figure 12.5). This development has enormously increased man's reserves of relatively easily exploited iron, for great volumes of these enigmatic sediments, found only in ancient Precambrian rocks, are found on every continent (Figure 12.6). Because of these reserves, we are assured of an abundant supply of this essential metallic resource for many centuries to come.

(a)

(b)

FIGURE 12.5 Iron ores and iron mining. (a) Close-up and (b) distant view of typical banded iron formations, exposed in western Australia. The ore mineral (hematite) is concentrated in the darker layers. (c) Mining iron ore in Minnesota. (a, b: Brian J. Skinner; c: Standard Oil Co., N.J.)

(c)

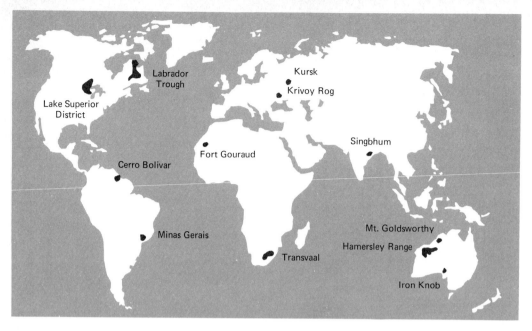

FIGURE 12.6 Location of the major Precambrian banded iron formations. (Modified from Skinner, "Earth Resources," 1969.)

MANGANESE, ALUMINUM, AND MAGNESIUM

Two of the three remaining primary metals have sedimentary sources, as does iron: *Manganese*, which is mostly used in the production of steel, and *aluminum*, used principally as a structural metal and electrical conductor, are both mined principally from tropical soils from which intense chemical weathering has removed other rock constituents, leaving behind an insoluble concentrate of aluminum (or manganese) oxides (Figure 12.7). Such deposits are widespread in the tropics, including parts of Australia, the Caribbean area, northern South America, and central Africa. It has been estimated that such reserves will meet all demands for these important metals until well into the twenty-first century.

Magnesium, the lightest metal used industrially, is used principally in alloys to make light, corrosion-resistant structural materials. It has an entirely different principal source from all other metals, for it is the one major mineral resource that is extracted directly from ocean water. Dissolved in the ocean are enormous quantities of many valuable elements, but the concentrations of most are so low that huge volumes of seawater must be processed to extract them, a procedure that has not yet proved generally profitable. Magnesium, the third most abundant dissolved element in ocean water (after sodium and chlorine), is an exception. It is extracted by adding to seawater dissolved calcium hydroxide, which causes the magnesium to precipitate as magnesium hydroxide (Figure 12.8). The

FIGURE 12.7   Filling a pit from which aluminum oxide (bauxite) has been mined, Jamaica. (Reynolds Aluminum Co.)

(a)

(b)

(c)

FIGURE 12.8   Magnesium extraction from sea water, Freeport, Texas. (a) Ocean water intake. (b) Large tanks in which calcium hydroxide is added to the ocean water to precipitate magnesium hydroxide. (c) Electrolytic cells which separate magnesium metal from other materials in solution. (d) Ingots of magnesium awaiting shipment. (Dow Chemical Co.)

(d)

oceans are so large that the potential supplies of magnesium and several other elements that might be extracted from them in the future are virtually inexhaustible.

12.2
FUELS

Mineral fuels are among the most crucial resources of all industrialized societies. Both coal and petroleum—the fuels that together supply the bulk of man's present energy needs—are the altered remains of ancient organisms that have accumulated in sedimentary rocks since early in Cambrian time.

Coal deposits, which are the compacted and altered remains of ancient land plants, were the first mineral fuels to be consumed on a large scale; they still provide more than half the world's energy (Figure 12.9). Although enormous quantities have already been extracted, coal-bearing sediments are so extensive that remaining reserves could supply man's energy needs for at least another 250 years. Unfortunately, petroleum, which generally is a cleaner and more easily transported fuel, is far less abundant.

Most petroleum is believed to have been derived from small marine animals and plants. When buried and compacted in sedimentary accumulations, their organic remains become altered to less complex liquid or gaseous compounds, which may then be trapped in porous surrounding rocks—principally sandstones or limestones—

FIGURE 12.9 A coal mine in Alaska. The coal beds are clearly visible as dark bands along the valley wall. (U.S. Bureau of Mines.)

(a)   (b)

FIGURE 12.10   (a) Oil wells in central Kansas. (b) Liquid petroleum flowing from a "well-head." (Standard Oil Co., N.J.)

to form petroleum reservoirs (Figure 12.10). Such reservoirs are most common in Cenozoic rocks and are less abundant in older rocks.

Because petroleum accumulations usually are smaller, more deeply buried, and more erratically distributed than are coal deposits, they are much more difficult to find and evaluate. Careful estimates of both known and probable petroleum reserves, however, suggest that only a 50- to 100-year supply remains even if consumption is held to present-day levels from now on. For this reason, countries such as the United States that depend heavily on oil and gas as fuels are already being forced to seek alternative energy sources. An increasing consumption of the more plentiful coal will undoubtedly be one result of declining petroleum fuel production, but still other alternatives exist.

Among the more promising is *nuclear energy* derived from the heat produced by the fission of uranium and related elements. Because relatively small amounts of uranium fuel can be made to produce large amounts of energy, nuclear power plants are already replacing those fueled by coal and petroleum and generating an increasing proportion of the world's electricity. The main difficulty with nuclear energy is disposing of nuclear plant waste products—particularly hot waters, which can endanger life in adjacent lakes and rivers, and radioactive wastes, which must usually be buried with the subsequent long-term risk of ground-water contamination.

Energy is also being obtained directly from the potential energy of waters on the earth's surface, both from man-made dams in streams and rivers as *hydroelectrical power* and from certain coasts where there are large tidal movements of ocean water. Furthermore, a few areas of hot springs are being directly tapped as *geothermal energy* for heating and for generating electricity, and much research is currently under way to harness more of the energy locked up in hot waters and rocks beneath the earth's surface. Careful projections show, however, that all of these potential sources combined are unlikely ever to account for more than a slight fraction of man's total energy needs.

There is, in addition, a far greater and as yet virtually untapped energy source: the direct radiation of the sun. Calculations show that the *solar energy* reaching a desert area only about one-tenth the size of Arizona could supply *all* the energy needs of the United States if it somehow could be trapped and stored. Many speculative schemes for such direct use of the sun's energy have been proposed, and some of these may become increasingly practical as petroleum reserves decline.

12.3
BUILDING MATERIALS, FERTILIZERS, AND INDUSTRIAL CHEMICALS

The remaining essential resources are mostly derived from sedimentary rocks, both detrital and chemical.

Man's principal uses of **detrital sediments** are for building materials: sand and gravel are used for fill and for making concrete, and clay is used for making bricks (Figure 12.11). Such materials are consumed in enormous volumes, yet they are so universally abundant that there is no danger of their exhaustion. However, supplies conveniently close to the point of use are diminishing in many heavily populated areas, and so they must be brought from increasing distances at greater costs.

Of greater immediate concern than an ultimate shortage of these materials are the widespread, landscape-marring pits and quarries that result from their removal. With careful management such blight can be avoided and the areas reclaimed for constructive uses after the materials are removed. This reclamation work is often

FIGURE 12.11 Sand and gravel being removed from under water, Maryland, (U.S. Bureau of Mines.)

expensive, however, and relatively few cities or regions as yet require it.

In contrast to the comparatively restricted uses of detrital sediments, **chemical sediments** and the sedimentary rocks derived from them have many applications. Limestone, the most abundant chemical sedimentary rock, is used chiefly as the major ingredient of cement (Figure 12.12). By far the most versatile chemical sediments, however, are **evaporite sediments,** which provide not only gypsum—the principal component of plaster and wallboard—but most mineral fertilizers and industrial chemicals as well.

As ocean or lake waters evaporate, the dissolved materials are precipitated principally as the minerals gypsum and halite. At several earlier intervals in earth history, large marine basins containing evaporite accumulations were far more extensive than they are today; as a result, the continents' veneer of sedimentary rocks contains abundant deposits of both gypsum, for building materials, and halite, which is used principally by the chemical industry (Figure 12.13). Less common, but still adequate for any foreseeable demand, are potassium evaporite minerals and phosphorus deposits, both used mainly as fertilizers.

Still less common are deposits of native sulfur formed in only a few regions by the action of bacteria on the gypsum of certain

FIGURE 12.12   Limestone quarry and cement plant, southern Sweden.

FIGURE 12.13   Evaporite minerals. Map showing the areas known or believed to be underlain by evaporite deposits in the United States and Canada. (From Skinner, "Earth Resources," 1969, after U.S. Geological Survey Bulletin 1019-J and A. D. Huffman.)

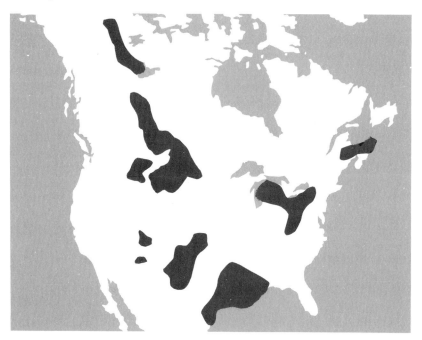

GEOLOGY AND HUMAN CONCERNS

evaporite deposits. Sulfur is a prime industrial chemical, used principally to make the sulfuric acid required for the processing of many other chemical products. For this reason, the relative scarcity of easily tapped native sulfur deposits has led to a search for alternative sources. Fortunately, sulfur occurs in abundance in many other forms and is now being extracted in large quantities as a byproduct of the processing of both natural gas and the sulfide ore minerals of copper, lead, and zinc.

12.4
MINERAL RESOURCES AND THE FUTURE

Although much has been written about the need to conserve the earth's finite supply of mineral resources, many modern planners feel that concern for future shortages of most of these minerals has been premature. Such elements as iron, aluminum, magnesium, and potassium make up a large fraction of the earth's crust; with improved methods of extraction (and perhaps recycling), their supply will probably last indefinitely. There are also large potential supplies of manganese, phosphorous, coal, building materials, halite, and sulfur. Among the principal mineral resources, only copper, zinc, lead, and petroleum appear to be relatively limited. The history of technology suggests, however, that satisfactory alternative resources are usually developed as the supply of one resource drops, and thus even these seemingly essential materials may become obsolete in the future. Aluminum, for example, is already replacing copper in many applications. Similarly, coal and nuclear energy are beginning to replace petroleum as a principal source of electrical power.

Perhaps more serious than the ultimate shortage of essential mineral resources is the immediate problem of extracting and using them in ways that do not threaten other aspects of human existence. For example, unreclaimed quarries, strip mines, oil fields, and gravel pits blight large areas of the land surface, while even larger areas are scarred by the abandoned debris that result from processing and consuming mineral resources and that, unlike most animal and plant remains, do not quickly disappear through organic decay. Likewise, the potential hazard of long-term radioactive contamination will become increasingly serious as nuclear energy is increasingly exploited. In growing recognition of these problems, many conservationists now feel that the emphasis over the next decades should be shifted from merely searching for new mineral resources to perfecting techniques that minimize the damage of extracting and consuming them.

WATER RESOURCES

A second major area in which geology is of direct service to man concerns the discovery, use, and conservation of water resources. Most liquid water occurs on land as slowly moving ground water; this source accounts for about 3,000 times the volume of water found in lakes and streams. As yet, however, less than one-third of the water used by man comes from wells tapping this large ground-water resource. The rest comes from the more easily exploited surface waters found in streams and in both natural and man-made lakes.

Most of the water used by man, whether for public water supply (about 10 percent of the total used), agriculture (about 45 percent), or industry (about 45 percent), is not actually *consumed* (Figure 12.14). Instead, it is returned with varying degrees of change to streams or the ground-water reservoir, where it may be reused again and again in a continuing cycle. For this reason, man's potential supply of fresh water is greater than any foreseeable need—with two important qualifications.

The first concerns the *location* of the water. Arid regions normally lack surface water in streams or lakes, and the deep-lying ground water in some of these areas is prohibitively expensive to exploit by wells (Figure 12.15). Thus neither agriculture nor industry with large water requirements is practical in most arid regions, and even municipal water supplies there may be limited and costly. In short, water resources are not evenly distributed on the land surface and must generally be exploited where they occur.

The second important reservation concerns not the location but the *quality* of water resources. Most human uses require relatively pure, clean waters; but wastes are frequently added that make these waters impure. Traditionally, such "used" waters have been returned to streams or the ground-water reservoir with little or

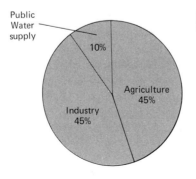

Public Water supply

10%

Agriculture 45%

Industry 45%

FIGURE 12.14 Principal uses of water in the United States.

GEOLOGY AND HUMAN CONCERNS

FIGURE 12.15 Irrigation agriculture (young orange trees) based on groundwater wells, southern Arizona. (U.S. Department of Agriculture.)

no treatment, so that contaminants were removed either slowly, by natural processes, or more quickly by man himself before he used the waters again. Along large rivers, for example, upstream cities and industries find relatively pure water that they use and return to the river with impurities, which must then be removed by consumers farther downstream. The well-known results of this and similar practices are the polluted lakes, rivers, and streams that now plague most industrialized nations. Fortunately, there is increasing concern for both the economic and aesthetic costs of such practices, and hopefully the pattern will be reversed in the future by requirements that waters be processed immediately *after* use so that they will be clean and pure when returned to their natural sources.

Unlike waters of the land, ocean water is not a direct resource because large-scale removal of the ocean's dissolved salts has not yet proved practical. Like lakes and streams, however, the ocean is used by man as a receptacle for his waste products. Coastal cities normally discharge sewage directly into the sea with little or no treatment; they also dump enormous quanities of solid waste and debris onto the ocean floor (Figure 12.16). Fortunately, the ocean is so large that these processes have as yet had little apparent effect on the waters and life of the open sea. In many partially enclosed near-shore waters, however, such waste disposal has led to destruction of marine life, including important fishery resources, as well as to pollution levels that restrict recreational swimming and boating. Hopefully, increased awareness of this condition may lead to corrective action before any large-scale damage is done to the overall balance of life in the ocean.

FIGURE 12.16 Solid wastes being hauled to ocean dumping grounds. (J. Paul Kirouac.)

GEOLOGY AND ENGINEERING

Geology makes yet another important series of contributions to man through the field of engineering. Many natural hazards that may threaten homes, buildings, bridges, and other man-made structures can be recognized and anticipated through geologic study. Of major concern in such studies are problems involving earthquakes and slope failures or other erosional processes. This section considers these problems.

12.5
SEISMIC HAZARDS

In Chapter 7 we introduced the topic of earthquakes primarily in terms of their value in learning about the earth's interior. Of greater general concern to most humans are the seismic hazards that frequently accompany strong earthquakes. In an average year, ten earthquakes causing widespread death and devastation occur somewhere on the earth; about 100 others cause serious local destruction; 1,000 do some damage; 100,000 are strong enough to be felt as tremors; and about 1 million can be detected by seismographs. Although earthquakes may occur anywhere on the earth's surface, they are primarily localized along plate boundaries, and the most frequent and destructive are concentrated in the seismically active zone around the margins of the Pacific Ocean (compare Figures 7.2 and 8.22).

The principal cause of natural earthquakes is believed to be faulting (see Section 7.2). There are four types of hazard associated with moderately strong-to-major seismic events produced by faulting (Figure 12.17):

1. **Ground rupture** If a structure is built across a plane of faulting that extends to the earth's surface, considerable damage can result.
2. **Shaking** Shaking is the primary cause of earthquake damage. It may take several tens of seconds for the strong motions of P, S, and L (surface) waves to die out, and accelerations equal to the force of earth gravity have been measured near the epicenters of earthquakes.
3. **Seismic sea waves** (often called tsunamis or tidal waves, the latter being a misnomer) Vertical ocean-floor movements or large submarine landslides can generate large irregularities in water level that spread outward as waves. Upon reaching shallow coastal waters, the waves steepen and heighten until they break, much in the manner of normal surf—except that heights as great as 50 or 60 m (160–200 feet) have been reached. Although seismic sea waves travel at velocities up to 450 mi/hr across the Pacific Ocean, due to their low height and the great distance between successive wave crests while moving in the deep ocean environment, they go unnoticed by ships at sea. They are dangerous, then, only when slowed and heightened in shallow water. One tsunami alone, for example, killed more than 27,000 Japanese in 1896.
4. **Ground failures** Landslides, rock avalanches, severe settlement, and other forms of slope failure are frequently triggered by rapid ground accelerations and prolonged ground shaking.

For most citizens the aspect of an earthquake that is of most concern is its intensity (review Section 7.3), especially as it pertains to their dwellings. What are the principal factors affecting how the building you live in will respond to an earthquake? In addition to the magnitude of an earthquake (over which you have no control) and the distance away from the epicenter (over which you have relatively little control), there are two other considerations of prime importance. One is that structures constructed on rigid bedrock suffer much less damage from shaking than do those built on poorly consolidated material. During the 1906 San Francisco earthquake, for example, buildings constructed on loose sandy soils and compacted but still watersoaked muds along the margins of San Francisco Bay were far more severely damaged than those resting on the bedrock of the city's higher hills. Another significant factor in a structure's ability to withstand strong shaking concerns its construction: design, materials, and quality of workmanship are all important. A fact that should be reassuring to most citizens is that a well-constructed one- or two-story frame house is one of the safest places to be during a strong earthquake, although special care must always be taken to avoid falling objects such as brick facings and chimneys.

(a)

FIGURE 12.17 Principal seismic hazards. (a) Ground rupture. (b-c) Before and after shaking. (d) Seismic sea wave. (e) Slope failure. (a: Karl V. Steinbrugge; b-c: The American Iron and Steel Institute; d: Mansell Collection; e: J. R. Stacy, U.S. Geological Survey.)

(b)

(c)

GEOLOGY AND HUMAN CONCERNS

(d)

(e)

The United States government has recently launched extensive research efforts designed to increase our understanding of earthquakes. Though still highly tentative, the ultimate goal of these investigations is the prediction and possibly even the control of potentially devastating earthquakes. The only predictive capability that currently exists, however, is a long-established system for warning island and coastal communities around the Pacific of possible seismic sea waves. Because tsunamis travel 40 to 50 times slower than earthquake waves, there is ample time to determine if an earthquake has occurred where a tsunami might be generated and, if it has, to predict accurately the time of its arrival at any geographic position.

More understanding of the underlying mechanism for earthquakes will be required, however, before predictions of major seismic events can be made. Perhaps we may never achieve this, but at present we are simply too ignorant to know. As for means of controlling an earthquake or reducing its strength, there are some encouraging models under development at present; but they, too, are in very preliminary form. The next ten years should see great progress in this area of geologic research.

12.6
SLOPE STABILITY HAZARDS

In the perspective of geologic time, all natural hillsides are undergoing rapid change, but our concern in this section is with the much shorter time intervals of human life and of the useful existence of man-made structures. A principal concern of engineering geology is to understand the geologic factors controlling the development of natural slopes in order to predict and prevent those activities that cause them to become unstable. Hillsides everywhere are constantly undergoing adjustments to maintain a stable slope angle. Such **natural slope angles** are controlled primarily by three factors: (1) strength of rock and soil; (2) orientation of planar structures such as bedding, fracture, and foliation planes; and (3) climatic conditions, and especially the amount of water. Natural slope angles range from the vertical and even overhanging cliffs in regions such as Yosemite Valley, where the strong granite rock is sparsely jointed, to slopes of only a few degrees in weak shale deposits. Slopes with angles in excess of 40 degrees and still in equilibrium are rare.

Man's entry upon the scene is often attended by his residential or industrial development of the natural environment, which too often involves changes that artificially upset slope equilibrium and thereby trigger slope failure. Figure 12.18 graphically depicts examples of three such adverse changes: overloading, oversteepening by undercutting, and introducing excess water. Seismic shaking is another important contributor to landslides. Figure 12.19 shows an unfortunate and dramatic result of failing to evaluate carefully a region's geologic setting before making cuts and fills for a subdivision.

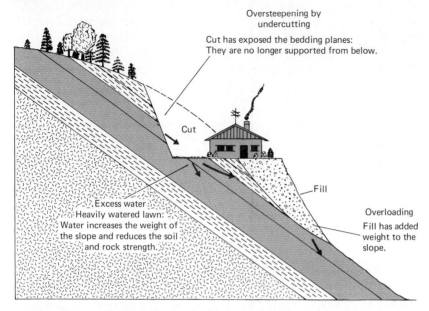

Oversteepening by undercutting

Cut has exposed the bedding planes: They are no longer supported from below.

Cut

Excess water: Heavily watered lawn: Water increases the weight of the slope and reduces the soil and rock strength.

Fill

Overloading

Fill has added weight to the slope.

FIGURE 12.18   Composite diagram of factors contributing to slope failure. There are, of course, many other configurations whereby undercutting, overloading, and excess water contribute to slope failure.

FIGURE 12.19   Homes destroyed by landsliding in southern California.

12.7
COASTAL EROSION

Many emergent coasts, such as those along the western coast of North America, display a variety of geologic hazards and inconveniences to man. Attack at the base of a sea cliff (Figure 10.14) during short episodes of high surf causes undercutting, thus oversteeping the cliff, which eventually causes landsliding and rock avalanching as a means of restoring the slope to equilibrium. Along the coast

FIGURE 12.20 Home and cliff at Seal Cove, California. Home is already showing distress from slope creep; eventual destruction is inevitable unless home is removed. (W. R. Cotton.)

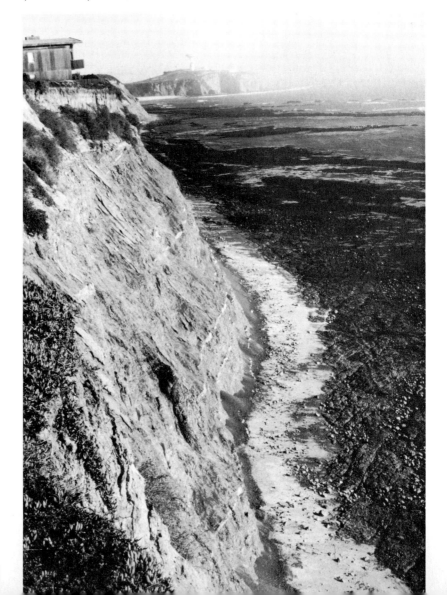

of central California, for example, rates of cliff retreat averaging 2 ft per year are not uncommon, and local occurrences of several times that rate are known. An unwary home builder, easily beguiled by the prospect of an attractive view from an ocean bluff, may fail to anticipate the precariousness of his setting in the not-too-distant future (Figure 12.20). In regions where the sea cliffs are composed of highly resistant rock, on the other hand, cliff retreat and landsliding may not pose any significant threat.

Along many coastlines man has interfered with the equilibrium of longshore beach transport (see Section 10.5) with disastrous results. In order to create a recreational facility such as a boat harbor or to enhance and protect a sandy beach, breakwaters and groins are often constructed to reduce wave and surf energy in the near-shore environment. More often than not, serious erosional activities are the undesirable side effects of such efforts. Consider the simple case shown in Figure 12.21: As the longshore transport moves sediment down the coast, an equilibrium is maintained as long as the backwash of the waves and surf is capable of carrying as many grains *out* as were brought *in* by the onwashing wave front. But what happens if the deposited grains are piled up in relatively quiet water created by a groin or breakwater? Not only is there insufficient energy to carry sand back out to deeper water, but down the beach from the groin the onrushing surf is without sediment to exchange as it strikes the beach. As a result, severe erosional changes are apt to occur.

FIGURE 12.21   Disruption of long-shore transport equilibrium. Net effect is deposition on the up-current side and erosion on the down-current side of an obstruction.

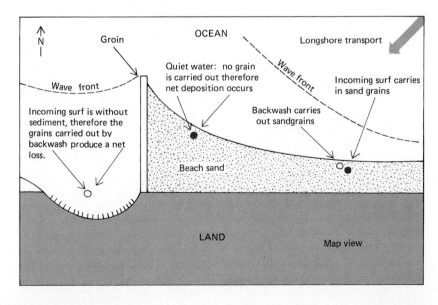

12.8
THE NEED FOR RISK-ZONING

In addition to the more dramatic geologic hazards associated with earthquakes, slope failures, and coastal erosion, increased urbanization in many parts of our country has initiated or aggravated problems involved with flooding and soil erosion, expansive soils, contamination of ground water, and regional ground subsidence. All of these problems are avoidable if we apply current knowledge of engineering geology and soils engineering. Regrettably, however, a large communication gap exists between members of the geological and engineering professions, on the one hand, and, on the other hand, between geologists and most city and county officials who must provide for protection of the public. We are just now beginning to bridge this gap, and in the next few years most communities will acquire significant geologic inputs into their planning programs. Those cities and counties located in seismically active zones or containing hillslope areas subject to development will benefit measurably by developing thorough risk-zoning studies and appropriate codes and ordinances. Only in this way can the average citizen be protected against geologic hazards to the same degree that government protects him against inadequate electrical wiring and plumbing in the buildings he frequents and inhabits.

SUMMARY OUTLINE

MINERAL RESOURCES

12.1 Metals: These are principally copper, lead, and zinc extracted from minerals of igneous origin; iron, manganese, and aluminum extracted mainly from concentrations in sedimentary rocks and soils; and magnesium, extracted directly from ocean water.

12.2 Fuels: Coal and petroleum are presently our principal energy resources, but replacements must be found for them since their deposits are limited and nonrenewable; nuclear and direct solar energy appear to be the only practical long-term alternatives.

12.3 Building materials, fertilizers, and industrial chemicals: These resources are mostly derived from sedimentary rocks, both chemical and detrital.

12.4 Mineral resources and the future: Future concerns will be to provide substitutes for depleted resources and to minimize the detrimental environmental impact of extraction and use.

WATER RESOURCES

Fresh water is a valuable resource from both an economic and an aesthetic standpoint; energetic efforts to limit water pollution are in order.

12.5 *Seismic hazards*: Four types of hazards associated with earthquakes are ground rupture, shaking, seismic sea waves, and ground failure; the possibility of controlling major seismic events is still remote.

12.6 *Slope stability hazards*: Hillsides generally stand at natural slope angles; their failure can be induced by overloading, oversteeping, or introducing excess water.

12.7 *Coastal erosion*: Cliff retreat is an ongoing process that creates hazards in some areas; man's interference with the beach's longshore transport can also be disastrous.

12.8 *The need for risk-zoning*: Risk-zoning studies and appropriate codes and ordinances are necessary steps toward protecting the public from potential geologic hazards.

ADDITIONAL READINGS

*BOLT, B. A.: *Earthquakes: A Primer*, W. H. Freeman & Company, Publishers, San Francisco, 1978. An excellent account of earthquake hazards.

BONATTI, E.: "The Origin of Metal Deposits in the Oceanic Lithosphere," *Scientific American*, February 1978.

*HODGSON, J. H.: *Earthquakes and Earth Structure*, Prentice-Hall, Inc., Englewood Cliffs, N.J., 1964. A brief, popular introduction stressing the relation of earthquakes to man.

*FAGAN, J. J.: *The Earth Environment*, Prentice-Hall, Inc., Englewood Cliffs, N.J., 1974. Chapters 2 and 4 provide good, brief reviews of water and energy resources.

*SKINNER, B. J.: *Earth Resources*, 2nd ed., Prentice-Hall, Inc., Englewood Cliffs, N.J., 1976. An authoritative and readable introduction to mineral resources.

* Available in paperback.

13

Extraterrestrial Rocks

ALTHOUGH THROUGHOUT THIS
book we have investigated terrestrial rocks and minerals as the principal means for understanding the earth, rocks collected from beyond the earth also have an important contribution to make to our knowledge of how the earth was formed. In this chapter, then, we shall direct our attention to meteorites and to the moon—the only nonterrestrial elements of our solar system thus far sampled for careful study.

METEORITES: SAMPLES OF THE SOLAR SYSTEM

The "shooting stars" seen streaking across the sky on any dark night are caused by materials originally left in space during the formation of the solar system and now captured by the earth's gravity. The bright streaks are formed as the materials plunge into the dense atmosphere, where they are heated, and usually vaporized, by friction with gas particles at heights of 40 to 100 km (25 to 60 mi). Such objects are called **meteors** if they are completely vaporized, and **meteorites** if a part of them survives the fall through the atmosphere and reaches the earth's surface.

13.1
METEORS AND METEORITES

Telescopic analysis of the light produced by the fiery paths of meteors shows them to be of two sorts. Most are composed of low-density masses of very light material that leave behind faint trails as they are vaporized in the atmosphere. This most common kind of meteor is believed to be composed of small frozen gas particles left behind by passing comets, a conclusion strengthened by the fact that such meteors are particularly abundant when the earth's orbit crosses that of a comet (Figure 13.1). Meteors composed of frozen gases are readily vaporized in the atmosphere and are thus never preserved on the earth's surface as meteorites.

 The second kind of meteor appears to be caused by much more dense metallic or stony material entering the earth's atmo-

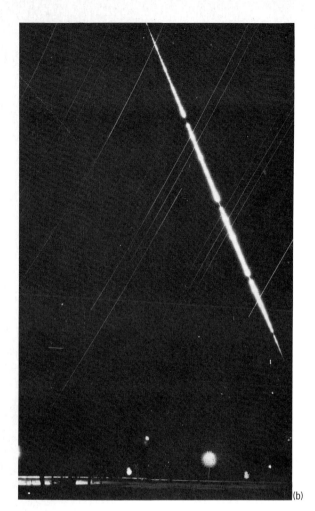

(a)

(b)

FIGURE 13.1 Meteors. (a) Meteors are most common when the earth's orbit crosses that of a comet. Most meteors are believed to be small, frozen masses of cometary debris that fall into, and are vaporized by, the upper atmosphere. (b) Photograph of a typical meteor. (b: Smithsonian Astrophysical Observatory.)

sphere from space. This type of meteor leaves an intense "fireball" as it passes through the atmosphere. In contrast to the cometary meteors, a small number of these heavier meteors are not completely vaporized, but instead reach the earth's surface, at which point they are classified as meteorites. We have already made reference to meteorites because of their extraordinary significance in helping us understand many aspects of the earth: In Section 7.6, we saw that certain inferences about the nature of the earth's interior are based on the overall composition of meteorites, whereas in Section 5.7, we noted that radiometric dating of meteorite minerals gives important clues concerning the age of the earth. In this section we shall review the characteristics of meteorites in more detail, emphasizing their importance as samples of the solar system beyond the earth.

About 500 meteorites the size of an orange or larger reach the earth's surface each year. Most fall in the ocean; only about 150 descend on land, and of these an average of only about 4 per year are recovered for study.

Although most meteorites are less than a meter in diameter, occasionally much larger masses, up to a kilometer or more in diameter, reach the earth's surface, where they make huge craterlike holes known as *astroblemes* (Figure 13.2). These are caused by the dissipation of their tremendous energy of motion as they collide with the

FIGURE 13.2   Astroblemes, the impact craters of large meteorites. The map shows sites of four large North American astroblemes that are believed to have been formed within the past 2 million years. Many older craters, now much modified by erosion, are also known. (a) Vertical aerial view of the New Quebec crater, which is about 3 km (1.8 mi) in diameter. (b) Oblique view of the Barringer crater, which is about 1 km (0.6 mi) in diameter. (a: Canada, Department of Energy, Mines, and Resources; b: American Museum of Natural History.)

(a)

(b)

earth. It has been estimated that only one such large meteorite falls every 10,000 years.

At least 20 large astroblemes are known on the earth's surface today. Most of these probably formed in the last few million years of earth history, whereas earlier ones most likely have been largely destroyed by erosion. In spite of the large masses of the meteorites that form astroblemes, meteorite fragments are rare in and near the craters. Apparently, such meteorites are largely vaporized by the enormous heat created by their impact with the earth. It is therefore principally the smaller meteorites that survive their fall to the earth's surface and become available for study.

13.2
METEORITE COMPOSITION AND ORIGIN

In overall composition, meteorites fall into three groups (Figure 13.3): some, called **stony meteorites**, are made up entirely of various silicate materials; others, called **iron meteorites**, are composed exclusively of metallic iron and nickel; still others, called **stony-irons**, contain mixtures of both metal and silicate. Most of the 1,600 or so meteorites recovered and preserved in the museums of the world are irons; this is because after they fall, these iron meteorites resist destruction by weathering far more readily than do the silicate minerals of stony meteorites. In addition, masses of metallic iron are far more likely to be recognized and preserved as exceptional materials than are stony meteorites, which are easily mistaken for ordinary rocks. For these reasons, it is impossible to estimate the relative proportion of meteorite types that reach the earth's surface by looking at *all* recovered meteorites. Instead, such estimates are based on studies of the much smaller number of meteorites, about 700 in all, that were *seen to fall* and then collected immediately. About 93 percent of such meteorite *falls*, as they are called, are of the stony type; irons make up most of the remainder, with stony-irons accounting for less than 2 percent (Figure 13.3). It thus appears that the material arriving at the earth's surface from elsewhere in the solar system is composed predominantly of silicate minerals, just as is the earth itself. The composition and structure of these meteoritic silicates differ, however, in many important respects from silicates found on earth.

Most stony meteorites are made, at least in part, of small glassy spheres about 1 to 2 mm (millimeters) in diameter (Figure 13.4). These spheres, in turn, are composed of dark magnesium- and iron-rich silicate minerals, particularly olivine and pyroxene. These small silicate spheres are called **chondrules**, and the meteorites containing them are referred to as **chondrites**.

FIGURE 13.3 Meteorites. (a) Relative proportions of stony, stony-iron, and iron compositions among meteorites actually seen to fall. Most meteorites are stony "chondrites" containing small, glassy spheres of silicate minerals. (b-d) Cut and polished surfaces of typical meteorites. (b) Stony chondrite. The specimen, found in Mexico, is about 10 cm (4 in.) long. (c) Stony-iron. The dark masses are silicate minerals and the light matrix is iron. The specimen, found in Arizona, is about 5 cm (2 in.) long. (d) Iron. The specimen, found in Arizona, is about 25 cm (10 in.) long. (b-d: Smithsonian Institution.)

The origin of chondrules, which make up a large fraction of the material reaching the earth from space, is uncertain, because similar structures are not found among the silicate minerals of the earth. Chondrules look as if they formed from a heating-and-rapid-cooling process that first melted some preexisting material and then quickly "froze" small drops of the melt into spheres. Radiometric dating indicates that most of them solidified about 4.5 billion years ago, at the same time that the earth is believed to have consolidated. This observation suggests that they may be particles of matter that were melted by an initial solar heating and then "froze" as they moved away from the sun in the early history of the solar system. This suggestion is strengthened by the fact that their composition

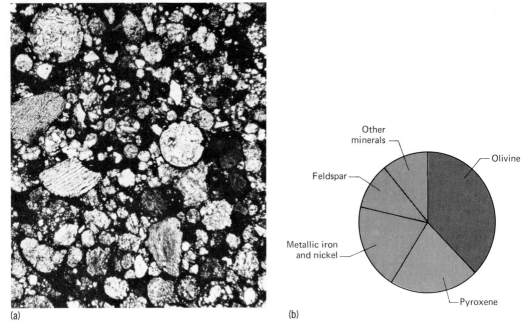

(a)   (b)

FIGURE 13.4   Chondrites. (a) Microscopic view of a typical chondrite showing the characteristic rounded, glassy spheres ("chondrules") made up of silicate minerals. The spheres are 1 to 2 mm in diameter. (b) Mineral composition of a typical chondrite. Olivine and pyroxene predominate. (a: John A. Wood.)

is remarkably uniform and shows about the same relative proportion of nonvolatile elements as does the sun (Figure 13.5). Indeed, one rare type of chondrule-bearing meteorite, called *carbonaceous chondrites*, even contains some of the more volatile solar elements, such as carbon, hydrogen, and oxygen, chemically combined into silicates and other solid minerals. Both because of their composition and their age, chondritic meteorites, particularly the carbonaceous chondrites, are believed to represent relatively unchanged samples of the primordial material that was initially dispersed from the sun to form the planets and other objects of the solar system.

Even if we knew that chondritic meteorites represented the primordial building materials of the solar system, we would still have to account for the small proportion of meteorites that do not contain chondrules (principally the irons and stony-irons, but also including a few nonchondrule-bearing stony meteorites called achondrites—see Figure 13.3). There are two general theories for the origin of these materials. Some workers believe that they condensed directly from solar gases, just as did the chondrites. Others feel that they have a secondary origin—from chondrites that at some time were swept together into large (several kilometers) bodies in

FIGURE 13.5   The relative compositions of chondritic meteorites and the sun. If the large volumes of solar hydrogen and helium are omitted, the remaining elements show almost identical abundance, a fact which supports the hypothesis that chondrites are fragments of solar matter. (From Glasstone, "Sourcebook on the Space Sciences," 1965, after Chapman and Larson.)

which internal melting could take place. Under such circumstances, the heavier iron and nickel content of the silicates might have accumulated near the center of the bodies. If such differentiated bodies were later broken up—for example, by impact with each other— then the fragments might well resemble the small proportion of iron, stony-iron, and achondritic meteorites that reach the earth.

THE MOON

For many years, meteorites provided the only materials from beyond the earth that were available for direct scientific study. Beginning in 1969, however, samples returned to the earth from the moon have added a new dimension to our understanding of the solar system. Before turning to the nature and implications of these dramatically important lunar materials, it will be useful to review some more general conclusions about the moon that have come from many years of astronomical calculations and observations of its surface features.

Most of the nine planets have one or more satellites in orbit around them, yet the earth-moon system is unique because of the very large size of the satellite in comparison with its attracting body (Figure 13.6): The moon has a diameter about one-quarter as large as the earth's, whereas most planetary satellites have diameters less than one-twentieth the size of their respective planets. Indeed, the moon is half the size of Mars and two-thirds as large as Mercury;

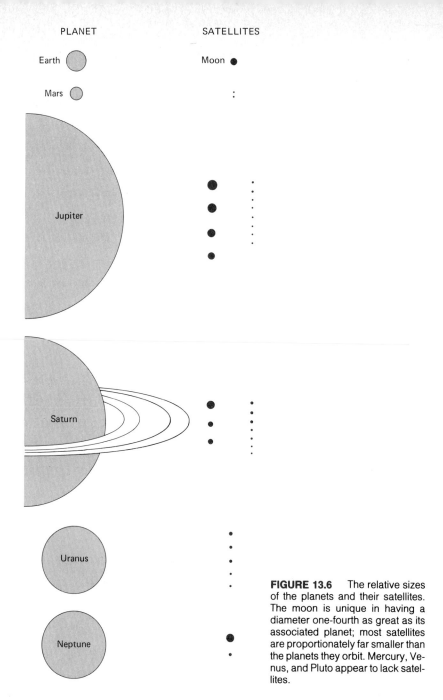

FIGURE 13.6 The relative sizes of the planets and their satellites. The moon is unique in having a diameter one-fourth as great as its associated planet; most satellites are proportionately far smaller than the planets they orbit. Mercury, Venus, and Pluto appear to lack satellites.

were it in orbit around the sun rather than the earth, it would qualify as a full-scale terrestrial planet.

By means of astronomical calculations, the moon's diameter, total mass, and distance from the earth have long been established. The diameter and mass having been determined, the average density of lunar materials was easily computed to be 3.3 g/cm³, about the same as the materials of the earth's upper mantle but far lighter than the earth's *overall* density of 5.5 g/cm³. This was taken to suggest that the moon lacks the heavy iron core of the earth's interior and is instead dominated by silicate minerals throughout. Because the moon is made up of lighter materials, its total *mass* is only about one-eightieth that of the earth, even though its diameter is one-fourth as great. The earth's far greater mass is the principal reason that a body as large as the moon can be held in orbit by the earth's gravitational attraction.

The moon completes one revolution around the earth every 27 days and, like the sun and planets, rotates about a central axis. Rather surprisingly, however, its period of rotation is the same as its period of revolution—about 27 days—so that the moon always shows the same hemispherical face when viewed from the earth. Because of the tilt of the lunar axis of rotation, and because of minor wobbles in the moon's orbital motion, slightly more than half the lunar surface, or about 60 percent, can be observed at one time or another from the earth. The remaining 40 percent, called the farside—to distinguish it from the visible earthside—is forever hidden from earth-based observation.

13.3
THE LUNAR SURFACE

Before the recent flurry of space exploration, information about the lunar surface could only be gathered by earth-based telescopes. Today, however, artificial satellites have provided detailed photographs of the entire surface, including the long-hidden farside, and astronauts of the Apollo missions have sampled the moon's surface rocks.

From afar, the most prominent features of the lunar earthside are large dark patches surrounded by lighter areas; both have been directly observed by everyone, for they are readily visible to the unaided eye (Figure 13.7). Early telescopic observations showed the dark areas to be relatively smooth and flat regions that contrasted sharply with the more irregular and rugged terrain of the lighter regions around them. Because they bear a superficial resemblance to the earth's oceans, the dark, smooth areas were long ago named maria (Latin for "seas"; the singular is *mare*); the lighter regions of high relief are known as the lunar highlands. The maria cover about one-third of the moon's earthside hemisphere; one of the most surprising discoveries of recent lunar exploration was that the maria are virtually absent from the long-hidden farside (Figure 13.7).

MARIA AND HIGHLANDS

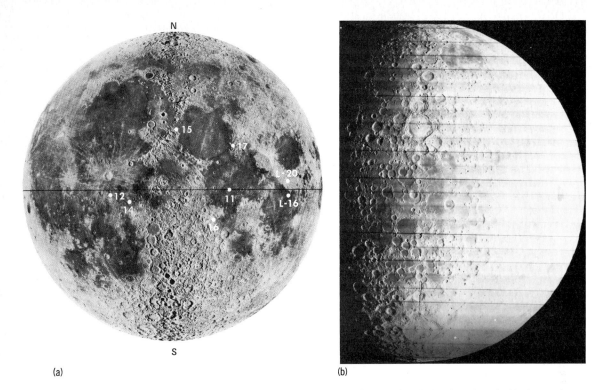

FIGURE 13.7 (a) Composite photograph of the lunar earthside, showing the distribution of maria (dark areas) and highlands (light areas). The dots indicate sites of samples returned to earth by the Apollo 11, 12, 14, 15, 16, 17, and Luna 16, 20 missions. (b) A portion of the lunar farside as photographed from an orbiting satellite. The farside is dominated by highlands and lacks the large maria of the nearside. (a: Lick Observatory; b: NASA.)

For reasons that are still uncertain, the farside is covered almost entirely by rugged highlands.

On close inspection, the margins of many of the maria show traces of the rugged relief of the surrounding highlands protruding through the flat mare surface, giving the impression that the mare material rests on top of an older highland surface (Figure 13.8). For this reason, it has long been postulated that the dark maria are huge lava flows that spread to fill large rugged depressions on the highland surface. This idea has now been confirmed by samples from the mare surfaces, which show their dominant rocks to be dark basaltic lavas. Except at the mare margins, the lavas completely cover the older highland surface that underlies them. Judging from the exposed highlands, this buried surface probably had mountains at least 6,000 m (20,000 ft) high. The complete burial of such rugged topography indicates that an enormous volume (and thickness) of lava was generated to form the maria at some stage in the moon's history.

(a)

(b)

FIGURE 13.8 Mare lavas. (a) A mare margin, showing the partial filling and burial of highland craters by flat, dark mare materials. Such evidence first suggested that the maria might be dark lava flows that cover an older highland surface. (b) Lobe-shaped pattern, suggesting lava flow, on a mare surface. (a, b: NASA.)

CRATERS The highland regions that cover about two-thirds of the lunar earthside and most of the farside are completely unlike the more familiar mountainous highlands of the earth. Instead of the narrow, linear belts of folded rock that form the earth's mountainous regions, most lunar mountains appear to be the more-or-less-altered remains of circular depressions or craters, which, next to the larger-scale maria and highlands themselves, are the most prominent features of the lunar surface (Figures 13.7 and 13.9). It is clear that the moon has not undergone "plate tectonics" interactions. Topographic features are not the result of compression and tension at plate boundaries.

The millions of craters visible in detailed photographs of the moon's surface come in numerous sizes and a variety of shapes. The smallest are only centimeters across, contributing to a highly pitted surface, and the largest have diameters of hundreds of kilometers. Many of the craters are fresh-looking and cup-shaped, whereas others are more dishlike, with flat bottoms and relatively low, irregular rims that give the appearance of having been modified by erosion. In general, craters with diameters of less than about 8 km (5 mi) tend to be cup-shaped and regular, whereas larger craters show a complete spectrum of shapes, from regular to strongly modified. The overall depths of the craters (distance between the crater floors and the tops of the surrounding rims) tend to vary with crater size; the largest craters, with diameters of tens of kilometers, have maximum depths of about 6,000 m (20,000 ft).

Craters occur on the surfaces of both the maria and highlands, but their size and distribution differ markedly in the two regions (Figure 13.9). Large craters, with diameters of several kilometers or more, are about ten times more abundant in the highlands than on the maria. It is largely the modified rims of thousands of such large craters that give the highlands their rugged relief.

The origin of lunar craters has long been a subject of debate. On the earth, similar structures are known to form by either of two processes: On the one hand, circular, craterlike volcanoes result from surface outpourings of lava; on the other hand, the impact of large meteorites also leaves craters, called astroblemes, on the earth's surface (see Section 13.1). By analogy with the earth, both internal volcanism and external meteorite impacts have been cited to explain the craters of the moon.

Volcanism has undoubtedly produced some lunar craters, yet recent exploration has made it clear that most were formed by meteorite impacts. Remember that although millions of objects from space are captured each day by the earth's gravitational field and plunge toward its surface, most are vaporized as they enter the earth's dense lower atmosphere, and only a few reach the surface. Although the moon, on the other hand, has far less mass and consequently exerts less gravitational attraction for such objects than does

FIGURE 13.9 Typical craters of the lunar highlands (a, b) and maria (c, d) in oblique and vertical views. (a-d: NASA.)

the earth, lunar gravity is still sufficiently strong to cause a continuous capture of materials. But more important, the moon lacks an atmosphere to cause melting and dissipation, and thus every captured object, both large and small, eventually plunges into its surface at high velocity. Countless millions of such impacts have probably given rise to most of the craters that cover the lunar surface.

OTHER SURFACE FEATURES

In addition to maria, highlands, and craters, there are other, less common features observable on the lunar surface. Small linear faults can be seen to break the rocks in a few areas, yet the numerous large faults associated with the earth's moving crustal plates are absent. Likewise, large-scale folded rocks similar to those that make up most of the earth's mountain ranges are not seen on the moon, although some mare lavas show small-scale foldlike structures called **wrinkle ridges** (Figure 13.10). These are believed to have been caused by compression or collapse of the cooling lava.

Two additional features of the lunar surface are of interest because they have few analogues on the earth. The first are **rays,** thin coatings of light-colored dust that radiate for great distances from large, fresh lunar craters (Figure 13.10). These rays, which can be seen from the earth only during a full moon, apparently form as lunar rocks are pulverized, and the resulting dust is scattered, by the force of large meteorite impacts. The second features

FIGURE 13.10 Lunar wrinkle ridges (a) and rays (b) (see text). (a, b: NASA.)

(a)

(b)

FIGURE 13.11 Lunar rilles, troughlike valleys thought to be due to the collapse of tubular cavities in mare lava flows. Aerial view of several rilles near a mare margin. (NASA.)

are rilles, long, narrow, troughlike valleys that occur in and around many large craters on the surface of the maria (Figure 13.11). On the earth, somewhat similar valleys, but on a smaller scale, are caused by the shrinkage and collapse of tubular cavities in lava flows. Most lunar scientists believe that lunar rilles have a similar origin.

13.4
LUNAR MATERIALS

Telescopes and satellite cameras have provided a wealth of knowledge about features of the lunar surface, yet these instruments supply very little information about the *composition* of the materials that make up the maria, highlands, and other surface features. By employing an analogy with the earth's crust and by noting as well that the maria resemble huge lava flows, lunar scientists long assumed that the moon's surface is dominated by igneous rocks. This hypothesis has been abundantly confirmed, in the years since 1969, by several hundred kilograms of lunar materials that have been returned to earth and subjected to exhaustive analyses. Although generally similar to certain igneous rocks of the earth's crust, these lunar samples also have many distinctive characteristics.

LUNAR SOIL

Because the moon lacks water and an atmosphere to produce earth-style weathering, its surface was long believed to expose much barren rock. One of the surprising initial findings of lunar exploration was that the moon's solid surface is almost everywhere covered by a deep layer of fine-grained "soil" particles, just as are most regions of the earth (Figure 13.12). On the moon, however, this soil debris originates from an entirely different kind of weathering than do earth soils.

In the first place, it is clear that the moon has probably always lacked the significant fluid cover that plays such a fundamental role in weathering and shaping the earth's surface. Just as on the earth, past volcanic outpourings from the interior of the moon undoubtedly released large quantities of water vapor, carbon dioxide, and other gaseous materials. Calculations show, however, that because of the moon's relatively small mass, the normal molecular motions of even the heavier gases would rather quickly cause them to escape its gratitational field and be lost to space. For this reason, it seems improbable that the moon has *ever* had the extensive fluid cover required to cause weathering of its surface rocks.

Instead of forming from weathering by water and atmosphere, the debris that covers the lunar surface is the result of **space weather-**

(a)

(b)

FIGURE 13.12 Lunar soil. (a) Typical view of the thick layer of rock debris that covers the moon's surface. A sample bag in the foreground and astronaut in the background provide scale. (b) Close-up view of a spacecraft imprint in fine lunar soil material. (a, b: NASA.)

ing—the continuous abrasion of the lunar surface by large and small meteorite impacts. Acting in countless numbers over billions of years, these impacts have pulverized the underlying bedrock and redistributed the resulting debris by "splashing," to produce the moon's soil cover.

The thickness of the lunar soil layer can be estimated from telescopic observations of lunar craters. Craters tend to show a somewhat different shape as they become deep enough to penetrate the underlying bedrock. Such observations show that the soils are thinner over the maria than over the highlands, which presumably, have been subjected to a much longer interval of space weathering. On the maria, the soil is usually between 2 and 10 m (33 ft) thick; in the highlands it may reach a maximum thickness of about 20 m (66 ft).

With one or two possible exceptions, all of the lunar materials so far returned to the earth have been pebble-, sand-, and dust-sized particles from the thick lunar soil, rather than direct samples of the underlying rock. All of this material shows evidence of igneous origin, yet much of it has distinctive secondary textures caused by space weathering within the soil layer (Figure 13.13).

When a meteorite strikes the lunar surface, its impact energy melts some of the preexisting soil material at the point of impact and scatters this molten rock over a wide area, where it quickly cools to form small spheres of glass. These secondary spheres are a common constituent of lunar soils. Beyond the zone of fusion is a zone in which the impact energy does not melt the soil but instead compresses and welds together small and large soil fragments to

FIGURE 13.13 "Space weathering" and the origin of lunar soil materials. Continuous bombardment of the lunar surface by meteorites creates a soil layer composed of small glass spheres (dark color), composite breccia fragments (crosshatched pattern), and fragments of relatively unaltered bedrock (gray). ("The Lunar Soil" by John A. Wood, August 1970.)

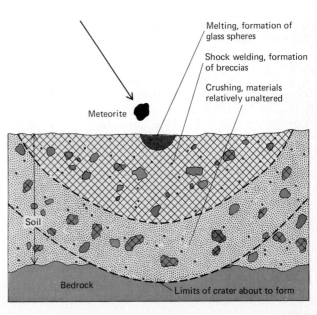

Meteorite

Melting, formation of glass spheres

Shock welding, formation of breccias

Crushing, materials relatively unaltered

Soil

Bedrock

Limits of crater about to form

(a)

(b)

(c)

FIGURE 13.14   Lunar soil constituents. (a) Small glass spheres that average about 0.2 mm in diameter. (b) Breccia fragments of all sizes. Breccias are composed of heterogeneous rock particles welded together by meteorite impacts. The photograph shows a large breccia boulder, about 1 m (3.3 ft) across, made up of clearly visible light- and dark-colored rock components. (c) Relatively unaltered bedrock fragments of all sizes. Shown is a large boulder of mare basalt. (a: E. C. T. Chao; b, c: NASA.)

form a heterogeneous solid rock called **breccia**. Like the molten soil, breccia fragments are widely scattered by the energy of impact. Beyond the zone of breccia formation is a third zone in which soil materials—and, if the meteorite is a large one, the underlying bedrock—are crushed and scattered with no change in texture other than fragmentation into progressively smaller and smaller particles.

The meteorite impacts of space weathering thus produce three principal textures of materials in the lunar soil: small glass spheres, heterogeneous breccia fragments, and relatively unaltered rock fragments (Figure 13.14). The breccia and unaltered rock fragments may be of various sizes, ranging from dust and sand up to large boulders.

LUNAR ROCKS   The bulk of the larger rocks returned from the moon are heterogeneous breccias whose included particles show a complex history of fragmentation and welding by meteorite impacts. Analyses of these, supplemented by studies of the less common unaltered rock fragments and sand and dust particles, indicate that the lunar soil is derived from at least three fundamental kinds of underlying igneous rock: mare basalts, premare basalts, and anorthosites (Figure 13.15).

Mare Basalts. Most of the lunar rock samples, which were collected from the soils that cover the maria, are dominated by dark basalt fragments that apparently come from the underlying lavas. These are made up largely of plagioclase feldspar and pyroxene, as are earth basalts, but they differ in containing more iron and far less sodium and certain other minor elements than do most basalts found on earth.

Premare Basalts. A second, quite different kind of basalt fragment is particularly abundant in soil debris believed to be derived from the highlands that bound and underlie the maria. Compared with the mare materials, these "premare" basalts have a higher proportion of plagioclase feldspar and less pyroxene and other dark minerals. As a result, they are relatively enriched in aluminum and silicon and poor in iron and magnesium. They also contain much more radioactive potassium and uranium than do the mare basalts, but they resemble them in having little sodium. Because of their associa-

FIGURE 13.15 Lunar rocks. The underlying bedrock from which the lunar soils are derived appears to be dominated by three distinctive igneous rocks composed of varying proportions of plagioclase feldspar and pyroxene. Dark, pyroxene-rich basalts form the mare lavas, whereas lighter basalts and anorthosites appear to make up the highlands. The photographs show small lunar rock specimens magnified about 100 times. (Basalts: U.S. Geological Survey; anorthosite: John A. Wood.)

Plagioclase

Pyroxene, olivine

MARE BASALT

Plagioclase

Pyroxene

PREMARE BASALT

Pyroxene

Plagioclase

ANORTHOSITE

tion with the highlands, these basalts are assumed to antedate those of the maria.

Anorthosites. Unlike the basalts, the third principal moon rock is of a type that is rare on the earth. This rock, called **anorthosite**, is similar to gabbro, the coarse-grained version of basalt, except that it is light-colored and composed largely of plagioclase feldspar, with little additional pyroxene or other iron-bearing minerals. Because of the dominance of white feldspar crystals, anorthosites are very light in color and contrast sharply with the dark lunar basalts. Like the premare basalts, lunar anorthosites appear to be derived from the highlands.

Thus the three principal lunar rocks predominate in different regions. The well-sampled maria are composed of iron-rich basalts, whereas the less intensively sampled highlands apparently contain both aluminum-rich basalts and anorthosites. This general compositional difference, based on a relatively few sample locations, has been confirmed by sensitive instruments orbiting in lunar satellites, which show the highlands to be everywhere more aluminum-rich than the maria. Such instruments also suggest that the radioactive premare basalts may be confined to the northwest quarter of the earthside, with anorthosites dominating other highland regions.

THE MOON'S
INTERIOR

In addition to providing direct samples of the moon's surface rocks, the most recent lunar explorations began to investigate the materials of the moon's hidden interior. As on the earth, these investigations are based on surface measurements of the moon's internal wave propagation, gravity, and magnetism.

The most revealing glimpses of the lunar interior are provided by *moonquakes* recorded by sensitive seismographs placed on its surface (Figure 13.16). At least three widely spaced seismograph stations are required to locate accurately an earthquake or moonquake, and in 1971 the third such lunar station was established. The instruments have since shown that the moon is seismically very quiet compared with the earth. All recorded moonquakes are very small, and their total energy release is about a million times less than that of all earthquakes over a comparable period.

The most surprising result of lunar seismic measurements has been the discovery that most moonquakes are sharply concentrated in both time and space. They tend to occur twice each month, when the moon is farthest from and closest to the earth; thus they appear to be caused by tidal effects of the earth's gravity. In addition, about 80 percent of the moonquake energy appears to come from one very small region at a depth of about 800 km (Figure 13.16). The reason for this peculiar localization is unknown, but the mere presence of moonquakes at such a great depth—about halfway to the

FIGURE 13.16 Moonquakes. (a) Astronaut setting up a seismograph at the Apollo 15 site. (b) Index map showing the location of lunar seismic stations established on the Apollo 12, 14, 15, 16, and 17 missions. Most moonquakes, which are far less energetic than earthquakes, appear to be concentrated at great depth beneath the small area shown by the color marker. (a: NASA.)

moon's center—indicates that the moon's deep interior is far more rigid than is that of the earth. Earthquakes are confined to the outermost one-tenth of the earth's radius.

Because of their small magnitude and their temporal and spatial concentration, moonquakes reveal relatively little about the moon's internal structure. Larger shock waves caused by the impact of abandoned spacecraft, however, have permitted the construction of crude seismic velocity-depth curves, which suggest that the lunar interior is layered, as is that of the earth: A rather sharp discontinuity at about 70 km (110 mi) appears to separate an overlying "crust" from an underlying "mantle." Wave velocities within the lunar crust are about what would be expected in basalts and anorthosites similar to those exposed on the lunar surface. Higher mantle velocities suggest denser and more rigid underlying materials, perhaps similar to the ultramafic materials of the earth's mantle. Little is known of the deeper interior because the relatively low energy of the spacecraft impacts and the location of the seismic stations in relation to them have so far made it difficult to measure deep wave velocities.

Satellite measurements of lunar gravity reveal only one unusual feature: anomalous concentrations of massive materials that floor several of the smaller maria. The exact nature of these surface concentrations of heavy materials is unknown, yet they confirm the earthquake evidence of a relatively strong and rigid lunar interior. On the more plastic earth, such masses would slowly sink into isostatic equilibrium rather than remain supported at the surface.

Unlike the earth, the moon today virtually lacks a magnetic field. This observation is in harmony with the moon's overall low density, which strongly suggests that the moon lacks a liquid iron core like the one that causes the earth's magnetism. There is, however, one disquieting magnetic puzzle: All lunar rocks tend to show strong *remnant magnetism,* which indicates that a significant magnetic field was present when they formed. The nature and origin of this earlier magnetic field are but two of the many unsolved problems of the moon's history.

13.5
LUNAR HISTORY

As with the earth, a principal reason for studying the present configuration of the moon is to understand its long and complex past. Likewise, our understanding of lunar history, like that of the earth, rests on two principal chronological techniques: *superposition*, or the relative vertical relations of its surface features, and *radiometric dating* of its minerals.

SURFACE CHRONOLOGY
Long before the first lunar samples were returned to the earth in 1969, a large body of information about the moon's history had been compiled by applying the venerable principle of superposition (see Section 5.1) to its surface features. We have already noted the most important conclusion to arise from such study: The edges of the flat maria can be seen to be superimposed on the more rugged topography of the surrounding highlands, thus showing clearly that mare lavas are younger than the adjacent highlands (see Figure 13.8). Furthermore, careful observations of the maria themselves reveal that some of them are composed not of single large lava flows but of several smaller flows that apparently formed at different times. Because the maria lack the abundant large craters of the highlands, it is also clear that many more large meteorites collided with the lunar surface *before* the maria were formed than did afterward.

By the application of similar reasoning, it is also possible to determine the relative ages of many large lunar craters, both those of the highlands and the less abundant ones that occur on the maria.

Often two craters, or the widely scattered debris thrown from them, can be seen to be superimposed, so that their relative ages are easily determined. More commonly it is necessary to infer the relative ages of craters by their degree of modification by later meteorite impacts (see Figure 13.9). By carefully combining all such evidence of relative age, lunar scientists have been able to compile, from telescopic photographs alone, detailed "geologic" maps of the lunar surface showing the relative ages not only of such major features as the maria and highlands but also of many individual craters and smaller lava flows as well (Figure 13.17).

FIGURE 13.17 Lunar surface photograph (a), and a geologic map (b) compiled from it. The region shown, a part of the mare margin and adjacent highlands, contains materials formed during the four principal events of lunar history: highland rocks (oldest); premare craters; mare rocks; and young craters. (a: NASA; b: modified from F. A. Mutch, "Geology of the Moon," 1970, after Titley.)

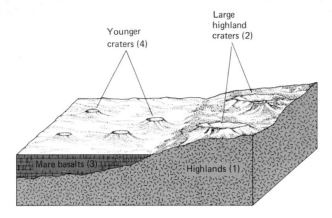

FIGURE 13.18 Schematic diagram of the four principal events of lunar history: (1) formation of highland rocks (oldest); (2) premare highland cratering; (3) partial highland flooding by mare basalts; and (4) younger cratering.

From such studies a basic fourfold division of major events in lunar history has emerged: First came the solidification and differentiation of the highland rocks; then massive, large-scale cratering of the highlands; next filling of some of the largest highland craters with the mare basalts; and finally, smaller-scale cratering of both the mare and highland surfaces (Figures 13.17 and 13.18).

RADIOMETRIC AGES AND THERMAL HISTORY

The major events of lunar history are clearly recorded in its surface features; yet until actual moon rocks were available for radiometric dating, there was no reliable means of determining the absolute ages of these events. Earlier estimates of the age of mare surfaces had been made from the abundance of their small craters. By determining the average number of meteorites reaching the earth today and making corrections for the moon's smaller mass and other factors, lunar scientists could calculate the time required to produce a given density of craters, assuming that the rate of meteorite infall remained constant. Such estimates first suggested that the mare surfaces are very old in terms of earth history, having formed perhaps 3.0 billion years ago. This conclusion has been amply confirmed by radiometric dating (Figure 13.19).

All mare basalts so far dated have ages in the range of 3.0–4.0 billion years. Thus even these relatively late features in lunar chronology were formed near the time of origin of the oldest known earth rocks. Dates from the lunar highlands are older—from 4.0 to 4.6 billion years—indicating that most of the rocks now exposed on the moon's surface originated early in its history. Except for continuous cratering, they have remained relatively unchanged for 3.0 billion years, or since early Precambrian time on the scale of earth history (Figure 13.19).

In addition to providing absolute ages for the highlands and maria, lunar rocks also raise fundamental questions about the moon's early differentiation and thermal history. Like the rocks of the earth's

FIGURE 13.19 Comparative histories of the earth and moon. The principal events of lunar history, including highland formation, highland cratering, and mare formation, are revealed by radiometric dating to be very old, having taken place during the early Precambrian interval of earth history.

crust, lunar rocks are quite *unlike* the olivine- and pyroxene-dominated meteorites, which are presumably similar to the solar materials from which they consolidated. Lunar surface basalts probably formed from a partial melting of such underlying ultrabasic materials, just as do earth basalts, but there is as yet no satisfactory explanation of the consistent differences in composition between the mare and premare basalts, nor for the fact that both appear to be concentrated on only the earthside of the moon.

A further puzzle is the source of the heat that produced these early internal meltings and then shut down to leave the moon relatively inactive for the past 3.0 billion years. It is unlikely to have been the impact energy of the large meteorites that caused the lava filling of the mare basins, for radiometric dates show that lavas from individual maria formed not all at once but over several hundred million years of lunar history. Likewise, if the interior were once heated by radioactive dacay, it should *still* be hot, for there is no way for most of the heat to escape the insulating effect of the moon's outer rock layers. Yet the present moonquakes occurring halfway to the center of the moon show that its interior is now cool and rigid.

Still other puzzles are associated with the light-colored anorthosites that apparently dominate the highlands. Anorthosites are relatively rare rocks on earth, but several regions in which they occur have been intensively studied, and their origin is well understood. They form when basaltic magmas are cooled very slowly deep beneath the earth's surface, rather than being extruded as lava to cool relatively rapidly. When cooled slowly, the first crystals to form are heavy magnesium- and iron-rich silicates that tend to sink to the bottom of the liquid magma, leaving the remaining fluid enriched in lighter calcium and silicon. These elements then crystallize to form an upper layer of feldspar-rich anorthosite. On the earth this process occurs, rather infrequently, in deep-seated magma chambers, some of which are now revealed at the surface by subsequent erosion. If the lunar highlands consist largely of anorthosite, as now seems probable, then a wholesale melting and differentiation of a thick outer layer of ultrabasic materials must have occurred very early in lunar history. Once again, the source of the enormous heat required for this melting is unknown.

Finally, there is the question of the large-scale meteorite impacts that produced the intensive early cratering of the highland surface. These impacts must have been concentrated in a relatively short interval of lunal history—after the consolidation of the highland rocks more than 4.0 billion years ago but before the origin of the mare basalts that fill many of the enormous craters and have maximum ages of almost 4.0 billion years. Fragments from the debris of one of the largest lava-filled mare craters suggest that the material was very hot, even partially melted, for a puzzlingly long interval after it was ejected. Small meteorite fragments in the debris also indicate that the impacting object was made up mostly of iron. Beyond that, little is known of this major phase of lunar history.

ORIGIN OF THE MOON

Still other puzzles surround the ultimate origin of the moon and its long-term interactions with the earth. The moon almost certainly consolidated about 4.5 billion years ago from smaller masses of cosmic matter, along with the sun, earth, and planets. It may even have accreted from fragments initially in orbit around the primitive earth [Figure 13.20(a)]. If it did, however, it is difficult to explain the differences in density between the two bodies and the concentration of most of the heavier materials in the earth's core. On the

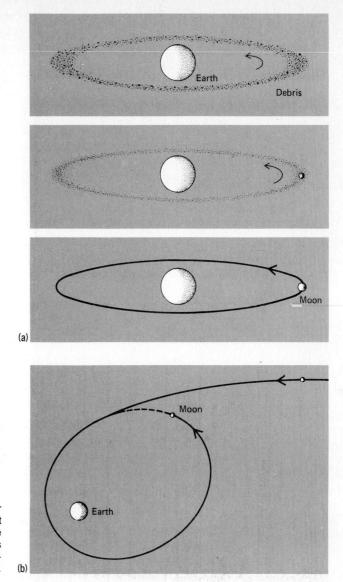

(a)

(b)

FIGURE 13.20 Hypotheses of lunar origin. (a) Accretion from debris in orbit around the primitive earth. (b) Capture of an independent body by the earth's gravitational field. There are serious objections to both hypotheses (see text).

other hand, there are also suggestions that the moon may not have been a satellite of the earth for all of its history. These suggestions come from considerations of the motions of the two bodies and the interactions of their gravitational fields.

The gravitational tides caused on the earth by the moon have the effect of gradually slowing down the earth's rate of rotation by transferring some of its rotational energy to the moon's energy of revolution about the earth. This causes the moon to become progressively more distant from the earth as the earth's rate of rotation decreases. Furthermore, the rate at which the moon is now receding from the earth can be calculated using historical records of ancient lunar eclipses. When the rate so obtained is projected into the past, it suggests that the moon came very close to the earth only 2.0 billion years ago and thus could not have been a satellite of the earth for all of its history.

Using such reasoning, some have suggested that the moon was originally a separate body, perhaps a fifth "terrestrial" or "inner" planet (along with Mercury, Venus, the earth, and Mars) that was somehow captured by the earth's gravity [Figure 13.20(b)]. There are, however, many difficulties with this idea. Other calculations suggest that if a body as large as the moon approached the earth, it would most probably not be captured but merely have its path deflected. Furthermore, if the moon had been very near the earth as recently as 2.0 billion years ago, it would have produced enormous tidal effects and frictional melting of most of the earth's crustal rocks, events for which there is no geological evidence. In short, the question of the origin of the earth-moon system remains a fundamental problem of planetary science.

SUMMARY OUTLINE

METEORITES: SAMPLES OF THE SOLAR SYSTEM

13.1 Meteors and meteorites:
Every year millions of frozen cometary gas accretions and heavier solid fragments from space are captured by the earth's gravity, but most are vaporized as they fall through the atmosphere; about 150 meteorites reach the land surface each year, but only about 4 are recovered for study.

13.2 Meteorite composition and origin:
Most meteorites are composed of small glassy spheres of olivine and pyroxene that may represent materials melted by the initial heating of the sun; the smaller quantities of iron and other meteorites may have had a similar origin or may be fragments of larger, differentiated planetary bodies.

THE MOON

13.3 The lunar surface:
Maria and highlands: The most conspicuous features of the lunar earthside are flat, dark maria and light, rugged highlands; only highlands occur on the long-hidden farside.
Craters are circular depressions of many sizes and shapes that cover the maria and highlands; some were probably caused by internal volcanoes, but most are the result of meteorite impacts.

EXTRATERRESTRIAL ROCKS

Other surface features include small faults and foldlike wrinkle ridges, rays of debris from crater-producing impacts, and long, sinuous channels called *rilles*.

13.4 Lunar materials:

Lunar Soil: Rocks of the lunar surface are almost everywhere covered by a thick layer of pebble-, sand-, and dust-sized debris produced by meteorite impacts.

Lunar rocks are of three principal types—iron-rich basalts that form the maria and aluminum-rich basalts and light-colored anorthosites that occur in the highlands.

The moon's interior: The moon's interior shows faint, localized moonquakes at great depths and an earthlike outer layering, but it lacks a magnetism-producing fluid iron core.

13.5 Lunar history:

Surface chronology: Superposition of lunar surface features shows the principal events of lunar history to have been, from oldest to youngest, highland formation, massive cratering, mare formation, and finally less intensive cratering.

Radiometric ages and thermal history: Highland differentiation, cratering, and mare filling took place between about 4.1 and 3.0 billion years ago, relatively soon after the moon's origin; the source of the heat for highland differentiation and basalt flooding is a major mystery.

Origin of the moon: The moon may have originally consolidated from materials in orbit around the primitive earth, or it may have been subsequently captured from elsewhere by the earth's gravity.

ADDITIONAL READINGS

BOWKER, D. C., and J. K. HUGHES: *Lunar Orbiter Photographic Atlas of the Moon*, National Aeronautics and Space Administration, Washington, 1971. A definitive collection of lunar surface photographs.

GOLDREICH, P.: "Tides and the Earth-Moon System," *Scientific American*, 226, no. 4 (1972), 43–52. A popular review of the problem of the moon's origin.

MASON, B.: "The Lunar Rocks," *Scientific American*, 225, no. 4 (1971), 48–58. A popular review of the first several groups of lunar samples.

MUTCH, T. A.: *Geology of the Moon, A Stratigraphic View*, Princeton University Press, Princeton, N.J., 1972. A detailed but readable introduction to lunar surface chronology, with excellent illustrations.

WOOD, J. A.: "The Lunar Soil," *Scientific American*, 223, no. 2 (1970), 14–23. A popular review article.

* WOOD, J. A.: *Meteorites and the Origin of Planets*, McGraw-Hill Book Company, New York, 1968. A readable, intermediate-level survey.

* Available in paperback.

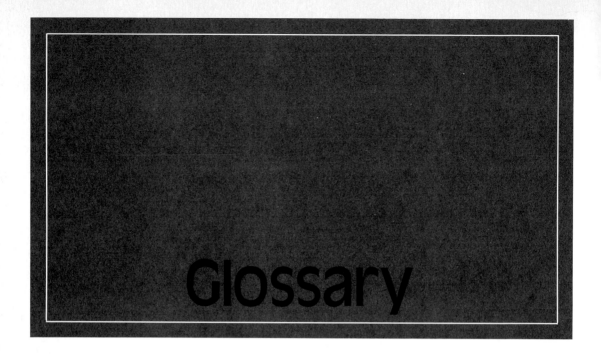

Glossary

Aa (lava) A relatively viscous, blocky surfaced basalt flow.

Achondrites Stony meteorites that do not contain small glassy spheres.

Alluvial fans Fan-shaped deposits of sediment formed at the base of highland terrain in arid regions.

Alluvial valleys Flat-floored valleys covered by thin deposits of alluvium.

Alluvium Sediment deposited from a stream.

Aluminum oxides Earthy masses of small crystals that commonly have resulted from intense chemical weathering; sometimes found as larger gem stones such as ruby (Al_2O_3).

Aluminum silicates Isolated tetrahedra silicates in which aluminum is the principal metallic element (e.g., Kyanite, Al_2SiO_5).

Amphibole (mineral group) Double chain silicates commonly rich in iron and magnesium ions.

Angular unconformity An unconformity in which the older rocks have been folded and eroded prior to deposition of the younger rocks.

Anhydrite A sulfate mineral; $CaSO_4$.

Anorthosites Coarse-grained plagioclase-rich rocks; the dominant rock of the lunar highlands.

Anticlines Archlike folds having limbs that are dipping away from each other.

Aphanitic texture A rock texture in which individual grains are too small to be seen by the unaided eye.

Aquifer A body of rock that holds and yields significant volumes of water.

Aragonite A carbonate mineral, $CaCO_3$.

Arkose Sandstone that contains abundant feldspar and quartz.

Artesian wells Free-flowing water wells.

Asthenosphere A weak (plastic) zone of mantle rock lying beneath the lithosphere.

Astrobleme A circular landscape feature resulting from a meteorite impact.

Atom The smallest particle of an element possessing the essential characteristics of the element.

Atomic number The number of protons in each atom of an element.

Attitudes Symbols used on maps to show the strike and dip of beds.

Axial dipole magnetic fields A magnetic field caused by two opposing poles at opposite ends of an axis.

Axial plane An imaginary surface that divides the opposite limbs of a fold.

Axis of a fold An imaginary line on the earth's surface that divides the opposite limbs of a fold.

Bajada Many alluvial fans joined together to make a continuous apronlike feature of sediment.

Barchan A sand dune occurring on hard, flat surfaces; crescent-shaped with its slip face on the downwind side.

Barrier islands Small islands resulting from redistributed coastal sediments.

Basement The oldest rocks occurring in an area; usually plutonic or metamorphic.

Batholith A large mass of intrusive igneous rocks; exposed only by extensive erosion.

Bauxite An aluminum-rich weathering product formed in tropical climates.

Beach A zone within which fragments are actively moved on shore, off shore, and parallel to the shore.

Bedding The layering of sedimentary accumulations; stratification.

Bed load Particles bounced or rolled along a stream bottom during transport.

Benioff Zone An inclined plane of earthquake foci; caused by subduction.

Bergschrund An air gap formed between the moving glacier and the bedrock at the head of a valley glacier; a region of intense frost-wedging.

Berm The portion of a beach that is above water level.

Biogenic chemical sediments Crystalline sediments produced by the life processes of water-dwelling plants and animals.

Biogenic sedimentary structures Features of a sedimentary rock produced by organisms following deposition (e.g., worm burrows, etc.).

Body waves Seismic waves (P and S) that travel through the interior (body) of the earth.

Breccia Large angular fragments forming a rock; may be of either volcanic or sedimentary origin.

Calcite A common carbonate mineral; $CaCO_3$ —the principal constituent of limestone.

Caldera A roughly circular feature resulting from collapse around the summit of a volcano.

Capillary waves Small irregularities on a water surface resulting from wind.

Carbonate group Minerals composed in part of the CO_3^{-2} ion group.

Carbonate rocks Rocks composed of carbonate minerals; limestone and dolomite are most common.

Catastrophism The eighteenth-century view that the earth had repeatedly undergone incredibly violent upheavals of the sort not presently observable; Georges Cuvier was the chief proponent.

Channel deposits Coarse alluvial deposits.

Chemical sediments Accumulations of chemically precipitated crystalline material; characterized by granular texture.

Chemical weathering Chemical decomposition of rock-forming minerals.

Chert Sedimentary rock composed of exceedingly fine-grained quartz and opal.

Chondrites Stony meteorites containing small glassy spheres.

Chondrules Small glassy spheres of silicate material; commonly found as a component of stony meteorites called chondrites.

Cinder cone A relatively small volcano formed by pyroclastic eruptions from a single vent.

Cirque A bowllike feature of glacial origin at the head of a glaciated valley.

Clastic texture A rock texture resulting from the accumulation of eroded fragments; rounded grains and pore (void) spaces among grains are usually apparent.

Clay minerals Sheet silicates that result from chemical weathering processes; very small crystal sizes.

Cleavage The tendency to fracture along planar surfaces; common in many minerals.

Cliff glaciers Valley glaciers of very small size.

Color One of the physical properties used to describe a mineral is its color.

Columnar jointing The development of many-sided columns in igneous rock because of cracks resulting from contraction during cooling.

Composite volcanoes Volcanoes consisting of interlayered flows and fragmental ejecta (tuff and breccia); usually andesitic in composition.

Compound A substance composed of two or more elements.

Concordant Igneous bodies emplaced parallel to the layering of an older rock are *concordant intrusives.*

Conglomerate Sedimentary rock composed of sand- and gravel-sized fragments.

Contact metamorphism Metamorphism from heat effects near the margin of a pluton.

Continental drift The theory that the continents of the earth have moved laterally about with respect to each other.

Continental shelves The submerged edges of continents.

Continental slopes The relatively steep slopes separating continental shelves and deep ocean floors.

Convection currents Fluid motions caused by density differences; hypothesized as a possible cause of plate motions in plate tectonic theory.

Coordination of atoms or ions Refers to the number of one-size particle (atoms or ions) that can pack around another size particle.

Core (of the earth) The earth's innermost zone; separated from the overlying mantle by a major seismic discontinuity.

Core-mantle discontinuity The seismic discontinuity separating the earth's mantle and core.

Correlate The demonstration of equivalencies between separated rock units; usually attempts are made to show *age* equivalencies.

Cosmic ray-induced nuclides Radioactive nuclides of short half-life produced by collisons between cosmic rays and atmospheric gases.

Covalent bonding Atoms that are held together by sharing each other's outermost electrons.

Craters (lunar) Circular depressions on the moon's surface.

Creep Slow downslope movements of soil and rock.

Cross bedding Within each major bed there are inclined layers; produced by directional currents of wind or water.

Crust The outer, rocky shell of the earth; generally less than 60 km thick.

Crystalline Possessing an ordered space lattice structure.

Crystalline space lattice A long-range three-dimensional pattern of repeated atoms or ions that characterizes all minerals.

Curie temperature The temperature at which heated magnetized solids lose their magnetism.

Current charts Charts showing the general pattern of surface currents in the ocean.

Currents (ocean) Motions in oceans that transport water from one location to another.

Deflation The removal of small particles of sediment by wind action.

Delta A large deposit of sediment at the mouth of a river.

Dendritic drainage The pattern of a stream system characterized by an irregular form, much like the branching pattern of a tree.

Density The mass per unit volume of a substance (e.g. the density of pure gold is 19.3 grams per cubic centimeter).

Desert pavement A pavementlike surface of large fragments produced by deflation; found in some desert regions.

Deserts Regions having little moisture or vegetation.

Detrital sediments Accumulations of eroded particles; characterized by clastic texture.

Dike A discordant intrusive body.

Dip The direction and amount (in degrees) of a bed's downward inclination as measured from the horizontal.

Dip-slip (faults) Fault movements of an up-down nature.

Disconformity An unconformity characterized by strata above and below it being essentially parallel; there is a significant age difference between them however.

Discordant Intrusives that are cross-cutting to the layering or fabric of an older rock.

Dissolved load Ions, involved in stream transport, that result from weathered rocks.

Dolomite The mineral or sedimentary rock

composed primarily of the mineral dolomite [CaMg (CO$_3$)$_2$]; the rock and the mineral have the same name.

Dome volcanoes Formed by the emplacement of very viscous magma in the throat of a volcanic vent.

Double refraction The ability possessed by some minerals to convert one light ray into two light rays that are polarized perpendicular to each other.

Drag fold A small fold on the limb of a larger fold.

Drift All glacially derived sediment, including stratified outwash deposits.

Drifts (in the oceans) Water that is moving slower than the ocean currents.

Drumlins Mounds of morainal material that have been overridden and streamlined by moving ice.

Dynamic metamorphism Metamorphism characterized by extensive shearing of mineral assemblages.

Earthquakes Natural movements of the earth usually caused by large-scale faulting.

Earthside The 60 percent of the moon's surface visible from earth.

Eddy A large region of relatively stable and immobile surface water in the center of an ocean gyre.

Elastic rebound theory A model describing faulting as the mechanism for generating earthquakes.

Electron An important subatomic particle possessing very little mass and an electric charge of −1.

Element A pure substance that cannot be broken down by ordinary chemical reactions.

Empirical formula The simplest combining proportions of elements to make a compound (e.g., SiO$_2$ or Al$_2$O$_3$).

Engineering geology The application of geologic and engineering principles to construction projects and other developments that affect man.

Eolian sediments Sedimentary accumulations of wind-blown fragments.

Ephemeral streams Streams that flow only after rainfalls.

Epicenter The point on the earth's surface located directly above an earthquake focus.

Epochs The time subdivisions of periods on the geologic timescale.

Equatorial countercurrent A one-directional ocean current flowing eastward near the equator.

Eras Major units of geologic time (e.g., Paleozoic era).

Erosion The dynamic process of transportation and deposition of rock debris.

Erratics Glacially deposited boulders located far from their source.

Eskers Winding ridges of glacial-fluvial deposits.

Estuaries Lagoonlike elongate bodies of water caused by the "drowning" of stream valleys by ocean water.

Evaporite sediments Nonbiogenic chemical sediments resulting from the evaporation of waters containing soluble elements (e.g., rock salt, gypsum, etc.).

Exfoliation The formation of planar or curved layers of rock by jointing and weathering.

Extrusive igneous Volcanic activity.

Farside The 40 percent of the moon's surface not visible from earth.

Fault-block mountains Mountain structures originating from large-scale dip-slip faulting, usually normal-slip.

Faults Fractures in rock along which movement of one side with respect to the other has occurred.

Feldspar (mineral group) Framework silicates in which ions of potassium, calcium and sodium are necessary because some alumina tetrahedra exist in the structure (e.g., KAlSi$_3$O$_8$); orthoclase and plagioclase are the most common varieties.

Firn Roughly spherical ice particles that develop from snow.

Flood plains Flat valleys partially filled by stream sediments.

Fluvial environment The sedimentary environment of flowing streams.

Focus The point (or region) of an earthquake's origin. Earthquake foci range from very shallow to several hundred kilometers in depth.

Fold mountains Mountain structures formed

largely by large-scale folding of sedimentary rocks.

Folds The result of primarily plastic rock deformation; typically either archlike or troughlike.

Foliated texture A rock texture showing minerals oriented in nearly parallel, sheetlike planes.

Formation The basic unit of rock that is depicted on a geologic map.

Fossil Evidence of the form of a once-living organism (e.g., molds, casts, or actual shells).

Fracture zone A scar in the earth's lithosphere that is currently aseismic, but was caused by transform fault movement at some time in the past.

Free oscillations Seismically induced vibrations of the earth as a whole; caused only by large earthquakes.

Frost wedging The principal process of mechanical weathering; expansion of water into ice forces water-filled cracks in rocks to open.

Gabbro Plutonic igneous rock composed of pyroxene and plagioclase; a mafic rock.

Garnets Isolated tetrahedra mineral group containing a variety of metallic ions (Mg, Al, Ca, Fe, etc.).

Generating area (for waves) The region where strong winds produce wave motions.

Geologic Column All the rocks of the earth's crust; geologists have ordered them into relative age relationships with each other.

Geologic map A map showing the distribution of different rocks as they would look if soil were removed.

Geologic structure sections Cross-sectional view of the rock formations beneath the earth's surface.

Geologic timescale The division of all earth history into units of time called eras, periods, and epochs.

Geosyncline A large elongate basin within which great thicknesses of sedimentary rocks have accumulated.

Glacial ages Time episodes of worldwide glacial advances.

Glaciers Moving bodies of ice on the land.

Gneiss A coarsely foliated metamorphic rock; shows banding of mineral segregations.

Goethite An iron oxide mineral; FeO(OH).

Grabens Down-faulted blocks of the earth's crust; troughlike basins.

Graded bedding Type of bedding in which each individual bed shows a progressive particle size decrease going from bottom to top.

Graded stream A hypothetical stream that is neither downcutting nor depositing; a stream in equilibrium between erosion and deposition.

Granite Plutonic igneous rock rich in quartz and feldspar; a silicic rock.

Granite gneiss A metamorphic gneiss having a mineral composition similar to granite.

Granular texture A rock texture formed by crystals of approximately equal size becoming intergrown.

Gravel Fragments of rock larger than 2 mm in diameter.

Gravimeters Sensitive instruments that measure slight variations in the force of the earth's gravity at different locations.

Gravity The property of all bodies of matter that causes them to be attracted to each other.

Gravity anomalies Slight variations from the average gravitational force of the earth.

Gravity waves Large wind waves capable of movement even after the wind stops blowing.

Groundmass The fine-grained portion of a porphyritic texture.

Ground water Water confined in the pore spaces of rock and soil.

Guyots Flat-topped submarine mountains.

Gypsum A sulfate mineral; $CaSO_4 \cdot 2H_2O$.

Gyres Large circular patterns of surface currents in the oceans.

Half-life The average life of a radioactive nuclide; the amount of time required for half of an initial amount of a nuclide to decay.

Halide (minerals) Minerals composed of metallic ions combined with ions of the halogen group (e.g., Cl^{-1}, Br^{-1}, F^{-1}, etc.).

Halite A halide mineral; NaCl.

Hanging valleys Tributary valleys that drop off abruptly into their main valley; frequently occupied by waterfalls.

Hematite An iron oxide mineral; Fe_2O_3.

Highlands (lunar) Light-colored, high-relief portions of the moon's surface.

Homocline A large region where all the beds are dipping in the same direction.

Horns Sharp-peaked mountains resulting from glacial erosion.

Horsts Up-faulted blocks of the earth's crust.

Hot spot Surface volcanism *above* a mantle plume; a region of intraplate volcanism.

Hydrosphere World-encompassing sphere of water; oceans, lakes, streams, etc.

Hydrothermal ore deposits Valuable bodies of minerals that were deposited from hot, water-rich gases and liquids; associated with igneous processes.

Hypothesis A tentative statement of how two or more phenomena might be related; an educated guess.

Icebergs Large floating masses, broken off from glaciers, that have drifted into the ocean.

Ice sheets Massive bodies of glacial ice such as those found in Antarctica and Greenland.

Igneous rocks Rocks formed by crystallization from a hot molten mass called *magma*.

Intensity (earthquake) The Modified Mercalli Intensity Scale describes the amount of damage done at *any* geographical location. It ranges from I to XII.

Internal waves Waves that move beneath the surface of the ocean; their origin is not well understood.

Intrusive igneous Pertains to the crystallization of magma beneath the earth's surface.

Ion A particle of atomic size that possesses an electric charge by virtue of gaining or losing electrons.

Ion groups Combinations of ions that possess an overall charge (SiO_4^{-4}, CO_3^{-2}, etc.).

Ionic bonding Ions held together by attraction between their opposite electrical charges.

Ionic diffusion The migration of ions under high temperature and pressure within a solid lattice structure.

Iron meteorites Meteorites composed predominately of iron, but typically containing some nickel.

Iron oxides A group of minerals resulting from iron and oxygen combining in different proportions (e.g., Fe_2O_3).

Island arcs Curving chains of volcanic islands associated with oceanic trenches.

Isoclinal (folds) Folds having both limbs dipping parallel to each other.

Isomorphism The phenomenon of a mineral's composition varying within fixed limits while its structure remains constant.

Isoseismal map A map delineating geographic localities that experienced equal modified Mercalli intensities during an earthquake.

Isostasy The concept that rocks of the earth will attain a gravitational equilibrium with each other if given sufficient time; this also suggests that lower density rocks "float" on higher density rocks.

Isotope See **Nuclide**.

Joints Fractures in rock that lack significant displacement.

Kames Moundlike glacial-fluvial deposits.

Karst topography Regions showing distinctive topographic features resulting from dissolution of limestone by ground water.

Kettles Depressions formed by melting of large blocks of ice that were incorporated with morainal debris.

Laccolith A concordant intrusive body that domes up the overlying sedimentary rocks.

Landslides Rapid downslope movements of soil or rock by mass wasting.

Laterite A soil type rich in iron oxides.

Lava Magma that has erupted onto the earth's surface.

Law A statement of how phenomena might be related that is almost certainly correct; supported by massive evidence and logic.

Limb of a fold The side of a fold; the portion of a fold between two adjacent axes.

Lime muds Mud-sized grains of calcite derived from organic remains.

Lime sands Sand-sized fragments of calcite derived from organic remains.

Limestone Sedimentary rock composed predominantly of calcite; $CaCO_3$.

Lithosphere The rigid outer skin of the earth; composed of the entire crust and 60–80 km of the upper mantle.

Longshore transport The movement of a beach parallel to the shoreline.

Low-velocity zone A region of sharp velocity decrease in the earth's upper mantle; called the *asthenosphere*.

Luster The manner in which a mineral reflects light (e.g. metallic, glassy, etc.).

Maar volcano A large explosion crater mantled with pyroclastic debris.

Mafic Refers to rocks or minerals rich in magnesium and iron; relatively low in silicon and oxygen (e.g., basalt and pyroxene).

Magma Hot molten rock material, usually high in silicate composition.

Magnetite An iron oxide mineral; Fe_3O_4 (sometimes indicated by $Fe_2O_3 \cdot FeO$).

Magnetometers Sensitive instruments used to measure the earth's magnetic field.

Magnitude (earthquake) The Richter Magnitude Scale describes the maximum amount of ground movement measured at a fixed distance from an earthquake's focus. This scale usually ranges from 1 to 9, although larger and smaller values are possible.

Main magnetic field (of the earth) The principal component of earth magnetism; originates deep in the earth.

Mantle (of the earth) The thick, rigid zone of the earth's interior that lies between the crust and the core; about 80 percent of the earth's volume is in the mantle.

Mantle plume A rising zone of hot molten magma from the mantle; creates volcanism *within* a plate.

Marble Metamorphosed limestone.

Mare basalts Plagioclase- and pyroxene-rich rocks of the lunar maria.

Maria Dark, relatively smooth areas of the moon's surface.

Marine sediments Sediments that accumulate on the ocean floor—either shallow or deep.

Marine terrace A relatively flat feature of surf erosion.

Mass number (atomic) The number of protons plus neutrons in each atom of an element, often known as "atomic weight."

Mass wasting Movements of rock or soil by the direct action of gravity (e.g., a rock fall).

Matter The stuff of the universe that occupies space and has mass.

Mechanical weathering Physical disintegration of rock.

Meanders Broad loops in the course of a stream channel; they reduce the gradient of the stream bed.

Mélange A mappable region of different rocks brought together by mixing through intense deformation.

Metallogenic provinces Geographic regions characterized by concentrations of valuable metallic ore bodies.

Metamorphic rocks Formed from preexisting igneous or sedimentary rocks by profound modifications of texture and/or composition while remaining essentially solid; heat, pressure, and chemically active fluids are the principal agents.

Metamorphism The process that produces metamorphic rocks; causes changes in the composition and texture of igneous or sedimentary rock.

Meteors Extraterrestrial materials that vaporize upon entering the earth's atmosphere.

Meteorites Extraterrestrial material that reaches the earth's surface.

Mica (mineral group) Sheet silicates; muscovite and biotite are the most common varieties.

Microcline A feldspar mineral having the same composition as orthoclase but a different lattice structure; $KAlSi_3O_8$.

Migmatite Rock showing an intimate mixture of granite with metamorphic material.

Mineral A naturally occurring inorganic solid of fixed chemical composition (e.g., quartz: SiO_2).

Model (scientific) A mental construct of how nature might function; it may be mathematical, mechanical, or verbal.

Moho discontinuity The seismic discontinuity at the base of the earth's crust (hence, top of mantle). See **Mohorovičić discontinuity.**

Mohorovičić discontinuity The seismic discontinuity separating the crust and the mantle; called the "Moho."

Monocline A fold having only one flexure, thus just one inclination.

Moraine Glacial deposits having ridgelike, moundlike, or other distinctive forms.

Mountain ranges Elongate zones of topographically high terrain.

Mud The accumulation of clay-sized particles; grains are less than 1/256 mm in diameter.

Native element minerals Minerals composed of uncombined elements (e.g., gold, diamond, etc.).

Natural slope angle The angle of slope that is maintained by natural erosional processes.

Neap tides Tides in their lowest ranges; neap tides occur twice each month.

Neptunism An eighteenth-century view that all rocks were deposited from a world-encompassing ocean; promulgated by A. G. Werner.

Neutron An important subatomic particle possessing no electric charge and one unit of atomic mass; found only in an atom's nucleus.

Noble gases Inert gases that tend not to combine with other elements to form compounds; each atom contains eight outermost electrons.

Nonbiogenic chemical sediments Crystalline sediments formed by inorganic processes (e.g., rock salt).

Nonconformity An unconformity in which the older rocks are nonstratified (e.g., granite).

Normal-slip faulting Dip-slip faulting that locally lengthens the earth's crust.

Nucleus (atomic) The massive central region of an atom or ion in which all the protons and neutrons are located.

Nuclide Different weights (caused by varying numbers of neutrons) of a given element are called *nuclides* (e.g., U^{235} and U^{238} are different nuclides of uranium). The term *isotope* is interchangeable with *nuclide*.

Oblique-slip (faults) Fault movement with components of both dip-slip and strike-slip.

Obsidian Volcanic glass of silicic composition; usually dark in color.

Ocean-floor spreading The separation of lithospheric plates along midoceanic ridges.

Oceanic ridge-rise system A world-encircling belt of mountains and broad rises found on the ocean floor.

Oceanic trenches Long, narrow zones of very deep ocean floor; usually parallel to a continental margin.

Olivine (mineral group) Fe-Mg-bearing isolated tetrahedra minerals.

Ooliths Rounded, sand-sized particles of calcite showing a concentric pattern of growth.

Ophiolite (suite) An assemblage of mafic and ultramafic igneous rocks formed at a spreading ridge; covered by deep marine sedimentary deposits such as chert, limestone, and shale.

Organic evolution The developmental changes in the living world through time.

Organic reefs Interlocking skeletons of living and dead marine life; commonly rich in algae and corals.

Original horizontality Steno's view (1669) that at the time of origin, sedimentary layers are essentially horizontal.

Orthoclase A feldspar mineral; $KAlSi_3O_8$.

Outwash plains Stratified deposits resulting from glacial meltwater.

Overbank deposits Fine-grained (clay and sand) alluvial deposits that settle out following the flood stage of a stream.

Overturned fold A fold having one limb deformed more than 90°; on that limb, older layers are above younger layers.

Oxidation number The number of electrons gained, lost, or shared by an element when it forms an ion or a compound.

Pahoehoe (lava) A relatively fluid, gas-rich, basalt flow; often ropy in surface appearance.

Paleomagnetism The study of the nature of the earth's magnetic field as it existed in the geologic past.

Pangea A large continent that existed in late Paleozoic time; subsequently split apart into our present continents.

Paradigm A model or "ground rule" that serves as a foundation to thinking.

Parallel bedding Individual layers of sediment that are parallel to each other and distinguished by slight differences in color or particle size.

Partial melting Because feldspar melts at a

lower temperature than mafic minerals such as olivine and pyroxene, local concentration of silicic magma could be produced by heating and partial melting of mafic (mantle) rock.

Pedalfer A soil type rich in aluminum and iron.

Pediment A relatively flat, eroded bedrock surface extending laterally from the base of a mountain front.

Pedocal A soil type rich in calcium carbonate.

Peneplane The most mature surface of stream erosion; flat, having minimum relief.

Perennial streams Streams that flow continuously.

Periodic table A grouping of chemical elements indicating those that have similar properties.

Periods Basic units of geologic time; the time subdivisions of eras.

Phase diagram A diagram depicting the conditions under which matter will occur in different composition or states (e.g., bases, solids, liquids).

Phenocryst The larger crystals in a porphyritic texture.

Physical sedimentary structures Features of a sedimentary rock formed at the time of its deposition (e.g., cross bedding, graded bedding, etc.).

Piedmont The region extending laterally from the base of a mountain front; comprises a pediment and a bajada in desert regions.

Plagioclase An isomorphic feldspar mineral group; ranges between $NaAlSi_3O_8$ and $CaAl_2Si_2O_8$.

Plates Large slabs of lithosphere that are the principal units of plate tectonics; the earth has twelve major plates and several minor ones.

Plate tectonics A model for the upper mantle and crust of the earth that envisions interactions of large, rigid lithospheric plates of rock as the cause of most deformation and volcanism.

Playa lakes Ephemeral lakes formed in arid regions.

Plunging fold A fold whose axis is inclined downward from the horizontal; usually has a "hairpinlike" outcrop pattern of the limbs.

Plutonic Pertains to the environment of rock origin deep within the earth; deep intrusive igneous rocks are plutonic in origin.

Plutons The general name for relatively massive, intrusive igneous bodies.

Poorly sorted sediment Accumulation of many different grain sizes (e.g., clay, sand, and gravel).

Porphyritic texture A volcanic rock texture in which larger crystals, called *phenocrysts*, are surrounded by smaller crystals or glass.

Premare basalts Plagioclase-rich lunar basalts that are older than the mare basalts.

Primary nuclides Radioactive nuclides that have persisted since the earth first formed.

Primary waves (P waves) Seismic waves that cause compressional motion (forward and back) in the earth; the fastest moving seismic waves.

Proton An important subatomic particle possessing an electric charge of +1 and one unit of atomic mass; found only in an atom's nucleus.

Pyrite A sulfide mineral (fool's gold); FeS_2.

Pyroclastic debris Volcanic ejecta blasted into the air by explosive eruptions (tuff and breccia are common examples).

Pyroxene (mineral group) Single chain silicates; commonly rich in iron and magnesium ions.

Quartz A framework silicate; SiO_2.

Quartzite Metamorphosed quartz-rich sandstone.

Radial drainage The pattern of valleys that radiates from a central high elevation; as around a volcano.

Radioactive age (of a mineral) The length of time since a radioactive parent nuclide and the daughter nuclide were first held together in a closed system.

Radioactivity The spontaneous breakdown of the nucleus of an element to become a different element.

Rays (lunar) Thin coatings of light-colored debris radiating from young lunar impact craters.

Recumbent fold An overturned fold whose axial plane is nearly horizontal.

Regional metamorphism Metamorphism of a large region in response to deformational pressures and elevated temperatures.

Regression Movement of marine waters off the land; exposes recent marine deposits to erosion.

Rejuvenation The process in which a stream begins to erode more actively; usually results from uplifting or climatic changes causing increased amounts of rainfall.

Residual field The small field of earth magnetism that remains after subtracting the large dipole field.

Reversals in magnetic polarity The earth's main magnetic field has changed direction many times in the past (e.g., North magnetic pole became South magnetic pole).

Reverse-slip faulting Dip-slip faulting that locally shortens the earth's crust.

Ridges (in plate tectonics) Zones separating two lithospheric plates where new crust is being formed.

Rifts Regions where the earth's crust is pulling apart; typically formed near the center of midocean ridges.

Rilles Long, narrow, troughlike valleys that occur near and within large craters on the moon.

Rises (in plate tectonics) New crust zones having more subdued topography than ridges.

Roches moutonnées Asymmetrically rounded bedrock knobs resulting from glacial erosion.

Rock An aggregate of mineral material; volcanic glass is also rock, even though noncrystalline.

Roof pendants Bodies of preigneous rock engulfed by plutonic material; they "hang" into the younger igneous mass.

Sand Grains ranging in diameter from 1/16 mm to 2 mm.

Sand dunes Accumulations of mobile windblown sand into distinctive dune forms.

Sandstone Sedimentary rock composed primarily of sand grains cemented and compacted together.

Schist A metamorphic rock having a foliated texture commonly rich in micas.

Scientific method A term sometimes used to describe the process of hypothesis testing by experimentation.

Scientific revolution When one major scientific paradigm is replaced by another.

Sea Complex ocean waves found in a generating area.

Sea ice Thin layers of ice formed from ocean water in cold polar climates.

Secondary waves (S waves) Seismic waves that cause transverse motion (sideways shearing) in the earth.

Sedimentary rocks Formed on the earth's surface by the settling out of fragments of preexisting rocks or dissolved substances; they are layered.

Seif dune A longitudinal sand dune resulting from variable wind directions.

Seismic discontinuities Surfaces or narrow zones in the earth's interior across which there are rather abrupt changes in seismic wave velocities.

Seismic moment A measure of the energy liberated during the faulting that produces an earthquake; the product of the fault's surface area, its average displacement, and the rigidity of the displaced rocks.

Seismic sea waves Large destructive waves that are generated by submarine faulting or landsliding. They sometimes strike coastlines with wave heights as great as 50 or 60 meters. (Also called *Tsunamis*.)

Seismic waves Elastic vibrations transmitted through the earth; earthquake waves.

Seismograms Records of earthquakes produced on seismographs.

Seismographs Instruments used to record the passing of seismic waves.

Semidiurnal (tides) Tides having a regular pattern of two high tides and two low tides each day.

Shale Sedimentary rock composed of clay-sized fragments; sometimes called *mudstone*.

Shear stress The application of force on a body in a manner that would cause its two sides to move past each other.

Shelf ice Continentally derived glacial ice floating on an adjacent sea.

Shells (electron) Energy levels in which electrons are surrounding the nucleus of an atom;

higher energy levels are farther from the nucleus.

Shield areas Exposed cores of ancient mountainous terrain; the nuclei of continents.

Shield volcanoes Large, broad volcanoes that build up from repeated outpourings of fluid lava; usually basaltic in composition.

Silicate group Minerals containing silicon-oxygen tetrahedra as fundamental building blocks.

Silicate melt Liquid silicate material; magma.

Silicic Refers to rocks and minerals rich in silicon and oxygen (e.g., granite and quartz).

Sill A concordant intrusive body.

Slate A fine-grained, foliated, metamorphic rock.

Soil Altered rock debris, typically containing a variable organic content.

Soil profile The characteristic structure of a soil as seen in cross section.

Sole markings Physical sedimentary structures found on the bottom (sole) of sedimentary strata that result from turbidity current deposition.

Space weathering The continuous abrasion and shattering of the moon's surface by small meteorite impacts.

Specific gravity The ratio of a substance's density to the density of water; a number without units (e.g., the Specific gravity of Quartz is 2.65).

Spheroidal weathering Rounded surfaces on rock resulting from greater rates of chemical attack at the corners and edges of rock masses.

Spring tides Tides in their greatest ranges; twice each month.

Stock An intrusive igneous body that is exposed for less than 40 square miles; smaller than a batholith.

Stony-irons Meteorites composed of both silicate and metallic material.

Stony meteorites Meteorites composed of silicate materials.

Stratification Layering (bedding) in sedimentary rocks.

Streak The color of a mineral in its finely powdered form.

Streams Ribbons of flowing water on the lands.

Striated pebbles Scratched and abraded fragments that result from glacial transport.

Strike The directional trend of a bed as seen on a horizontal erosion surface.

Strike-slip (faults) Fault movement of a horizontal nature; often called *transcurrent faults.*

Subduction zones Zones where lithospheric plates descend deep into the earth's mantle.

Submarine canyons Step and deep canyons eroded through continental shelves and slopes.

Sulfate group Minerals composed in part of the SO_4^{-2} ion group.

Sulfide (minerals) Minerals composed of metallic elements combined with sulfur.

Superposed stream A stream that flows across resistent rocks as the result of inheriting its drainage course from one established at an earlier time.

Superposition Law stating that in a undeformed sequence of sedimentary strata, the oldest layer is on the bottom and is overlain by successively younger layers.

Surf Breaking water waves that rush onto the land.

Surface currents Horizontal ocean water movements in the upper hundred meters or so.

Surface waves Seismic waves that travel only in the outer layers of the earth (e.g., *L* waves).

Suspended load Solid particles undergoing stream transport in a primarily suspended state.

Swell Relatively simple ocean waves that have spread from the generating area.

Synclines Troughlike folds having limbs that are dipping toward each other.

Systems (of rock) The basic time-rock unit; a system comprises all rocks formed during a geologic period.

Talus Fragments of rock that have fallen in response to gravity alone.

Tarns Small lakes occupying the bottom of cirque basins.

Tectonic inclusion A large unbroken mass of rock included with an extensively sheared mélange.

Tectonics The study of large scale movements of the earth.

Terrestrial sediments Sediments that accumulate on land; including lake and stream deposits.

Tetrahedron A four-sided geometrical solid; each face is an equilateral triangle.

Texture (rock) The relationships among the grains of a rock that pertain to their (1) size distribution, (2) orientation, and (3) the manner in which they fit together; texture is the most genetically significant rock characteristic.

Theory A confidently held statement of how phenomena might be related; supported by abundant evidence.

Thrust fault A reverse fault in which the fault plane has a shallow dip.

Tidal wave The misnomer that is often applied to seismic sea wave.

Tides World-encircling ocean movements caused by solar and lunar gravitational attractions.

Till Sediment deposited directly from glacial ice.

Topographic profile A side view of the earth's surface along a given line.

Transcurrent faults Strike-slip faults.

Transform faults A special class of strike-slip faults where actual displacement takes place only between two major plate features (e.g., movement occurs only in the region between two spreading ridges).

Transgression Movement of the marine environment across the land; initiates deposition of marine sediments in new regions.

Transition zone A middle region of the earth's mantle separating the upper mantle from the lower mantle.

Trellis drainage A stream drainage pattern in which valleys run parallel to each other due to erosion into steeply dipping beds on the limbs of folded sedimentary rocks.

Triple junction A place on the earth where three lithospheric plates are in contact with each other.

Tsunamis Seismic sea waves.

Tuff Fine volcanic ash that has been consolidated into rock.

Turbidite sequence An accumulation of turbidity current deposits, usually characterized by graded beds showing sole markings.

Turbidity currents Sediment-laden currents of water that commonly deposit graded beds and sole markings upon reaching deep water.

Ultramafic (rocks) Refers to rocks that are very low in silicon–oxygen content (e.g., mantle rocks composed of olivine and pyroxene).

Unconformity A surface of contact between rock units that represents a significant time gap in the continuity of the rocks; a buried erosion surface.

Uniformitarianism The assumption that matter and energy have acted in an unchanging manner throughout all of earth history (i.e., natural laws have always existed).

U-shaped valleys Broad-floored, steep-walled mountain valleys; usually of glacial origin.

Velocity-depth curves Curves showing how P-wave and S-wave velocities change with depth in the earth.

Ventifacts Wind-faceted pebbles and cobbles formed by "sandblasting" in desert regions.

Volcanic Igneous activity involving the eruption of magma (lava) onto the earth's surface.

Volcano A cone or domed-shaped feature resulting from successive eruptions of lava or other volcanic ejecta from a localized vent.

V-shaped valleys Steep-walled, narrow-bottomed, stream-cut valleys.

Water gap A mountain ridge through which a stream valley has been eroded.

Water table The upper surface of ground-water saturated rock.

Wave base The depth of water motion in a wave; about half the wave length.

Waves Temporary disturbances of a medium (e.g., ocean water) that transmit energy but do not permanently displace the medium.

Weathering Chemical and mechanical breakdown of rock near the earth's surface.

Well-sorted sediment Accumulation of grains that are nearly the same size (e.g., all clay).

Wind waves Surface waves produced by wind blowing across a body of water.

Wrinkle ridges Small-scale, foldlike structures on lunar maria.

Xenolith A "foreign" rock incorporated in a younger intrusive igneous rock.

Index

451

Exfoliation, 301, 302
Extrusive igneous rocks, 69–70

F

Fans, alluvial, 131, 132, 354–56
Farallon plate, 102–105
Farside, lunar, 417–18
Fault-block mountains, 215–16, 256, 258–59,
  289, 292–95
Fault offset, 197, 199
Faults, 193–200, 281–82, 286–89
  and elastic rebound theory, 226
Fault scarp, 355
Fault slip, 197, 199
Faunal succession, law of, 158–59
Feldspar, 48, 57, 175, 300
Fertilizers, 382, 392–95
Firn, 361–62
Flash floods, 354
Flood basalts, 78
Floodplain, 313–14, 326
Fluvial environments, 126–30
Fold mountains, 213–16, 256–57, 260, 289
Folds, 193–94, 200–204
Foraminifers, 111–12, 142
Formation, rock, 192
Fossils, 13, 125, 156
  dating techniques, 156–60
Fractures, 193
Fracture zones, 289
Fragment relationships, in age-dating rocks,
  152–53
Framework silicates, 53, 56–58
Free oscillations, 220–21
Frost wedging, 297–98, 365, 367
Fuels, 382, 390–91

G

Gabbro, 74
Garnets, 46, 52, 54
Gases, noble, 32
Generating area, of waves, 337, 339
Geological time scale, 161, 162, 176–77
Geologic clocks, radioactive nuclides as,
  172–75
Geologic column, 161
Geologic maps, 189–92, 205–208
  contour, 206–208
  isoseismal, 230, 232
  of lunar surface, 431

Smith's, 156–58
  typical, 190–91
Geologic structure sections, 205–208, 209
Geology:
  modern, 7–18
  scientific uniqueness of, 4–7
Geophysical Laboratory of the Carnegie
    Institution, 87
Geosynclines, 260, 262, 289
Geothermal energy, 392
Glacial ages, 375–78
Glacial deposits, 372–75
Glacial environments, 133, 134, 353
Glacial episodes, 375–78
Glacial epochs, 375–78
Glacial moraines, 372–75
Glacial till, 372–75
Glaciated valleys, 362–71
Glaciers, 353, 359–78
  defined, 361–63
Gneisses, 96–98
Goethite, 61, 385, 386
Gorda plate, 292–95
Grabens, 256, 259
Graded bedding, 121, 123–25, 138, 203–204
Graded stream, as equilibrium concept,
    321–324
Grand Canyon region, 145–49, 182–86
Granitic gneisses, 98
Granitic rocks, 74, 86, 90–92, 178, 188–89, 300
Granitization, 91–92
Gravel, 108, 109, 393
Gravimeters, 248, 249
Gravity:
  acting on water masses at high elevations,
    222
  anomalies, 250
  defined, 248–49
  earth, and deep crust, 247–52
  effect of sun and moon on ocean, 341–42
  and groundwater, 308
  isostasy, 249–51
  lunar, 420, 422
  and mass wasting, 315–17
  and streams, 311–15
Gravity waves, 337
Great Basin, 259, 289, 292–95
  evolutionary sequence of landforms, 355–56
Greenland:
  granite rocks, 178
  ice sheets, 360, 363, 378
Ground failures, 399–404
Groundmass, 69
Ground moraines, 372
Ground rupture, 399–400

Mid-ocean ridges, 270
Migmatites, 92
Minerals:
  aluminum oxides, 61
  aluminum silicates, 52
  amphiboles, 48, 55
  anhydrite, 61
  aragonite, 60
  calcite, 48, 60
  carbonates, 45, 59–60
  chain silicates, 52–55
  clay, 56, 108, 109, 300, 302
  cleavage, 41, 59
  color, 50–51
  composition of, 44–47
  crystalline, 39
  defined, 28
  dolomite, 60, 61
  evaporites, 112–13, 115, 131–32, 354, 356
  garnets, 52
  goethite, 61, 385, 386
  gypsum, 48, 61, 361, 382, 393
  halides, 46, 47, 62
  hematite, 45, 61, 385, 386
  ion groups, 45
  iron oxides, 61
  isomorphic, 58
  luster, 50–51
  magnetite, 61, 274, 385, 386
  of mantle, 243–45
  mica, 46, 48, 55, 175
  microcline, 48, 58
  mineral resources, 381–95
  native elements, 46, 62–64
  nonsilicate, 59–64
  olivines, 48, 52, 58, 243–47
  oxides, 46, 61–62
  properties of, 47–51, 58
  pyrite, 62, 63
  pyroxenes, 48, 54–55, 243–47
  quartz, 48, 57, 108, 300, 302
  radioactive nuclides, 169–71, 179–80
  resources, 381–95
  rock-forming, 48
  silicates, 45, 51–59
  streak, 50–51
  structure of, 39–44
  sulfates, 45, 59, 61
  sulfides, 46, 62
Mines, 218, 219
Mixed tides, 343
Models (see Scientific models)
Modified Mercalli scale of intensity, 230–32

Moho discontinuity, 233–34, 251
Mohorovicic, Andrija, 223, 234
Monocline, 204
Moon, 415–36
  composition, 423–28
  density, 417
  diameter, 416
  history of, 430–36
  interior of, 428–30
  origin of, 434–36
  radiometric dating of meteorites and rocks,
    178–79, 413
  rocks, 426–28
  soil, 423–26, 427
  surface, 417–23
  thermal history, 332–34
  and tidal changes, 341–42
Moonquakes, 428–29
Moraines, glacial, 372–75
Mountain building, 104, 182–86, 256, 289
Mountain ranges, 182–86, 193, 250–52
  continental, 256–66
  fault-block, 215–16, 256, 258–59, 289,
    292–95
  fold, 213–16, 256–57, 260, 289
  force of gravity, 250–52
  on ocean floor, 266–72
  volcanic, 256, 258, 292–95
Mount Fuji, 76
Mount Kilimanjaro, 359
Mount Rainier, 76
Mud cracks, 130
Muds, 108, 109
  lime, 138–39

N

Native elements, 46, 62–64
Natural slope angles, 402
Nazca plate, 283–85
Neap tides, 342
Neogene Period, 162
Neptunism, 6, 11, 154
Neutrons, 35, 169
Nevadan orogeny, 104
Newark deposits, 215–16
Nitrogen-14, 171–74
Noble gases, 32
Nonbiogenic chemical sediments, 110–12,
  113–14
Nonconformities, 167–68